MATHEMATICAL ANALYSIS
FOR BUSINESS DECISIONS

IRWIN SERIES IN QUANTITATIVE ANALYSIS FOR BUSINESS

Consulting Editor

ROBERT B. FETTER *Yale University*

MATHEMATICAL ANALYSIS FOR BUSINESS DECISIONS

By

- JAMES E. HOWELL, Ph.D.
  Associate Professor of Economics
  Graduate School of Business
  Stanford University

and

- DANIEL TEICHROEW, Ph.D.
  Head, Division of Organizational Science

- Case Institute of Technology

RICHARD D. IRWIN, INC.

1963 · HOMEWOOD, ILLINOIS

First Printing, February, 1963

Second Printing, January, 1964

Third Printing, August, 1964

Library of Congress Catalogue Card No. 63–8440

PRINTED IN THE UNITED STATES OF AMERICA

PREFACE

THE APPLICATION of mathematics to problems of business and industry has been increasing rapidly over the past ten years. In both university classrooms and executive offices, terms such as linear programming, optimizing models, decision theory, and management science have become commonplace. The use of mathematics as an important administrative tool can be expected to continue to expand at an even greater rate. A major reason is the intellectual revolution now underway in fields of business such as marketing, transportation, finance, and production—a revolution in which quantitative methods are going to continue to play a major role. Another important reason is that the use of computers will make more and better data available.

These developments have been anticipated and commented upon at some length by those interested in business education.[1] Out of this discussion has come a fairly general agreement about the minimum preparation for those anticipating administrative or managerial careers in business or government in the next few decades.

In particular, it is agreed that students should be exposed to the traditional pre-calculus materials, to calculus, and to that set of relatively recently developed subjects which is sometimes called "modern mathematics." It is also agreed, although put in many different ways, that the emphasis should be on using a result rather than on proving it, on understanding and interpreting abstract mathematical ideas rather than on developing them, and on ability to treat certain problems mathematically rather than on the internal development of the mathematics itself. Yet we agree with the

---

[1] See, for example, R. A. Gordon and J. E. Howell, *Higher Education for Business* (New York: Columbia University Press, 1959), pp. 159–63; F. C. Pierson *et al.*, *The Education of American Businessmen* (New York: McGraw-Hill Book Co., Inc., 1959), pp. 186–90; S. Goldberg, "Mathematics for Business Students," in *Views on Business Education* (Chapel Hill: School of Business Administration, University of North Carolina, 1960); R. K. Gaumnitz and O. H. Brownlee, "Mathematics for Decision Makers," *Harvard Business Review*, Vol. 34, No. 3 (May–June, 1956), p. 48; G. A. W. Boehm, "Mathematics II: The New Uses of the Abstract," *Fortune*, Vol. LVIII, No. 1 (July, 1958), p. 124.

view that one of the values of studying mathematics is the exposure to the concept of rigorous formulation and proof.

The present book is a direct outgrowth of all these considerations and represents our experience in teaching mathematics to business students. It is written for the student or the business practictioner who needs to learn enough about the possible uses of modern mathematics to be able to read the literature and understand recent developments in the several fields of business as well as to understand and be able to work with the ever-growing number of specialists who are becoming increasingly important in business, industry, and government.

Students intending to become specialists need more training in mathematics than is represented here. They should follow the regular curriculum in a mathematics department. Even the non-specialist will profit greatly from such a curriculum provided he has the time and background for several years of course work. Not many business students do have the time for they also must become familiar with a myriad of other topics—accounting, finance, economics, marketing, policy, and so on. Hence, courses such as the one represented by this book have an important role to play.

Specifically, this book contains the kinds and amounts of mathematics that we think should be included in a professional program in business administration at either the bachelor's or master's level. It can be used in a course offered either in the mathematics department or in the school of business. The book assumes no previous knowledge of mathematics except for a reasonable secondary school preparation in elementary algebra. It represents a one-semester course for average students with a good preparation. If used as a year course, additional materials might be needed: elementary materials for less well prepared students, more advanced materials for well prepared ones. The book has been used in the classroom with a variety of students, undergraduates and graduates; those with literally no mathematics since high school as well as those who had had a year's course in calculus in college. With appropriate adjustments in rate of coverage, amount of home work drill, and level of classroom presentation, the book was suitable for each situation.

It is assumed that the majority of students using this book will take no additional mathematics although presumably they will take courses in statistics and the other fields of business. The student will be well prepared for courses in production, statistics, managerial economics, managerial accounting, management science, or, if he wishes to be a specialist, more mathematics. He will also be prepared for advanced work in accounting, finance, marketing, and similar subjects, especially in those courses incorporating the newer developments. It should be emphasized that the primary value of a course based on this book is in the preparation it gives students for these other courses. A real but nonetheless secondary justification is that the mathematics has value in and of itself for the student who aspires to a managerial career in a world where science, technology, and formal decision-making techniques are and will become increasingly important.

Although the structure of the book reflects our own experiences in teaching these materials, it has been designed with the needs and tastes of others in mind. The following schematic suggests some of its flexibility.

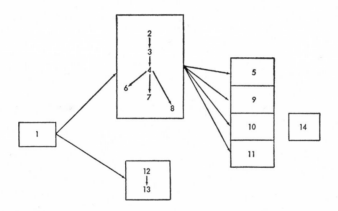

Although we prefer to introduce the sections on linear analysis after the calculus chapters, it is possible to assign Chapters 12 and 13 following Chapter 1. Chapter 12 on matrix algebra is a prerequisite to the chapter on linear programming. Linear programming is introduced as a technique for optimizing in certain situations where the techniques of the calculus are inapplicable. Understanding, rather than formal theorems and solution techniques, is stressed. The student will have a clear notion at the end of Chapter 13 of what linear programming is, but he will have no facility at "doing" linear programming without further work.

Chapters 2 through 8, internally related as shown in the

schematic, cover many of the topics typically found in college courses in calculus. The emphasis is on polynomials although other functions, particularly the exponential and the logarithmic, are treated. The derivative is introduced as a rigorous generalization of the intuitive notion of slope; the theory of extrema is presented early for motivational reasons; and multivariate analysis is introduced because of its importance in applications. The major theme of these chapters is that of optimizing.

Each of Chapters 5, 9, 10, and 11 stand alone even though they depend on Chapter 4 and, in some cases, on certain sections of Chapters 6, 7, or 8. These four chapters are concerned exclusively with applications. Chapters 5 and 11 contain cases of varying difficulty requiring varying levels of mathematical sophistication. The cases, which represent a major feature of the book, serve both to motivate the study of mathematics and to impress upon the student the nature of the role of mathematics vis à vis the other elements of a decision situation. Nearly all of them are taken from published accounts of the application of mathematics to particular business problems.

Chapter 9 introduces probability theory, partly as an example of an application of the mathematics and partly as a bridge to the study of statistics which the student will presumably pursue elsewhere. A case on optimizing the expected value of a random variable is included. In Chapter 10 the mathematics of finance and accounting is presented and then applied to certain decision-making situations. It rests on Chapters 4 and 6.

Chapter 14 is a description of a variety of optimizing situations encountered in management science and of the kinds of mathematics developed to cope with them. It rests on no set of chapters in particular, although it probably should not be assigned unless the student has been exposed to most of the rest of the book.

The preparation of this book would have been impossible without the support of a number of people. First, we wish to acknowledge our debt to our colleagues here at Stanford who encouraged the development of the course upon which the book is based. A major contribution was also made by Mr. Richard Kistler, formerly our course assistant. We also wish to acknowledge the assistance of Miss Margaret M. Renner who carried the manuscript through several drafts. Helpful comments were made at various stages by Professor Wain Martin and Mr. Ira Horowitz of Indiana

University, Professor C. Michael White of the University of Southern California, Dr. John Bishop, Harvard University, Professor Fred E. Kindig, University of Pittsburgh, Mr. John Lee of the Stanford Mathematics Department, and, especially, our colleague, Professor John Haldi.

JAMES E. HOWELL

DANIEL TEICHROEW

Stanford, California
   January 2, 1963

TABLE OF CONTENTS

CHAPTER 1

ELEMENTARY MATHEMATICAL RELATIONS

AT THE outset it is necessary to develop the elementary concepts of mathematics on which subsequent chapters will build. These concepts will serve not only as the foundations of the later analysis but will also be of value as aids to logical thinking about applied problems.

A brief introduction to these ideas—functions, equations, graphs, intersections, inequalities, etc.—may be useful even for the reader who is already familiar with them. On the other hand, the reader who finds the gap between his previous training and this chapter too great may wish to supplement this introduction by reference to one or another of the many excellent elementary or college algebra texts.

1. FUNCTIONS

The notion of a *function* is essentially that of a correspondence between two sets of objects; that is, it is a *rule* for relating particular objects in one set to particular objects in another set.

For example, one might say that the income of a salesman selling on commission is a function of how much he sells. In particular, it might be said that his income will be "high" or "low" depending on whether he makes "many" or "few" sales. The function in this case is the verbal rule relating "high income" to "many sales" and a "low income" to "few sales." "High income" and "low income" are the objects of one set, and "many sales" and "few sales" are the objects of another set, as in Figure 1–1.

The function in the example would be more interesting if it were numerically valued, that is, if the objects in each set were num-

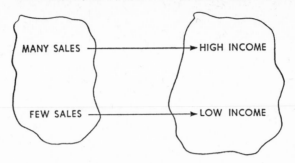

Figure 1–1

bers. Suppose the salesman receives a commission of $20 on each completed sale. Then the first set would consist of all numbers representing the number of sales he might make in (say) a month, and the other set would be a set of dollar amounts representing the income corresponding to each possible number of sales. The function would be the rule by which elements in the two sets were related. This function might be represented by the verbal description just given, or by a table:

Number of sales	0	1	2	3	4	5	· · ·
Dollars of commission income	0	20	40	60	80	100	· · ·

A more common and convenient convention, however, is the symbolic representation of the function. In the example, let n represent the number of sales, whatever it may be, and y represent the dollars of income; then the function or rule determining the salesman's commission of $20 per sale is written as:

$$y = 20n \qquad (1)$$

The function can be thought of as a "machine" whose inputs are the various values of n (0, 1, 2, 3, · · ·) and whose outputs are the corresponding values of y (0, 20, 40, 60, · · ·) as in Figure 1–2. The inputs and outputs are commonly called variables. A variable is merely a representation of something which can assume varying numerical values.

It is convenient and conventional to label the "input" variable the *independent* variable and the "output" variable the *dependent* variable. Thus, in equation (1), n is the independent variable and y the dependent one. The number 20 has several names: constant, coefficient, and parameter. If the amount paid per sale were a instead of 20, the function would be $y = an$ with a the parameter.

It is sometimes useful to be able to express the functional re-

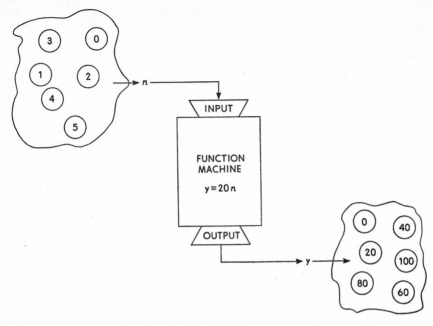

Figure 1–2

lation in general terms, saying only that income, y, is an unspecified function of the number of sales, n:

$$y = f(n) \qquad (2)$$

This notation does not mean that y equals f times n. Rather, it says that a variable y has its numerical value determined by a function or rule called f and by the numerical value of another variable, n. The symbol $f(n)$ is read "f of n."

This general formulation can be made more specific by showing what the rule is:

$$f(n) = 20n \qquad (3)$$

as in (1). This says that the rule, which uses information about the value of n, is that each numerical value of n is multiplied by 20. Thus, if $n = 15$,

$$f(15) = 20 \cdot 15 = 300 \qquad (4)$$

and, since y is $f(n)$,

$$y = 300$$

Changing $f(n)$ to $f(15)$ as soon as one particular value of n is specified indicates clearly the relative unimportance of the specific symbol n. It is simply a "placeholder" on each side of the equals sign in (3); one could as well have used s, S, β, or $*$. For example, if $f(s) = 20s$, $f(15) = 300$ as before.

Similarly, the representation of a function by the symbol $f(\ )$ is purely a matter of taste. Any number of symbolic representations, including the following, would have served as well:

$$g(n) = 20n \qquad y(n) = 20n \qquad F(n) = 20n$$
$$\psi(n) = 20n \qquad \theta(n) = 20n \qquad \text{etc.}$$

However, the letters f, g, F, and G are the most common forms, and they will be used frequently here.

It is important to note that there are two kinds of correspondence included within the concept of a function. There is said to be a one-to-one correspondence when each allowable value of the dependent variable is associated with a unique (that is, with one and only one) allowable value of the independent variable.

Example of a One-to-One Correspondence:

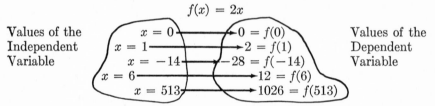

Values of the Independent Variable

Values of the Dependent Variable

There is said to be a many-to-one correspondence if more than one value of the independent variable will yield the same value of the dependent variable when the functional rule is applied.

Example of a Many-to-One Correspondence:

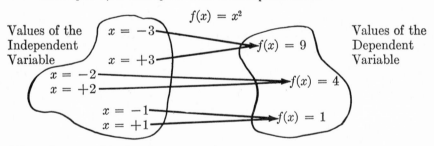

Values of the Independent Variable

Values of the Dependent Variable

The other two kinds of correspondence, one-to-many and many-to-many, are *not* functions as functions are defined here.

All of this simply means that one or many values of the independent variable may correspond to one value of the dependent variable, but more than one value of the dependent variable can never correspond to any one value of the independent variable.

In the salesman example there were two variables, y and n. This should not be misinterpreted as being typical of functions, for the dependent variable y can be a function of two, three, or a thousand independent variables. For example, suppose an investigator finds that a particular firm's sales S are a function of the price p it charges for its product, the amount of money it spends on advertising a, the country's population n, and per capita income y. This relationship could be shown as:

$$S = f(p, a, n, y) \tag{5}$$

Usually in such multivariable functions as this four-variable one, it is more convenient to label each independent variable with the same letter, say x, and then to distinguish among them with subscripts. Thus (5) might become

$$S = f(x_1, x_2, x_3, x_4) \tag{6}$$

where x_1 is price, x_2 is advertising expenditure, x_3 is population, and x_4 is per capita income. This might be compressed even more as

$$S = f(x_i) \qquad i = 1, 2, 3, 4 \tag{7}$$

If y is a function of two variables, x_1 and x_2, the functional relationship among them might be $y = ax_1 + bx_2 + c$, where a, b, and c are constants. Supposing that $a = 2$, $b = 3$, and $c = 1$, this becomes

$$y = 2x_1 + 3x_2 + 1 \tag{8}$$

The values which x_1 assumes do not depend on the values of x_2, or vice versa, but the value of y depends on both of the *independent* variables, as shown in Figure 1–3.

Functions can be manipulated in essentially the same way that numbers can. They can be added, subtracted, multiplied, and divided (provided the divisor is not zero). This property makes it possible to have functions which are combinations of other functions. Thus, it is meaningful to write

$$f + g, \quad F - G, \quad \frac{f}{g}, \quad F \cdot G, \text{ etc.}$$

where f, g, F, and G are functions. Suppose $f(x) = 2x$, $F(x) = 3x^2$, $g(x) = -16x$, and $G(x) = -12x^3$. Then a new function H could be defined as

$$H(x) = G + F + f + g$$

so that

$$H(x) = -12x^3 + 3x^2 + 2x - 16x$$
$$= -12x^3 + 3x^2 - 14x \tag{9}$$

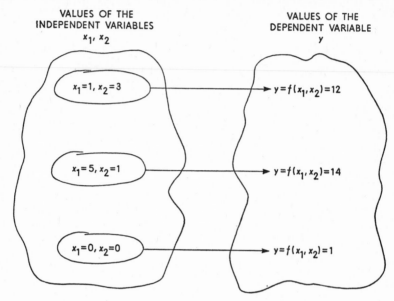

Figure 1–3

Another example of a combination of functions would be where

$$f(x) = (x - 3)^2$$
$$g(x) = (x + 1)$$

and

$$F = \frac{f}{g}$$

so that

$$F(x) = \frac{(x - 3)^2}{(x + 1)} \tag{10}$$

A somewhat more complicated operation with functions is that of expressing a "function of a function." Such a *composite function* might be written as $f[g(x)]$ or $y = G[f(x)]$. The process can be illustrated by an example. Suppose $y = G(x)$ where $G(x) = x^2$, and $x = f(n)$ where $f(n) = 3n$. Then, by substituting for x, it can be seen that y depends on n, that is, is a function of n.

$$
\begin{aligned}
y &= H(n) \\
&= G[f(n)] \\
&= G[3n] \\
&= (3n)^2 \\
&= 9n^2
\end{aligned}
\tag{11}
$$

Thus, y is said to be a composite function, H, and, in this case, $H(n) = 9n^2$.

The idea of the composite function is demonstrated in Figure 1–4 by reference again to the notion of a function as a "machine" for

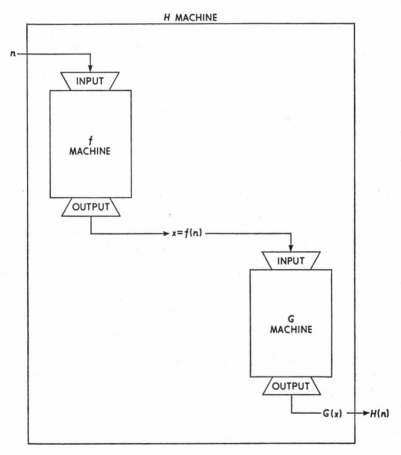

Figure 1–4

converting input values into outputs. Thus, values of n are inputs into the f machine, the outputs being the values $x = f(n)$. These outputs then become inputs into the G machine. The latter's outputs are, of course, the values, $y = G(x) = G[f(n)] = H(n)$. It is usually more convenient to call the composite function $H(n)$ rather than to refer to it by its constituent parts, $G(x)$ and $f(n)$.

The reader will come to appreciate the great power of the function concept and of the notation developed here after he has used both for some time. The exercises of this chapter will also serve to illustrate the meaning and importance of functions. Nearly all of this book is concerned in some way or another with functions, either functions of one variable such as $y = f(n)$ or functions of several variables such as $S = f(p, a, n, y)$.

2. GRAPHS OF FUNCTIONS AND EQUATIONS

A function has been defined as a rule for associating a value to a dependent variable, y, on the basis of a value for each of a number of independent variables. A diagram such as Figure 1–2 is useful for illustrating in *one* diagram the value of y for several values of the independent variable. In diagrams of this kind, the order in which the values of the dependent variables are shown is immaterial. However, in most practical problems the values of the independent variables can be ordered, e.g., placed in order of increasing or decreasing value. In such a case the functional relationship can be depicted best on a rectangular coordinate system.

If y is a function of one variable, the graph of y is the set of points (x, y), or, since $y = f(x)$, the set of points $[x, f(x)]$ in a two-dimensional space. If f is a function of two variables, x and y, the graph of f is the set of points (x, y, z) or $[x, y, f(x, y)]$ in a three-dimensional space for which $z = f(x, y)$. Conceptually, this view of a graph can be extended to a function having any number, say n, of independent variables; then the graph would be a set of "points" in an $(n + 1)$ dimensional space.

The concept of a two-dimensional graph involving one independent and one dependent variable is more familiar than the recognition of the function implicit in the graph. Consider a function relating the area of a square A to the length of one of its sides, s:

$$A = g(s) = s^2 \qquad s \text{ nonnegative} \qquad (12)$$

In order to display the graph of this equation, consider a few arbitrarily selected values of s and the corresponding values of g:

Where s is	0	$\frac{1}{2}$	1	2	3	4	5	6	$\cdots$
The function $g(s) = s^2$ is	0	$\frac{1}{4}$	1	4	9	16	25	36	$\cdots$

These pairs, each representing a point, $[s, g(s)]$, can be plotted

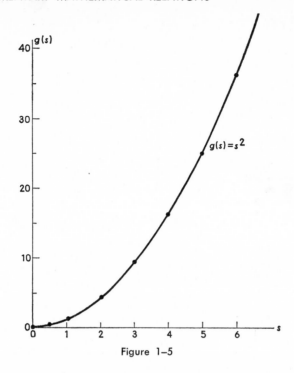

Figure 1–5

on the familiar rectangular coordinate system, as in Figure 1–5. The points are connected because of an implicit assumption that s can assume any nonnegative value. Note that the graph of the function is restricted to the positive quadrant. Obviously this is not true of all functions.

Note also that although it is common to speak of the "graph of a function," it would be more accurate to say the "graph of the equation defining a function" for the graph actually is of the equation. The graph of an equation, of course, is defined as the collection of points whose coordinates satisfy the equation.

The graph of the function $y = 3x - 2$ is displayed in Figure 1–6 where it is seen to be a line. A function of the form $y = a + bx$ where a and b are constants is said to be a *linear function* because of the shape of the associated graph; that is, the graph of the function is a straight line.

The function $g(s)$ in equation (12) and Figure 1–5 also has a special name. Or, rather, it is one example of a category of functions, the *quadratic functions*, whose distinguishing feature is that the highest exponent is a two; that is, the quadratic function is of the

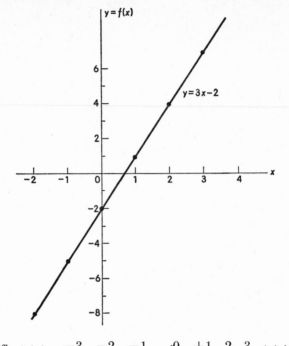

x	$\cdots$	-3	-2	-1	$\cdot 0$	$+1$	2	3	$\cdots$
y	$\cdots$	-11	-8	-5	-2	$+1$	4	7	$\cdots$

Figure 1–6

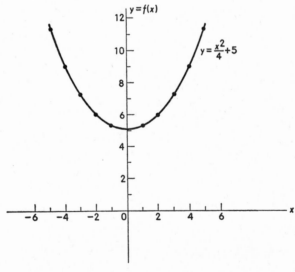

x	$\cdots$	-5	-4	-3	-2	-1	0	$+1$	2	3	4	5
y	$\cdots$	$11\frac{1}{4}$	9	$7\frac{1}{4}$	6	$5\frac{1}{4}$	5	$5\frac{1}{4}$	6	$7\frac{1}{4}$	9	$11\frac{1}{4}$

Figure 1–7

form $ax^2 + bx + c$ where a, b, c are constants (b and c may be zero but a may not be). Another example of a quadratic function is $y = x^2/4 + 5$. See Figure 1–7.

The functions and graphs examined thus far have been relatively simple. Consider now a more complex example, the functional relationship between the proportion of his taxable income that a taxpayer might pay under the federal personal income tax and his income. Let T designate taxes in dollars; Y, taxable income; and P, the proportion T/Y. Taxes are a function of income, say $T = f(Y)$. Hence, $P = f(Y)/Y$; that is, P is a composite function of Y. Designating this new function as $g(Y)$, it is possible to write

$$P = g(Y) \tag{13}$$

The federal tax laws are written so that P increases as Y increases, but it increases in "jumps" as Y moves from one bracket to another. For example, for certain taxpayers the situation is as shown in this table:

Taxable Income (Y)	Tax (T)
Not more than $2000	20% of taxable income
$2000 but not more than $4000	$400 plus 22% of excess over $2000
$4000 but not more than $6000	$840 plus 26% of excess over $4000
$6000 but not more than $8000	$1360 plus 30% of excess over $6000

etc.

The specific form of the function $g(Y)$ can be written as follows:

T	$P = \dfrac{T}{Y}$	
$.20Y$	$.20$	if Y is not more than $2000
$400 + .22(Y - 2000)$	$.22 - \dfrac{40}{Y}$	if Y is $2000 but not more than $4000
$840 + .26(Y - 4000)$	$.26 - \dfrac{200}{Y}$	if Y is $4000 but not more than $6000
$1360 + .30(Y - 6000)$	$.30 - \dfrac{440}{Y}$	if Y is $6000 but not more than $8000

etc.

Its graph is shown in Figure 1–8.

Functions come in what may seem to be a bewildering variety: functions of one variable, functions of two or more variables, combinations of functions, composite functions, etc. Some are complicated in the way that (13) is complex. Others are complicated in the sense that they are not defined everywhere over some interval, i.e., their graphs are not "smooth." Such is the case with the function (1) which related a salesman's commission income to his sales where the latter could be 0, 1, 2, 3, . . .

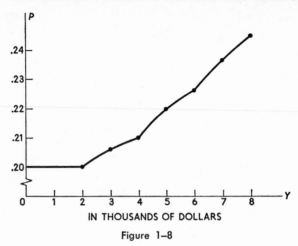

Figure 1–8

Figure 1–9 shows the graph of (1). This is a *discrete* function—as opposed to a *continuous* function such as (12). Note that the

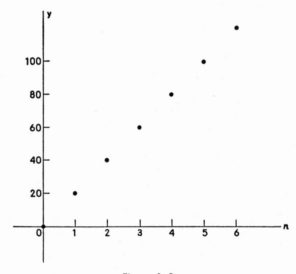

Figure 1–9

points represented by the dots in Figure 1–9 cannot be connected to form a smooth line since this would imply that the function, y, exists (is defined) for nonintegral values of n between, for example, $2\frac{1}{2}$ and $3\frac{1}{2}$, clearly an unrealistic statement in view of the original statement of the problem.

This raises the issue of restrictions which may be imposed on functions—such as the requirements set on (1) whereby n must be integral ("a whole number") and nonnegative. This is an example of a restriction imposed by the nonmathematical aspects of the problem. Some restrictions, on the other hand, are a result of conventions and definitions of mathematics. For instance, if

$$g(x) = \frac{1}{x + 2} \qquad (14)$$

the function g is not defined when $x = -2$ since division by zero is not a meaningful algebraic operation. In this book, and indeed in most mathematical writing, it is understood when writing expressions such as (14) that all possible values of the independent variable x are permitted except those which are explicitly prohibited or which, because of the mathematics, are impossible ($x = -2$ in the example).

Restrictions on the variables of functions are often stated in terms of inequality signs: $>$ and $<$. The reader will no doubt recall that "$<$" means "less than" and "$>$" means "greater than." An elementary understanding of the concepts and laws of inequalities is essential since inequalities are an important part of mathematical analysis. They also play a key role in many business applications of mathematics.

The concept of an inequality involves a comparison of two numbers, a and b. If a does not equal b, that is, if $a \neq b$, then one of the two is greater than the other; i.e., either

$a > b$, or, expressed another way, $b < a$
(read: "a greater than b or b less than a")

if a is the greater, or

$a < b$ or $b > a$

if b is the greater. Each of these four ways of expressing the two possible relations is termed an inequality.

The compound symbol

$a \geq b$ or $b \leq a$

called a "weak inequality" as opposed to the others which are "strong inequalities," expresses the idea that either a is greater than b *or* a is equal to b—only the third possibility, b greater than a, is excluded.

Inequality relationships are governed by the following laws:

1. If $a > b$ and $b > c$, then $a > c$.
2. If $a > b$, then $(a + c) > (b + c)$ for every c.
3. If $a > b$ and $c > 0$, then $(ac) > (bc)$.
4. If $a > b$ and $c < 0$, then $(ac) < (bc)$.
5. If a, b, and c are positive numbers and $a < b$, then $c/a > c/b$ and in particular $1/a > 1/b$.

One possible confusion in the algebra of inequalities arises from operations with negative numbers. Clearly $5 > 3$, but it is not always immediately obvious that $3 > -5$. Also the rule for multiplication of both sides of an inequality by a positive number seems more reasonable than the one for multiplication by a negative one where the direction of the inequality is reversed. These examples illustrate the point:

i) Multiply $5 > 3$ by $+2$ ii) Multiply $5 > 3$ by -2
   Solution: $10 > 6$ Solution: $-10 < -6$

iii) Multiply $-3 < 5$ by $+2$ iv) Multiply $-3 < 5$ by -2
   Solution: $-6 < 10$ Solution: $6 > -10$

Inequalities have "solutions" just as equations do. Suppose $y = 3x$. Then for any stipulated value of x there is a corresponding

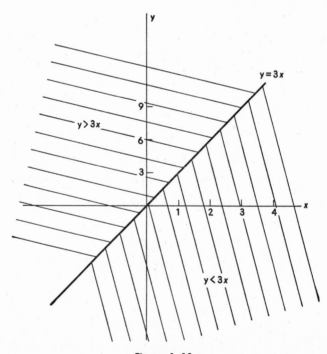

Figure 1–10

"solution" value of y. If $x = 15$, for example, the solution of the equation is $y = 45$; if $x = b$ the solution is $y = 3b$; etc. Suppose the inequality $y \geqq 3x$ is now considered. Then, for any stipulated value of x there is a corresponding *set* of solution values of y. For example, if $x = 15$ the solution set is $y \geqq 45$; i.e., y may be 45 or any number greater than 45.

Inequalities also have graphs. Consider $y = 3x$ again. Its graph is shown in Figure 1–10. The region *above* the graph of that equation would be designated as *the graph of the inequality* $y > 3x$. Similarly the region *below* is analytically represented by the inequality $y < 3x$. Thus the graph of the equation has partitioned the points in the plane into three sets: those points (x, y) which satisfy the equation and lie *on* the graph of the equation, those points which lie *above* the line, and those which lie *below*. Several of the exercises will further illustrate the point.

EXERCISES, SECTION 1

1. If $f(x) = 5 - 3x$
   find $f(3)$
   find $f(n)$

2. If $G(u) = \dfrac{u + 1}{u^2}$
   find $G(4)$
   find $G(x + y)$
   find $G(0)$

3. Find $f(5)$ where $f(x) = ax^2 + bx + c$ if
   a) $a = 2$, $b = 5$, $c = 1$
   b) $a = 1$, $b = 0$, $c = 5$

4. Find $G(4)$ where $G(u) = \dfrac{5u + a}{bu - 4}$ if
   a) $a = 5$, $b = 2$
   b) $a = 4$, $b = 1$

5. If $f(x_1, x_2) = 5x_1 + 6x_2 + 5$
   find $f(4, 3)$
   find $f(0, 1)$
   find $f(0, 0)$

6. If $h(u, v) = \dfrac{3a + 6u + v}{7(u - v)^2}$
   find $h(1, 0)$
   find $h(4, 6)$
   find $h(n, n)$

7. If $F(x) = 3x^2$ and $H(x) = 2x + 1$
   a) Determine $F(x) \cdot H(x)$

   b) Determine $\dfrac{F(x)}{H(x)}$

   c) Determine $F(x) + H(x)$

8. If $G(x) = 4x + 3$ and $h(x) = \dfrac{x^2 + 3}{x}$, find $A(0)$, $A(5)$, and $A(-6)$
where

   a) $A(x) = G(x) - h(x)$

   b) $A(x) = [G(x)] \cdot [h(x)]$

   c) $A(x) = \dfrac{G(x)}{h(x)}$

   d) $A(x) = G[h(x)]$

9. If $Y = f(s) = 3s^2$ and $s = F(u, v) = 2u + v$, express Y as a function
of u and v.

10. If $Y = g(a, b) = 3a + b$
     $a = f(u) = 2u^2$

     $b = h(u) = \dfrac{u}{u + 1}$

express Y as a function of u

11. If $F(y) = 4y^2 + 4y - 6$ and
     $G(x) = 2x - 1$
find $F(y) \cdot G(x)$

12. If $g(x_1, x_2) = 5x_1 + 6x_2^2$ and
     $h(g) = 3g^2$
compute $h(3, 4)$

EXERCISES, SECTION 2

13. Graph the following functions:

   a) $y = x + 5$

   b) $y = 6$

   c) $y = 3 + \dfrac{4}{x}$

   d) $y = x^2 - x$

14. Graph the following functions:

   a) $f(x) = x + 1$

   b) $g(x) = x^2 - 1$

   c) $x = 5$

   d) $h(x) = 16x^2 - \dfrac{3}{x}$

15. State whether the functions listed in Exercise 13 are linear, quadratic,
or neither.

16. State whether the functions listed in Exercise 14 are linear, quadratic,
or neither.

17. A worker's daily pay is based on the number of potato sacks which
he loads and packs. During a recent five-day period, his output and
pay were as follows:

	Day 1	Day 2	Day 3	Day 4	Day 5
Output (x)......	125	184	173	112	150
Pay (y)........	$7.50	$11.04	$10.38	$6.72	$9.00

Graph y as a function of x.

18. In a production situation, total production costs may be regarded as being made up of fixed costs—costs such as rent, administrative salaries, etc., which do not vary regardless of production level—and of variable costs, which do vary as production changes. Given the following information, graph the total cost of producing as a function of the number of units produced:

	Production Level			
	Zero Units	250 Units	300 Units	700 Units
Fixed costs.....	3000	3000	3000	3000
Variable costs......	0	3125	3750	8750

19. Graph the inequality

$$x + y > 5$$

Show on the graph that the point ($x = -2$, $y = 4$) does not satisfy the inequality.

20. Which of the following inequalities are correct and which are incorrect?
    a) $10 < -15$
    b) $-1 > 0$
    c) $a \geq a$
    d) $-3 < -5$
    e) $-(-2) < -1$

21. a) Multiply $x > 6$ by $+3$.
    b) Multiply $x > 2$ by -2.

22. a) If $2x \leq y$ and $y \leq 6$, what is the maximum value of x?
    b) Divide $x < 6$ by 2.

23. The Thule Company rebuilds and sells used refrigerators. It has 10,-000 square feet of warehouse space in which to store its inventory of refrigerators. If each refrigerator occupies 12 square feet, express the number of refrigerators which can be stored, in terms of an inequality.

24. A firm's fixed costs are $5000 per month. Variable costs are $1.50 per unit at all levels of production. Selling price of each unit is $2.75. Graph the firm's total revenue and total cost curves for the production range from 1000 units to 10,000 units. At what production level will costs be exactly equal to revenues?

25. The Argos Company enjoys a monopoly on the production of a certain rare mineral, being the owner of the only operating mine. Since

the market for this mineral is limited, the company has found that the price it can get for its product declines as its production goes up. It has, in the past, observed the following relationship between selling price and quantity produced:

Quantity (in Cwt.)	Price (per Cwt.)	Total Revenue
2	500	1,000
4	450	1,800
10	300	3,000
25	250	6,250
50	200	10,000
75	180	13,500
100	160	16,000
150	120	18,000
200	75	15,000
250	50	12,500

Fixed costs are $5000 per period; variable costs are $100 per cwt., regardless of production level.

a) Graph the revenue function and the total cost function on the same chart over the output range from 0 to 250 units per period (units being expressed in cwt., as per the above chart).

b) At what production level do you think the firm would wish to operate in order to gain the most profit?

26. The Clytemnestra Company has two warehouses and three retail outlets. Warehouse number one (which will be denoted by W_1) has a capacity of 12 units; warehouse number two (W_2) holds 8 units. These warehouses must ship the product to the three outlets, denoted by O_1, O_2, and O_3. O_1 requires 8 units, O_2 requires 7 units, and O_3 requires 5 units. Thus there is a total storage capacity of 20 units, and also a demand for 20 units. The question is, which warehouse should ship how many units to which outlet? (The objective being, of course, to accomplish this at the least possible cost.)

Costs of shipping from either warehouse to any of the outlets are known and are summarized in the following table, which also sets forth the warehouse capacities and the needs of the retail outlets:

	O_1	O_2	O_3	Capacity
W_1...............	$3.00	$5.00	$3.00	12
W_2...............	2.00	7.00	1.00	8
Needs (units)	8	7	5	

The table indicates, for instance, that it costs $3.00 to ship a unit from warehouse 1 to outlet 1; it costs $7.00 to ship a unit from warehouse 2 to outlet 2, etc.

This problem is a simple example of the so-called "transportation problem" encountered in operations research literature. The method for solving it belongs to the theory of linear programming, an advanced technique which will be considered later on in this text. However, this particular example may be solved graphically without recourse to advanced methods.

To accomplish this, let x represent the quantity shipped from warehouse 1 to outlet 1. Since the requirements of outlet 1 are 8 units, clearly

$$0 \leq x \leq 8$$

that is, x must be at least zero, since negative quantities can't be shipped, but x must not be greater than 8. It follows, then, that the quantity shipped from warehouse 2 to outlet 1 must be equal to $(8 - x)$.

Now let y represent the quantity shipped from warehouse 1 to outlet 2. Then, by the same reasoning expressed above,

$$0 \leq y \leq 7$$

and the quantity shipped from warehouse 2 to outlet 2 must be equal to $(7 - y)$. Consider the table below:

	O_1	O_2	O_3
W_1	x	y	$12 - x - y$
W_2	$8 - x$	$7 - y$	$x + y - 7$

Note that the quantities shipped from both warehouses to outlet 3 have been determined by simply subtracting the quantities shipped to outlets 1 and 2 from the total capacities of the warehouses.

To find the total cost of shipments, multiply the figures for costs in the first table by those for the quantities shipped in the second table. This gives the total cost function:

$$C(x, y) = 3x + 5y + 3(12 - x - y) + 2(8 - x) + 7(7 - y)$$
$$+ 1(x + y - 7)$$
$$= 94 - x - 4y$$

The problem now is to find values of x and y which will minimize the value of $C(x, y)$ and at the same time which will "fit" the requirements of the problem, namely, that x and y satisfy the six inequalities:

$$0 \leq x \leq 8$$
$$0 \leq y \leq 7$$
$$7 \leq x + y \leq 12$$

If these inequalities are graphed, the result will be a polygon formed by their intersections. Values of x and y which satisfy all the inequalities (i.e., all the restrictions on x and y) will be in or on this polygon; all other possible values of x and y are "inadmissible." Obviously, to *minimize* the expression $C(x, y) = 94 - x - 4y$, it is necessary to find value of $x + 4y$ which is as large as possible but such that x and y are still in or on the polygon. Therefore the point will be somewhere on the upper rim of the polygon. Linear programming theory states that only the values of the *corners* of the polygon need be examined in a situation like this.

Graph the six inequalities and determine their points of intersection (the corners of the polygon). Determine which values of x and y, represented by corners of the polygon, result in a minimum value for the cost function. Determine the minimum cost figure, and prepare a table showing how many units are shipped from each warehouse to each outlet.

CHAPTER 2

RATES OF CHANGE

T HIS chapter lays a foundation for the calculus. The notions of rate of change, limit, and continuity will be introduced. The derivative concept will be presented and defined in terms of rates of change and limits. Although limits are only briefly and informally treated, it should be realized that it is the limit concept which permits the transcendence to higher mathematics.

1. SLOPE OF A LINE AND RATE OF CHANGE

As was seen in Chapter 1, a straight line can be analytically represented by a function or an equation of the form

$$y = bx \text{ or } y = a + bx \tag{1}$$

If $b = -4$ and $a = 20$, then (1) can be represented by the graph in Figure 2–1.

Each variable and constant in $y = a + bx$ has a special name: y and x are the dependent and independent variables, respectively; b (the coefficient of the independent variable) is the *slope;* and a is the *intercept.* The intercept is the value of the function y when $x = 0$; that is, it is the height of the graph of the function when the latter "intercepts" the y-axis. In the example above, if $x = 0$, then $y = +20$; that is, the intercept is 20.

The slope of the line is positive when the line extends from the lower left of the coordinate system to the upper right, that is, when the line slopes up as x increases. When the line slopes down from upper left to lower right as x increases, the slope is said to be negative (as in Figure 2–1). Looked at in another way, positive slope means that y increases when x is increased and vice versa, whereas negative slope means that y decreases when x is increased.

The sign of the slope indicates whether y increases or decreases

21

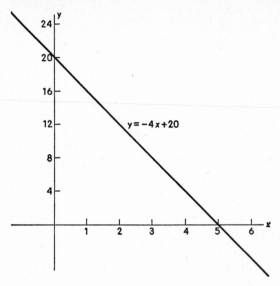

Figure 2–1

when x is increased; the magnitude of the slope indicates how much y is increased or decreased for each change in x. For example, $y(1) = 16$ and $y(2) = 12$ in (1). Thus y changes by four units for each unit change in x.

The notion of slope, which is intuitively reasonable, can be made precise in terms of the notation of "finite increments" or finite differences. Let $\Delta f(x)$ ("delta f-of-x") be defined as the *difference* between two values of a function $f(x)$ associated with two adjacent values of x, say, x_1 and x_2:

$$\Delta f(x) = f(x_2) - f(x_1) \tag{2}$$

If $f(x) = x$, then, by definition

$$\Delta x = x_2 - x_1$$

The definition in (2) has three corollaries which should be noted:

1. If $f(x)$ is a constant, $f(x) = c$, then $\Delta f(x) = 0$.
   Proof: $\Delta f(x) = f(x_2) - f(x_1)$. But $f(x_2) = c$ and $f(x_1) = c$, therefore $\Delta f(x) = c - c = 0$.

2. $\Delta cf(x) = c\Delta f(x)$ where c is a constant.
   Proof: $\Delta cf(x) = cf(x_2) - cf(x_1) = c[f(x_2) - f(x_1)] = c\Delta f(x)$

3. If f, g, and h are functions of the same variable, x, then $\Delta(f + g - h) = \Delta f + \Delta g - \Delta h$.

Proof: $\Delta[f(x) + g(x) - h(x)] = [f(x_2) + g(x_2) - h(x_2)] - [f(x_1) + g(x_1) - h(x_1)] = [f(x_2) - f(x_1)] + [g(x_2) - g(x_1)] - [h(x_2) - h(x_1)] = \Delta f(x) + \Delta g(x) - \Delta h(x)$

Consider now the application of (2) to the equation of a line, $y = a + bx$:

$$\begin{aligned} \Delta y &= \Delta(a + bx) \\ &= \Delta a + \Delta bx \\ &= b\Delta x \end{aligned}$$

Then, dividing both sides by Δx,

$$\frac{\Delta y}{\Delta x} = \frac{b\Delta x}{\Delta x} = b \tag{3}$$

But b is the slope of the line as stated above. Thus it has been shown that $\Delta y/\Delta x$ is the slope of (1).

This view of slope explains the sign of b: when y and x move in the same direction so that Δx and Δy have the same sign, the ratio $\Delta y/\Delta x$ is positive and so is b, otherwise $\Delta y/\Delta x$ is negative and $b < 0$. It is clear also why the slope of a horizontal line is said to be zero: $\Delta y/\Delta x = 0$ because $\Delta y = 0$ regardless of changes in x. Finally, the case of vertical lines can be explained. For such a case, slope is not defined since $\Delta x = 0$ and division by zero is inadmissible. (Because Δy is "infinitely large" it is sometimes said that a vertical line has a slope of infinity, but this is a convention rather than a consequence of the definition.)

The intuitive notion of the slope of a line is thus formalized as, where S is the slope,

$$S = \frac{\Delta y}{\Delta x} = \frac{\Delta f(x)}{\Delta x} \qquad \text{if } y = f(x) = a + bx \tag{4}$$

Because the graph of f is a straight line, it is clear that the slope at any point is the same as the slope at any other point, i.e., does not depend on the value of x, and is, in fact, S as just defined.

It will be useful to expand the slope definition of (4) so it is in a different form, rewriting it as

$$S = \frac{\Delta f(x)}{\Delta x} = \frac{f(x_2) - f(x_1)}{\Delta x} \tag{5}$$

since $\Delta f(x) = f(x_2) - f(x_1)$.

Then, because $x_2 = (x_2 - x_1 + x_1) = (x_2 - x_1) + x_1 = \Delta x + x_1 = x_1 + \Delta x$,

$$S = \frac{f(x_1 + \Delta x) - f(x_1)}{\Delta x}$$

or

$$= \frac{f(x + \Delta x) - f(x)}{\Delta x} \tag{6}$$

That (4) yields the same result for S as does (6) is illustrated by these two examples:

Example (i)

Given $y = m + bx$, find S.

Solution:

Method 1. $S = \dfrac{\Delta y}{\Delta x} = \dfrac{\Delta(m + bx)}{\Delta x} = \dfrac{0 + b\Delta x}{\Delta x} = b$

Method 2. $S = \dfrac{f(x + \Delta x) - f(x)}{\Delta x}$

$$= \frac{[m + b(x + \Delta x)] - [m + bx]}{\Delta x}$$

$$= \frac{b\Delta x}{\Delta x} = b$$

Example (ii)

Given $y = 612 - 12z$, find S.

Solution:

Method 1. $S = \dfrac{\Delta y}{\Delta z} = \dfrac{\Delta(612 - 12z)}{\Delta z} = \dfrac{\Delta(-12z)}{\Delta z} = -12$

Method 2. $S = \dfrac{612 - 12(z + \Delta z) - (612 - 12z)}{\Delta z}$

$$= \frac{-12\Delta z}{\Delta z} = -12$$

Consider now the function defined by $f(x) = bx^2$, whose graph is Figure 2–2. Application of (6) to this yields

$$S = \frac{f(x + \Delta x) - f(x)}{\Delta x} = \frac{b(x + \Delta x)^2 - bx^2}{\Delta x}$$

$$= \frac{b[x^2 + 2x\Delta x + (\Delta x)^2] - bx^2}{\Delta x}$$

$$= 2bx + b\Delta x \tag{7}$$

This expression for slope has no meaning here since it contains x and Δx. This is understandable since a serious error has been committed. A definition has been applied to a situation to which it is

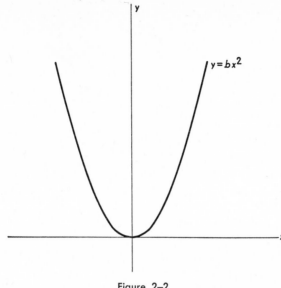

Figure 2–2

inapplicable: $y = bx^2$ is a curve (Figure 2–2), not a line, whereas
(6) so far has been shown to give the slope *only* when applied to
straight lines. The graph of $y = bx^2$ reveals that the function has a
different slope at each point; this is the reason why the formula for
S contains x. Hence there is no single number S which is the slope of
the graphic representation of $y = bx^2$ for all values of x.

It is clear from the graphs of functions which are not linear,
such as Figure 2–2, that it does not make sense to talk of *the* slope
of the function because the slope changes from one value of x
to another. The concept of slope must be broadened, and this is
done by speaking of the *rate* of change of the function *at a point*.
The fact that this rate of change refers to a particular point may
be emphasized by speaking of it as an instantaneous rate of change.

This chapter will have as its main concern the development of a
technique for defining and making explicit the rate of change (or
slope) of functions like that in Figure 2–2. The concepts of instantaneous rate of change and derivative will be developed for
this purpose. To do this, however, the concept of limit must first be
introduced.

2. LIMITS AND CONTINUITY

The concept of the limit is fundamental to the calculus. A good
deal of effort has been expended to make the concept rigorous. It

will, however, be approached here on an informal basis; in particular, the limit theorems will be offered without proof.

Suppose a variable y takes on the values

$$1\tfrac{1}{2},\ 1\tfrac{1}{4},\ 1\tfrac{1}{8},\ 1\tfrac{1}{16},\ 1\tfrac{1}{32},\ 1\tfrac{1}{64}\ \cdots \tag{8}$$

This variable is apparently getting closer and closer to the number 1, and it seems reasonable to describe this process by saying that *y is approaching 1 as a limit.* The philosophical conjecture—that it is doubtful y will ever equal 1 no matter how close it gets to 1—may be interesting, but it does not change the feeling that 1 is a limit of y. Two other examples of limits follow. The sequence

$$\tfrac{1}{1},\ \tfrac{1}{2},\ \tfrac{1}{3},\ \tfrac{1}{4},\ \tfrac{1}{5},\ \cdots \tag{9}$$

apparently approaches 0 as a limit. However, the sequence

$$1.5,\ 1.05,\ 1.005,\ 1.0005,\ \cdots \tag{10}$$

apparently approaches 1 as a limit.

Each of these examples involves a sequence of values for a variable, say y. Each sequence is described by actually showing a number of consecutive values of y which then imply how additional values might be obtained. A more exact approach is to describe analytically how each member of the sequence can be obtained. Consider the series in (8). An analytical representation might be

$$y = 1 + \frac{1}{2^n} \tag{11}$$

where n is a positive integer taking the value $n = 1, 2, 3, \ldots$. The limit of the sequence can be described by saying that the limit of the variable y, as n increases indefinitely, is 1. Or, symbolically,

$$\lim_{n\to\infty} y = \lim_{n\to\infty}\left(1 + \frac{1}{2^n}\right) = 1 \tag{12}$$

For the sequence in (9) and (10), the analytical representations might be, respectively:

$$\lim_{n\to\infty} y = \lim_{n\to\infty}\frac{1}{n} = 0 \tag{13}$$

and

$$\lim_{m\to\infty} y = \lim_{m\to\infty}\left(1 + \frac{5}{10^m}\right) = 1 \tag{14}$$

It is necessary now to distinguish between *the limit of a variable* and *the limit of a function of a variable.* The examples refer to the limit of the variable y. In fact, y is a function of the variable n. Thus, one can speak of

the *sequence* of n
the *limit* of the sequence of n
a *function* of n
the *sequence* of the function of n
the *limit* of the function of n as n increases

The reader should clearly distinguish between the variable, n; the limit of the variable (call this limit a); the function of the variable, y; and the limit of the function as the variable approaches *its* limit. It is the latter which is of most interest here:

$$\lim_{n \to a} y \quad \text{(read: "the limit of } y \text{ as } n \text{ approaches } a\text{")}$$

The examples given above were all for the case where n is a "discrete" variable. The concept also applies, and is much more useful, for the *continuous* case where the variable can take on any value in a specified interval. The limit in this case is defined as follows:

A function $f(x)$ is said to have a limit L as x approaches a if the values of the function $f(x)$ differ arbitrarily little from L for all values of x which lie close enough to a.

The mathematical notation is

$$\lim_{x \to a} f(x) = L \tag{15}$$

The limit may exist even though the value of the function for $x = a$ has no meaning. Even assuming that x, $f(x)$, and a all exist, however, it is still uncertain whether or not $f(x)$ exists when $x = a$ (i.e., whether the function is defined when the variable is at its limit). A case where the function is not defined when $x = a$ is where $f(n) = 1/n$ and $a = 0$. Since $1/0$ is not defined, $f(0)$ is not defined. Note, however, that $f(n)$ is defined for n "close to" a, no matter how close.

Also, even if n, $f(n)$, and a all exist, it is uncertain whether or not $f(n)$ has a limit as n approaches a. Thus, there are four cases:

$f(a)$ is defined and $f(n)$ has a limit as $n \to a$;
$f(a)$ is not defined but $f(n)$ has a limit as $n \to a$;
$f(a)$ is not defined and $f(n)$ has no limit as $n \to a$;
$f(a)$ is defined but $f(n)$ has no limit as $n \to a$.

Only those functions which do have limits (first two cases) will be considered.

The following rules are useful in determining limiting values of functions for given values of the variable:

1. The limit of a sum or difference of two (or more) functions is equal to the sum or difference of their limits:

$$\lim_{x \to a} [f(x) \pm g(x)] = \lim_{x \to a} f(x) \pm \lim_{x \to a} g(x)$$

For example,

$$\lim_{x \to 1} (x^2 - x) = \lim_{x \to 1} x^2 - \lim_{x \to 1} x = 1 - 1 = 0$$

2. The limit of a constant times a function is equal to the constant times the limit of the function:

$$\lim_{x \to a} cf(x) = c \lim_{x \to a} f(x)$$

For example,

$$\lim_{x \to a} 4x^2 = 4 \lim_{x \to a} x^2 = 4a^2$$

3. The limit of the product of two (or more) functions is the product of their limits:

$$\lim_{x \to a} f(x) \, g(x) = \lim_{x \to a} f(x) \cdot \lim_{x \to a} g(x)$$

For example,

$$\lim_{x \to 1} 4x^2 = 4 \left(\lim_{x \to 1} x \right) \left(\lim_{x \to 1} x \right) = 4$$

4. The limit of a quotient of two functions is the quotient of their limits provided that the limit of the denominator is different from zero:

$$\lim_{x \to a} \frac{f(x)}{g(x)} = \frac{\lim_{x \to a} f(x)}{\lim_{x \to a} g(x)}$$

For example,

$$\lim_{x \to 3} \frac{x + 1}{x^2 - 2} = \left[\lim_{x \to 3} (x + 1) \right] \div \left[\lim_{x \to 3} (x^2 - 2) \right] = \frac{4}{7}$$

In some cases, instead of approaching L, the value of $f(x)$ becomes larger and larger as x approaches a. By analogy, it can be said that the limit of $f(x)$ is infinite, since it corresponds to the case where L is not a finite number, i.e., tends to infinity. This is denoted by

$$\lim_{x \to a} f(x) = \infty \qquad (16)$$

It should be noted that x can approach a in two ways, i.e., x can be either $> a$ or $< a; x < a$ indicates that if x approaches a, it is always less than a, and vice versa for $x > a$.

The important concept of continuity of a function is derived from the notion of limits. A function $f(x)$ is said to be continuous for the value $x = a$ if both these conditions are met:

1. $f(a)$ exists and is finite.
2. $\lim_{x \to a} f(x) = f(a)$ whether a is approached from above or below.

For example, $f(x)$ is continuous for $x = a$ in Figure 2–3, but not in Figure 2–4. In the latter case $f(x)$ is said to be discontinuous for

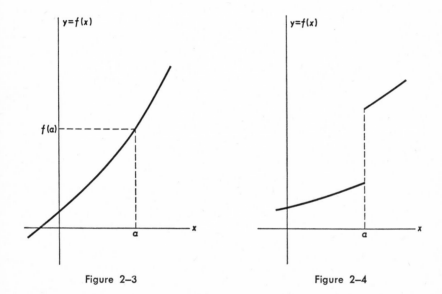

Figure 2–3   Figure 2–4

$x = a$. A function of $f(x)$ is said to be continuous in an interval if it is continuous for all values of x in that interval.

From the definition of a limit and the definition of continuity, it follows that the sum, difference, and product of two continuous functions are themselves continuous and that the quotient of two continuous functions is continuous at every point at which the denominator does not vanish. In addition, continuous functions of continuous functions are continuous. Thus, nearly all of the functions to be treated in this book are continuous; in particular, all polynomials are continuous and all rational functions (quotients of polynomials) are continuous except at points where the denominators vanish.

3. INSTANTANEOUS RATE OF CHANGE

It is now possible to consider what is meant by the rate of change of a nonlinear function. Let the instantaneous rate of change of a function, or the rate of change of a function at a point, be defined as

$$\lim_{\Delta x \to 0} \frac{\Delta y}{\Delta x} = \lim_{\Delta x \to 0} \frac{\Delta f(x)}{\Delta x} \tag{17}$$

Clearly, as seen in the preceding section, this limit does not always exist. When it does, however, it can be given an intuitive meaning just as in the linear case: it is the slope of the graph of the function.

In the case of the previously considered function, $y = bx^2$, the (instantaneous) rate of change is, using (6) and (17),

$$
\begin{aligned}
\lim_{\Delta x \to 0} \frac{f(x + \Delta x) - f(x)}{\Delta x} &= \lim_{\Delta x \to 0} \frac{b(x + \Delta x)^2 - bx^2}{\Delta x} \\
&= \lim_{\Delta x \to 0} \frac{bx^2 + 2bx\Delta x + b(\Delta x)^2 - bx^2}{\Delta x} \\
&= \lim_{\Delta x \to 0} (2bx + b\Delta x) \\
&= 2bx + 0 \\
&= 2bx
\end{aligned}
$$

The graphical interpretation of this limit is easy to follow. See Figure 2–5. Let x assume some value, say 3, and let $b = 1$. Construct a tangent line to f at the point $[3, f(3)]$. The slope of the tangent is 6; and by the theorem that two graphs which are tangent have equal slopes at the point of tangency, the slope of f is 6 at the point $[3, f(3)]$, i.e., when $x = 3$. But the formula says the same thing, since

$$\lim_{\Delta x \to 0} \frac{b(x + \Delta x)^2 - bx^2}{\Delta x} = 6 \text{ when } b = 1 \text{ and } x = 3$$

In other words, the instantaneous rate of change of y (or f) with respect to x at $x = x_0$ is the slope of the tangent to the graph of $y = f(x)$ at the point of tangency $[x_0, f(x_0)]$.

Rates of change at a point are of fundamental importance when they exist. In fact, a new function, to be called a *derivative*, will be defined as the instantaneous rate of change (rate of change at a point) of y with respect to x. Thus the *derivative* of a function f at the point x is

$$\lim_{\Delta x \to 0} \frac{f(x + \Delta x) - f(x)}{\Delta x} \tag{18}$$

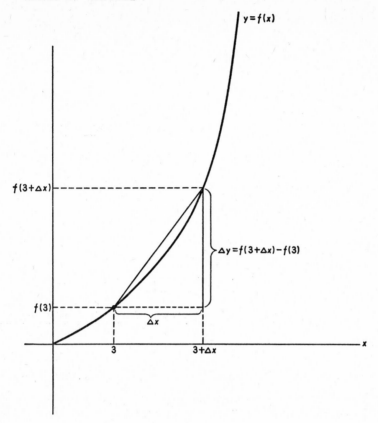

Figure 2–5

The definition in (18) shows that the derivative of a function is itself a function. It is designated in a variety of ways, the limit notation of (18) being the most cumbersome of these. Recalling that $y = f(x)$, each of the following is an equivalent and acceptable way of denoting the derivative of a function $f(x)$:

$$y' , f'(x) , D_x f(x) , \frac{dy}{dx}, \frac{df(x)}{dx} \qquad (19)$$

Each of these should be viewed as a complete symbol, not as a set of variables or functions related by certain operations. In particular, dy/dx is here defined not as a quotient or ratio but as a symbol for the derivative of a function $y = f(x)$.

Examples of application of (18):

    i) The derivative (instantaneous rate of change) of a constant is zero.

    If $y = f(x) = c$, where c is a constant, then

$$\lim_{\Delta x \to 0} \frac{f(x + \Delta x) - f(x)}{\Delta x} = \lim_{\Delta x \to 0} \frac{c - c}{\Delta x} = 0$$

ii) The derivative of a straight line is a constant.
If $y = f(x) = 2x$, then

$$\lim_{\Delta x \to 0} \frac{f(x + \Delta x) - f(x)}{\Delta x} = \lim_{\Delta x \to 0} \frac{2(x + \Delta x) - 2x}{\Delta x}$$

$$= \lim_{\Delta x \to 0} \frac{2x + 2\Delta x - 2x}{\Delta x}$$

$$= \lim_{\Delta x \to 0} \frac{2\Delta x}{\Delta x} = 2$$

iii) The derivative of a second-degree polynomial is a linear function of x.
If $f(x) = bx^2 + cx + a$, then

$$\lim_{\Delta x \to 0} \frac{f(x + \Delta x) - f(x)}{\Delta x}$$

$$= \lim_{\Delta x \to 0} \frac{b(x + \Delta x)^2 + c(x + \Delta x) + a - bx^2 - cx - a}{\Delta x}$$

$$= \lim_{\Delta x \to 0} \frac{bx^2 + 2bx\Delta x + b(\Delta x)^2 + cx + c\Delta x + a - bx^2 - cx - a}{\Delta x}$$

$$= \lim_{\Delta x \to 0} \frac{(2bx + c)\Delta x}{\Delta x} + \frac{b(\Delta x)^2}{\Delta x} = 2bx + c$$

The derivative gives information about the behavior of the function. In particular, the derivative relates the rate of change in the function to "infinitesimal changes" in the independent variable. Graphically, in the two-variable case, this means that the derivative is the analytical representation of the slope of the graph of the function. Since functions do not always have limits, they do not always have derivatives. This is equivalent to saying that a function does not always have a slope at every point.

Suppose $f(x)$ is *increasing* at some $x = x_0$. This means that a small increase in x causes an increase in y, and a small decrease in x causes a decrease in y. In other words, the signs of the related changes in x and y are the same. In the discussion of the slope of lines it was said that such a situation would be described by saying that the slope was positive since the ratio $\Delta y / \Delta x$ was positive. A similarly reasoned statement was made for a decreasing function: x and y move in opposite directions, $\Delta y / \Delta x$ is negative, and the slope is labeled negative.

Analogous reasoning applies to the more general case and to derivatives. If $f(x)$ is increasing at some $x = x_0$, it is said that the graph of the function has positive slope since $f'(x)$ will be positive and it *is* the slope. This and the opposite situation are summarized in the following theorem for which a proof is offered.

Theorem

> Suppose $f(x)$ has a nonzero derivative, $f'(x_0)$, at $x = x_0$. Then at $x = x_0$, $f(x)$ is an *increasing* function if $f'(x_0) > 0$, and a *decreasing* function if $f'(x_0) < 0$.

Proof:

> Assume that $f'(x) > 0$. Then, recalling that $f'(x_0) = \lim_{\Delta x \to 0} \Delta y / \Delta x$ since $y = f(x)$, if Δx is sufficiently near zero, $\Delta y / \Delta x$ will be so near $f'(x_0)$ that $\Delta y / \Delta x$ as well as $f'(x_0)$ will be *positive*. But if $\Delta y / \Delta x$ is positive, Δy and Δx have the same signs and $f(x)$ is increasing at $x = x_0$. Similarly, if $f'(x_0) < 0$, then Δy and Δx are of opposite signs if Δx is sufficiently near zero, and hence $f(x)$ is a decreasing function at $x = x_0$.

A function $y = f(x)$ is said to be *stationary* at $x = x_0$ if it is neither increasing or decreasing at that point; that is, if and only if $f'(x_0) = 0$. At such a point the slope of the curve is neither positive nor negative since it is zero—that is, the tangent at that point is horizontal. Figure 2–6 shows an example of a function which is first decreasing, then stationary, then increasing as x increases.

Much of the calculus is concerned with the process of finding the derivative of a function, a process called differentation. The

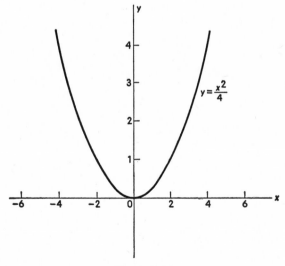

Figure 2–6

reader will want to develop some facility at this process in order to master the applications which are to follow. The next chapter will be devoted to the various techniques which permit differentiation of a wide variety of functions. Examples from business and economics will be introduced in the exercises and in later chapters.

EXERCISES, SECTION 1

Graph and determine the slopes of Exercises 1–10, assuming that the first-mentioned variable in each instance is the dependent one:

1. $y = 3x + 2$
2. $u = 4v - 6$
3. $r + 2s - 1 = 0$
4. $y = 6 - 2v$
5. $3y - 3x + 1 = 0$
6. $u = \dfrac{v}{3} - 4$
7. $y = 8$
8. $x = \dfrac{y - 2}{3}$
9. $v = \dfrac{u + 6}{4}$
10. $2s = 1 - r$

EXERCISES, SECTION 2

11. Suppose $y = f(x) = 2x + 1$ and $z = F(x) = x - 4$.
    a) Determine the limit of y as x approaches 2.
    b) Determine the limit of z as x approaches 2.
    c) Determine the limit of yz as x approaches 2.
12. Suppose $u = f(w) = 7w$, and $v = g(w) = w - 5$.
    Determine the limit of $(u + v)$ as w approaches 3.
13. If $r = f(t) = 3t - 14$ and $s = g(t) = 2t + 11$, find the limit of r/s as t approaches zero.
14. Find the limit of x^2 as x approaches 6.
15. Graph the equation $y = \dfrac{3x}{x^2 - 4}$ over the range $x = -5$ to $x = +7$. What is the value of y when $x = -1$? Toward what limit does $f(x)$ appear to be converging as x tends to infinity?
16. $f(x) = \dfrac{x^2 - 2}{x + 1}$ is undefined at the point $x = -1$. By successive approximations, or by inspection, determine the limit of $f(x)$ as x approaches -1.
17. Give that $y = f(x) = \dfrac{x^2 + 2x}{x^2 - 3x - 4}$, what limit does $f(x)$ approach as x approaches 4?

18.[1] Any investigation conducted in a technical organization invariably has as its end result the publication of a suitable report. Such reports are circulated and distributed to any members of the organization who might have some slight interest in the subject matter. As a consequence, most of the professional employees of such an organization find sizable stacks of internal mail on their desks each day, increasing rapidly with the size of the organization until essentially the whole day can easily be taken up perusing these communications.

The following notation will be used to formalize the relationship between organization size and efficiency:

n = number of professional employees;
m = number of reports turned out per year;
t_w = average net time in days to complete a report (including the investigation, analysis, writing, etc., but not counting any time spent reading other reports) per employee;
t_r = average time in days to read a report;
k = fraction of all reports received and read by the average professional employee.

On the assumption that everyone reads the km reports he receives in a year, the net time the average individual has left to do creative work is $(240 - kmt_r)$ days, taking 240 as the total number of working days per year and assuming that his only task is reading and writing reports. The number of reports he will therefore turn out in a year, on the average, is

$$\frac{240 - kmt_r}{t_w}$$

The above relation can be solved for m, as follows:

$$mt_w = 240n - kmt_r n$$
$$m(t_w + kt_r n) = 240n$$
$$m = \frac{240n}{t_w + kt_r n}$$

a) What will happen to the number of reports as n becomes very large? Using the definition of the limit as given above, the answer would be given by

$$\lim_{n \to \infty} m = \lim_{n \to \infty} \frac{240n}{t_w + kt_r n}$$
$$= \lim_{n \to \infty} \frac{240}{\frac{t_w}{n} + kt_r}$$
$$= \frac{240}{kt_r}$$

---

[1] Abridged from E. P. Adler, "Relationships between Organization Size and Efficiency," *Management Science,* Vol. 7, 1960, pp. 80–84.

Thus the maximum number of reports that can be produced by an organization which satisfies the assumptions, regardless of the number of personnel hired, is a fixed number which depends on the number of working days per year, the average time required to read a report, and the fraction of all reports received by the average employee.

b) What happens to the number of reports produced as the fraction of all reports received by the average employee is reduced?

EXERCISES, SECTION 3

19. Suppose $f'(x) = 0$ at the point $x = 5$.
    a) What is the slope of $f(x)$ at $x = 5$?
    b) Is $f(x)$ increasing, decreasing, or stationary at $x = 5$?
20. Suppose $y = 6x - 2$.
    a) What is the slope of y?
    b) What is the derivative of y?
    c) Is the function increasing or decreasing?
21. If $f(x) = 2x^2 + 4x$, what is $f'(x)$? (Use the "delta" method described in the chapter.)
22. If $f(x) = 3x^2$, find $f'(x)$.
23. Find the derivatives of the following, using the "delta" method.
    a) $2x + 1$
    b) $x^2 + 3x + 1$
    c) $x^3 - 1$
    d) $(x + 1)^2$
24. The cost of transporting the Thyrsis Company's finished products is $15 per ton to move the goods by rail from the plant to a central warehousing and shipping point four miles away. It costs $25 per mile to move a ton of goods from the warehouse to the distributors.
    a) Express the linear equation describing the cost per ton of shipping goods from the factory to the distributors, letting C = cost per ton and D = distance in miles from the warehouse to the distributors. Graph the equation. What is the slope of the line?
    b) What would it cost to ship a ton of goods to a distributor 14 miles from the warehouse, including the cost of shipping goods from the plant to the warehouse?
25. A store is attempting to reduce an overly large inventory and has marked down all items by 30% of the original markup over the wholesale price. The store customarily marks up its prices 50% above wholesale. For example, an item which cost the store $10 (wholesale price) would be marked up to a retail price of $10 + (.50) (10) = $15. Under the 30% markdown this item would be offered at $15 − (.30) (5) = $13.50.
    a) Construct the graph of the equation expressing the original retail price in relation to wholesale price. State the equation in algebraic terms.

    b) Determine the equation expressing the new, reduced retail price in relation to wholesale price. Graph it on the same graph as (*a*) above.

    c) On an item costing $150 wholesale, what was the original retail price? What is the new retail price?

26. Suppose a firm wishes to minimize the amount of inventory on hand in order to hold costs down. If there is a time lag between placing an order for a new supply and the actual receipt of the new items to replenish inventory, then the following situation might occur:

    If R = number of units on hand, and

      M = expected sales per day, and

       x = number of days between ordering and receiving goods,

then the firm will place an order for a new supply of goods when $R = Mx$.

    a) If x is very large, what will happen to inventory holding costs?

    b) If x approaches zero (i.e., delivery is almost immediate) what happens to the firm's optimum "order point"?

CHAPTER 3

DIFFERENTIATION OF FUNCTIONS

THE DERIVATIVE of the function $f(x)$ has been defined as

$$\lim_{\Delta x \to 0} \frac{f(x + \Delta x) - f(x)}{\Delta x} \tag{1}$$

and denoted by any of several symbols, $f'(x)$, $df(x)/dx$, $D_x f(x)$, etc. The process of finding $f'(x)$ was called *differentiation*. Differentiation by direct application of (1) is usually possible, as shown in the examples of the last chapter, but it is nearly always awkward and often laborious. This chapter will develop certain rules of differentiation, each resting on (1), which will permit the rapid, efficient differentiation of certain kinds of functions. The more common of these formulas or theorems the reader should memorize; for convenient reference they are collected in an appendix table.

Some of the examples and exercises will involve business and economic situations, but consideration of the most important applications of the differential calculus will be delayed until a theory of extreme points is developed in the following chapter. Because of their importance in both theoretical and applied work, this chapter will concentrate on techniques of differentiating polynomial functions.

1. ELEMENTARY DIFFERENTIATION THEOREMS

There are two simple differentiation formulas which follow from the discussion at the end of the last chapter. The first is that the derivative of a constant function is zero; the other is that the derivative of a variable with respect to itself is one. In symbolic form these two rules become Theorems 1 and 2:

Theorem 1

$$D_x(k) = 0$$

where k is any constant.

Proof:

$$f'(x) = \lim_{\Delta x \to 0} \frac{\Delta f(x)}{\Delta x} = \lim_{\Delta x \to 0} \frac{0}{\Delta x} = 0$$

Theorem 2

$$D_x(x) = 1$$

Proof:

$$f'(x) = \lim_{\Delta x \to 0} \frac{f(x + \Delta x) - f(x)}{\Delta x} = \lim_{\Delta x \to 0} \frac{f(x_2) - f(x_1)}{\Delta x}$$

$$= \lim_{\Delta x \to 0} \frac{\Delta x}{\Delta x} = \lim_{\Delta x \to 0} 1 = 1$$

The next differentiation rule, dealing with the very important *power function*, is less obvious. The power function is

$$f(x) = x^n$$

n a given real number and x a variable.

The definition of (1) can be applied to find the derivative of this power function:

$$D_x(x^n) = \lim_{\Delta x \to 0} \frac{(x + \Delta x)^n - x^n}{\Delta x} = \lim_{\Delta x \to 0}$$

$$\frac{(x + \Delta x - x)[(x + \Delta x)^{n-1} + (x + \Delta x)^{n-2}x + \cdots + (x + \Delta x)x^{n-2} + x^{n-1}]}{\Delta x}$$

$$= \lim_{\Delta x \to 0} [(x + \Delta x)^{n-1} + (x + \Delta x)^{n-2} x + \cdots + (x + \Delta x)x^{n-2} + x^{n-1}]$$

$$= x^{n-1} + x^{n-2}x + \cdots + xx^{n-2} + x^{n-1}$$

$$= nx^{n-1}$$

Thus it has been proven that

$$D_x(x^n) = nx^{n-1} \tag{2}$$

(This proof depended in its second line on the identity

$$a^n - b^n = [a - b][a^{n-1} + a^{n-2}b + a^{n-3}b^2 + \cdots + ab^{n-2} + b^{n-1}])$$

Now it is possible to differentiate some functions "on sight":

$$D_x(x^2) = 2x \qquad D_t(t^3) = 3t^2$$
$$D_u(u^5) = 5u^4 \qquad D_s(s^{3a}) = 3a(s^{3a-1})$$

Since the limit of a product is the product of the limits, the result of (2) can be extended to derive the more general rule,

Theorem 3

$$D_x(kx^n) = knx^{n-1}$$

where k is a constant. This theorem permits sight differentiations such as these:

$$D_x(4x^3) = 12x^2 \qquad \frac{d(5u^2)}{du} = 10u$$

$$D_s(3s) = 3 \qquad D_x(2x^{-8}) = -16x^{-9}$$

The next group of formulas has to do with the derivatives of sums, differences, products, and quotients. First, as might be expected, the derivative of the sum (or difference) of two functions is the sum (or difference) of their respective derivatives. Thus:

Theorem 4

$$D_x[f(x) \pm g(x)] = D_x f(x) \pm D_x g(x)$$

Proof:
Follows from the properties of limits in the preceding chapter.

Less obvious than Theorem 4, and hence somewhat more interesting, is this rule for differentiating a product: the derivative of a product of two functions is the first function times the derivative of the second plus the second function times the derivative of the first. In symbols this becomes

Theorem 5

$$D_x[f(x) \cdot g(x)] = f(x) \cdot D_x g(x) + g(x) \cdot D_x f(x)$$

Proof:

$$D_x(f \cdot g) = \lim_{\Delta x \to 0} \frac{[f(x + \Delta x) \cdot g(x + \Delta x)] - [f(x) \cdot g(x)]}{\Delta x}$$

$$= \lim_{\Delta x \to 0} \frac{[f(x + \Delta x)g(x + \Delta x)] + [f(x + \Delta x)g(x) - f(x + \Delta x)g(x)] - [f(x)g(x)]}{\Delta x}$$

$$= \lim_{\Delta x \to 0} \frac{f(x + \Delta x)[g(x + \Delta x) - g(x)] + g(x)[f(x + \Delta x) - f(x)]}{\Delta x}$$

$$= \lim_{\Delta x \to 0} f(x + \Delta x) \frac{[g(x + \Delta x) - g(x)]}{\Delta x} + \lim_{\Delta x \to 0} g(x) \frac{[f(x + \Delta x) - f(x)]}{\Delta x}$$

$$= \left(\lim_{\Delta x \to 0} f(x + \Delta x) \right)\left(\lim_{\Delta x \to 0} \frac{g(x + \Delta x) - g(x)}{\Delta x} \right)$$

$$+ \left(\lim_{\Delta x \to 0} g(x) \right)\left(\lim_{\Delta x \to 0} \frac{f(x + \Delta x) - f(x)}{\Delta x} \right)$$

$$= [f(x)] \cdot [g'(x)] + [g(x)] \cdot [f'(x)]$$

The theorem can, of course, be written as

$$\frac{d(f \cdot g)}{dx} = f\frac{dg}{dx} + g\frac{df}{dx}$$

Now it is necessary to turn to the case of differentiating a function h when h is given as a quotient of two functions; that is, $h(x) =$

$f(x)/g(x)$. If f and g were at all complicated, the application of the definition of (1) would be a tedious task, and one would be thankful for Theorem 6:

Theorem 6

$$D_x\left(\frac{f(x)}{g(x)}\right) = \frac{g(x)\, D_x\, f(x) - f(x)\, D_x\, g(x)}{[g(x)]^2}$$

In words, the theorem says that the derivative of a quotient is the denominator times the derivative of the numerator *minus* the numerator times the derivative of the denominator, divided by the square of the denominator. Note that the minus sign in the numerator means, unlike the case of a derivative of a product, that the order in the numerator is important.

Before proving Theorem 6 a few examples of its usefulness can be considered.

Example (i)

$$D_x\left(\frac{x^2}{x^3}\right) = \frac{(x^3)(2x) - (x^2)(3x^2)}{x^6} = \frac{2x^4 - 3x^4}{x^6} = -\frac{1}{x^2}$$

(This result could also have been obtained by the application of Theorem 3. How?)

Example (ii)

$$D_x\left(\frac{2x^2 + x}{x^3 - 3}\right) = \frac{(x^3 - 3)(4x + 1) - (2x^2 + x)(3x^2)}{(x^3 - 3)^2}$$

$$= \frac{4x^4 + x^3 - 12x - 3 - 6x^4 - 3x^3}{x^6 - 6x^3 + 9} = \frac{-2x^4 - 2x^3 - 12x - 3}{x^6 - 6x^3 + 9}$$

Example (iii)

$$\frac{d\left(\frac{3u + u^4}{8u}\right)}{du} = \frac{(8u)(3 + 4u^3) - (3u + u^4)(8)}{(8u)^2} = \frac{24u^4}{64u^2} = \frac{3u^2}{8}$$

Example (iv)

When

$$f(s) = \frac{s^4 + 2s^3 + 5s^2 + s + 6}{2s}$$

$$f'(s) = \frac{(2s)(4s^3 + 6s^2 + 10s + 1) - (s^4 + 2s^3 + 5s^2 + s + 6)(2)}{(2s)^2}$$

$$= \frac{3s^4 + 4s^3 + 5s^2 - 6}{2s^2}$$

A proof of Theorem 6 is now offered.

$$D_x\left[\frac{f(x)}{g(x)}\right] = \lim_{\Delta x \to 0} \frac{\dfrac{f(x + \Delta x)}{g(x + \Delta x)} - \dfrac{f(x)}{g(x)}}{\Delta x}$$

$$= \lim_{\Delta x \to 0} \frac{f(x + \Delta x)g(x) - f(x)g(x + \Delta x)}{\Delta x\, g(x)g(x + \Delta x)}$$

$$= \lim_{\Delta x \to 0} \frac{f(x)g(x) - f(x)g(x + \Delta x) - f(x)g(x) + f(x + \Delta x)g(x)}{\Delta x\, g(x)g(x + \Delta x)}$$

$$= \lim_{\Delta x \to 0} \frac{g(x)\left[\dfrac{f(x + \Delta x) - f(x)}{\Delta x}\right] - f(x)\left[\dfrac{g(x + \Delta x) - g(x)}{\Delta x}\right]}{g(x)g(x + \Delta x)}$$

$$= \frac{g(x)f'(x) - f(x)g'(x)}{[g(x)]^2}$$

2. COMPOSITE FUNCTIONS

If y is a function of u and u is a function of x, then y is also a function of x. It is said that y is a "function of a function," that is, it is a *composite function*. Such functions, first introduced in Chapter 1, are extremely important in applied analysis.

Suppose, as an example, that $y = 2u^3 + 4u^2$ and $u = 2x - 1$. Then y could be shown as an explicit function of x by substitution:

$$y = 2(2x - 1)^3 + 4(2x - 1)^2 \tag{3}$$

$D_x y$ could be found by expanding (3) and applying Theorems 1 through 6 as appropriate.

Often, however, it is inconvenient or impossible to substitute and simplify. In such cases a special theorem known as the "chain rule" is used. It is stated here as Theorem 7.

Theorem 7

If y is a differentiable function of u, and u is a differentiable function of x, then y is a differentiable function of x and $D_x y = D_u y \cdot D_x u$.

This "chain rule" is commonly written as

$$D_x f[g(x)] = f'[g(x)]g'(x)$$
$$= D_u f(u) \cdot D_x g(x)$$

or as

$$\frac{dy}{dx} = \frac{dy}{du} \cdot \frac{du}{dx} \tag{4}$$

The last form is somewhat unfortunate since it suggests, incorrectly, that the two derivatives on the right are fractions upon which some kind of "cancellation" can be performed, leaving dy/dx. It is, however, a convenient form in which to remember the theorem.

The following three examples illustrate the use of Theorem 7.

Example (i)

Suppose $u = 3 - v^2$ and $v = w^2 + 3w + 6$. Then

$$\frac{du}{dw} = \frac{du}{dv} \cdot \frac{dv}{dw} = (-2v)(2w + 3)$$

$$= -2(w^2 + 3w + 6)(2w + 3)$$

$$= -(4w^3 + 18w^2 + 42w + 36)$$

Note that v has been eliminated from the final form of the derivative by substituting the expression $w^2 + 3w + 6$ for v. For simplicity in handling the expression it may be desirable to make such a substitution; but, as will be shown later, it is not always convenient.

Example (ii)

Suppose

$$r = s^3 + \frac{1}{s} \text{ and } s = 3t^2 \tag{5}$$

Then

$$\frac{dr}{ds} = 3s^2 - \frac{1}{s^2}, \frac{ds}{dt} = 6t$$

and

$$\frac{dr}{dt} = \left(3s^2 - \frac{1}{s^2}\right)(6t)$$

$$= \left(27t^4 - \frac{1}{9t^4}\right)(6t)$$

$$= 162t^5 - \frac{2}{3t^3}$$

This could also be done by defining r explicitly in terms of t and differentiating. From (5)

$$r = (3t^2)^3 + \frac{1}{3t^2}$$

$$= 27t^6 + \frac{t^{-2}}{3}$$

and

$$\frac{dr}{dt} = 162t^5 - \frac{2t^{-3}}{3}$$

$$= 162t^5 - \frac{2}{3t^3}$$

The result, of course, is the same no matter which method is used; sometimes it will be easier to use the chain rule, and sometimes it will be easier to rewrite the function, as was done above, and perform a single differentiation. In this particular case, there is little difference in the computational work involved.

Example (iii)

Suppose $u = 3v^2$ and $v = c$, c a constant. Then

$$\frac{du}{dv} = 6v \; ; \frac{dv}{dc} = 0 \; ; \frac{du}{dc} = 0$$

A special case of Theorem 7 occurs when one of the constituent parts of the composite function is a power function. Consider this situation in general notation:

$$y = f(u) \; , \qquad u = g(x) = x^n$$

Then, by Theorem 7,

$$\frac{dy}{dx} = \frac{dy}{du} \cdot \frac{du}{dx} \qquad [= f'(u) \cdot g'(x)]$$

$$= nx^{n-1} \frac{dy}{du} \qquad [= nx^{n-1} f'(u)]$$

In other words, Theorem 7 can be used in the differentiation of *powers of functions.* Let $y = f(u) = u^n$. If u is a *variable,* it is known by Theorem 3 that

$$y' = nu^{n-1}$$

and no further analysis is needed. But if u is a *function,* say, $u = g(x)$, then Theorem 7 must be used to find y' since $y = f(u) = f[g(x)] = [g(x)]^n$, $dy/du = d(u^n)/du = n[g(x)]^{n-1}$, and $du/dx = g'(x)$. Then $dy/dx = y' = n[g(x)]^{n-1} g'(x)$ by Theorem 7. Thus Theorem 3 has been generalized to a new, more powerful formula, Theorem 8.

Theorem 8

$$D_x[f(x)]^n = n[f(x)]^{n-1} D_x f(x) \; , \; n \text{ a real number}$$

When $u = f(x) = x$, a variable, simple substitution shows that Theorem 8 reduces to Theorem 3:

$$D_x[f(x)]^n = n(x)^{n-1} D_x(x) = nx^{n-1}$$

Again, several examples serve to illustrate the theorem.

Example (i)

Suppose $y = (x^3 - 2x^2 + 3x + 1)^7$.

This expression could be multiplied by itself seven times, and the derivative of the result could then be obtained. Such an operation would be time consuming and complicated, however. It is easier, if the derivative is desired, to let

$$z = x^3 - 2x^2 + 3x + 1$$

Then $y = z^7$ and $dy/dz = 7z^6$ and $dz/dx = 3x^2 - 4x + 3$. Therefore, by the theorem,

$$\frac{dy}{dx} = (7z^6)(3x^2 - 4x + 3)$$
$$= 7(x^3 - 2x^2 + 3x + 1)^6(3x^2 - 4x + 3)$$

Example (ii)

Suppose $y = (ax^2 + bx + c)^n$. Let $z = ax^2 + bx + c$.

Then $y = z^n$, $dy/dz = nz^{n-1}$, $dz/dx = 2ax + b$, and, by the theorem,

$$\frac{dy}{dx} = n(ax^2 + bx + c)^{n-1}(2ax + b)$$

Example (iii)

Suppose $y = (4x^{4/3} - 12x^{2/3} + 9)^{1/2}$. Let $z = 2x^{2/3} - 3$.

Then $y = (z^2)^{1/2} = z$ (the possibility that $y = -z$ is ignored here). Thus

$$\frac{dy}{dz} = 1$$
$$\frac{dz}{dx} = \frac{4x^{-1/3}}{3}$$
$$\frac{dy}{dx} = \frac{4}{3x^{1/3}}$$

3. HIGHER-ORDER DERIVATIVES

If a function has a derivative for each value of x in some specified interval, then the derivative function is defined for that interval. If, in turn, the derivative function itself has a derivative for one or more points in the specified interval, then this new derivative is called the *second derivative* of the original function.

Thus, if $f'(x)$ is the derivative of $f(x)$, then $D_x[f'(x)]$, often designated $f''(x)$, is the *second* derivative of $f(x)$. Similarly, if $f''(x)$ has a derivative, it is possible to talk about the *third* derivative of $f(x)$, etc., for the *fourth, fifth, nth* derivatives (where n is any positive integer).

The only confusing aspect of these higher-order derivatives is the variety of symbols used for the same function. Some of these symbols are organized in the following table which shows the notation for certain higher-order derivatives of f at x:

Function	First Derivative	Second Derivative	Third Derivative	nth Derivative
$y = f(x)$	$f'(x)$	$f''(x)$	$f'''(x)$	$\cdots f^{[n]}(x)$
$y = f(x)$	$f'(x)$	$f^{[2]}(x)$	$f^{[3]}(x)$	$\cdots f^{[n]}(x)$
$y = f(x)$	$D_x f(x)$	$D_x^2 f(x)$	$D_x^3 f(x)$	$\cdots D_x^n f(x)$
$y = f(x)$	dy/dx	d^2y/dx^2	d^3y/dx^3	$\cdots d^ny/dx^n$

It should be noted that $f^{[n]}(x)$, the nth *derivative* of f, is *not* the same as $f^n(x)$, the nth *power* of f; that is,

$$f^{[n]}(x) = \frac{d^ny}{dx^n} \text{ but } f^n(x) = [f(x)]^n$$

Notational convention on this point varies somewhat. The distinction made here, however, will be adhered to in this book.

The differentiation formulas developed in the earlier sections of this chapter apply, with appropriate modifications, to differentiation at any level. This is demonstrated in the examples and exercises.

Example (*i*)

Let $y = x^3 - 2x^2 + 3x - 10$. Then

$$\frac{dy}{dx} = 3x^2 - 4x + 3$$

$$\frac{d^2y}{dx^2} = 6x - 4$$

$$\frac{d^3y}{dx^3} = 6$$

$$\frac{d^4y}{dx^4} = 0$$

Example (*ii*)

Let $f(x) = \frac{1}{x}$. Then

$$f'(x) = \frac{-1}{x^2}$$

$$f''(x) = \frac{2x}{x^4} = \frac{2}{x^3}$$

$$f'''(x) = \frac{-6x^2}{x^6} = \frac{-6}{x^4}$$

(How else could this example have been worked? Theorem 6 was used here.)

Example (iii)

Let $f(v) = (v^2 - 1)(1/v)$. Then

$$D_v f(v) = (v^2 - 1)\left(\frac{-1}{v^2}\right) + \left(\frac{1}{v}\right)(2v)$$

$$= \frac{1}{v^2} + 1$$

$$D_v^2 f(v) = \frac{-2v}{v^4}$$

$$= \frac{-2}{v^3}$$

and

$$D_v^3 f(v) = \frac{6v^2}{v^6} \quad .$$

$$= \frac{6}{v^4}$$

The significance of the first derivative was discussed in Chapter 2. It was noted that when a first derivative is positive, the function is increasing; when the first derivative is negative, the function is decreasing, and when the first derivative is zero, the function is constant. The second derivative bears the same relation to the first derivative as the first derivative to the function; that is, it provides information about whether the first derivative is increasing, decreasing, or stationary.

In particular, knowledge of f'' at a, b, and c in the cases shown in Figure 3–1 permits an inference in each case about the shape of D_x, just as knowledge of D_x permits an inference about the shape of the function itself. It follows, of course, that a knowledge of D_x^2 should also permit an inference about the function itself. Thus, in the first case shown in Figure 3–1, f'' is a positive constant. Hence, f' must be a line with positive slope, which in turn implies a quadratic like the one shown. Analogous reasoning applies in the column where h'' is a constant, but a negative one.

In the second case, g'' is a linear function with positive rate of change so that g' must be a quadratic and g will be a cubic, perhaps like the one shown. As the reader no doubt suspects by now, the third derivative gives information about the second, and so on. The next chapter will draw on these concepts.

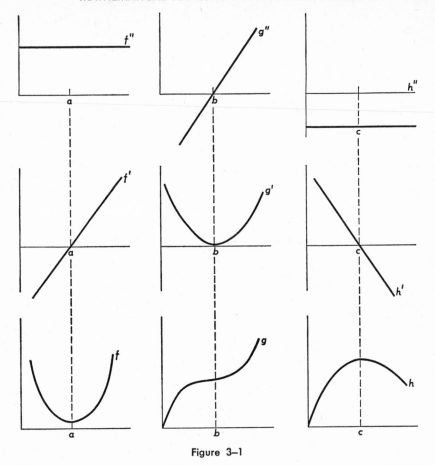

Figure 3–1

4. IMPLICIT FUNCTIONS

Often a function is defined only indirectly through an equation. Suppose the equation

$$5y - 2x = 15 \qquad (6)$$

is given. Clearly, (6) could be rearranged so that y is explicitly defined as a function of x:

$$y = \tfrac{1}{5}(15 + 2x)$$

$$= 3 + \tfrac{2}{5}x$$

Equally clearly, (6) could have been rearranged so x was defined in terms of y:

$$x = \frac{5y - 15}{2}$$

In equation (6), y is said to be an *implicit function* of x. If one solves for y by rearranging terms, y becomes an *explicit function* of x. It is often necessary to perform a mathematical operation on a function which is given implicitly. In simple cases the explicit function can easily be found before performing the operation; but it is not always convenient to do so and thus it is important to know that it may be possible to operate directly on the implicit form of the function.

It is relatively easy to differentiate implicit functions—at least, it is usually easier "to differentiate implicitly" than it is to solve for the explicit form and then to differentiate. In some instances it is impossible to obtain a simple specific form of the function. The technique of implicit differentiation will be illustrated in the examples, where, as is often the case, the "chain rule" will be the major tool.

It should be noted that two assumptions are made in each case: *that there is a function* f(x) *which, when substituted for* y, *will satisfy the original equation; and that this function does possess a derivative at the point or points in question.*

Up to this point, dy/dx has been expressed only in terms of x, i.e., the independent variable. However, when working with functions such as Example (i), it may be impossible or inconvenient to eliminate the dependent variable y from the expression for the derivative. This does not mean that the rate of change of y is dependent on y itself; recall that y is a function of x, and therefore the value of the derivative still depends only upon x even though it may be expressed in terms of both x and y.

The examples and exercises will further illustrate the differentiation of implicit functions.

Example (i)

Let $x^2 + 2xy + y^2 = 6$. Find dy/dx.

Solution:

Differentiate each term as usual, treating y as a function of x, as follows:

a) The derivative of x^2 with respect to x is, of course, $2x$.

b) The derivative of $2xy$ is treated as the product of two functions—$(2x)(y)$ where y is a function of x. Therefore the derivative is

$$(2x)\frac{dy}{dx} + (y)(2)$$

that is, the first term times the derivative of the second, plus the second times the derivative of the first (see Theorem 5).

c) The derivative of the third term, y^2, is $2y\dfrac{dy}{dx}$. (See Theorem 8.)

d) The derivative of 6 is zero.

The derivative of the implicit function is therefore

$$2x + 2x\frac{dy}{dx} + 2y + 2y\frac{dy}{dx} = 0$$

Collecting and rearranging terms, to solve for the derivative, yields

$$(2x + 2y)\frac{dy}{dx} + 2x + 2y = 0$$

$$\frac{dy}{dx} = -\frac{2x + 2y}{2x + 2y}$$

$$= -1$$

Example (ii)

A similar procedure for finding the derivative may be followed if

$$5y - \frac{6}{x^2} + \frac{12}{x} - 6 = 0$$

Solution:

$$5\frac{dy}{dx} + \frac{12}{x^3} - \frac{12}{x^2} = 0$$

$$\frac{dy}{dx} = \frac{12}{5x^2}\left(1 - \frac{1}{x}\right)$$

Example (iii)

If $x^2 + \dfrac{1}{y} + 2xy = 3$, find dy/dx for $x > 0$.

Solution:

$$2x - \left(\frac{1}{y^2}\right)\frac{dy}{dx} + 2x\frac{dy}{dx} + 2y = 0$$

$$\left(2x - \frac{1}{y^2}\right)\frac{dy}{dx} = -(2x + 2y)$$

$$\frac{dy}{dx} = \frac{-2(x + y)}{2x - \dfrac{1}{y^2}}$$

5. INVERSE FUNCTIONS

As indicated in the preceding section, an equation such as

$$5y - 2x = 14 \tag{7}$$

defines not one but two implicit functions:

$$y = f(x) = \tfrac{14}{5} + \tfrac{2}{5}x \quad \text{if } y = f(x) \tag{8}$$

and

$$x = g(y) = \tfrac{5}{2}y - 7 \quad \text{if } x = g(y)$$

If differentiation of (7) were the goal, one would have to distinguish clearly which derivative was required, for, obviously, there are two: f' and g'. If f is considered the original function, then g is said to be the *inverse function* of f. It is conventional to designate an inverse function by the notation f^{-1} if f is the original function. Of course, in the example, $g = f^{-1}$ and $f = g^{-1}$. Note that f^{-1} is the symbol for the function which is the inverse of f, and not a symbol for the reciprocal of f.

If $f(x)$ is continuous and either always increasing or always decreasing, there is a unique inverse, $x = g(y)$. If $f(x)$ is not always increasing or decreasing, there is no unique inverse function $g(y)$. There may be, however, two or more inverse functions. For example, if

$$y = x^2 \quad -\infty < x < \infty$$

there is no unique inverse. But there are two inverse functions:

$$x = g(y) = +\sqrt{y} \quad 0 \le y \le \infty$$

and

$$x = h(y) = -\sqrt{y} \quad 0 \le y \le \infty$$

An important characteristic of functions which are inverse is that their respective rates of change are in a reciprocal relationship. This can be seen in (8). The rate of change of f is the coefficient of x, i.e., 2/5; the rate of change of g is, analogously, the coefficient of y, 5/2. But 5/2 is indeed the reciprocal of 2/5. Thus, as Theorem 9 says, the derivative of an inverse function is the reciprocal of the derivative of the original function:

Theorem 9

If f and g are inverse functions and if g' exists and is non-zero,

$$f'(x) = \frac{1}{g'[f(x)]}$$

Theorem 9, stated here without proof, assumes an easy-to-remember form (but misleading, perhaps, since fractions are *not* involved) if it is recalled that $y = f(x)$ and $x = g(y)$, for then

$$f'(x) = \frac{dy}{dx}$$

$$g'(y) = \frac{dx}{dy}$$

and Theorem 9 becomes

$$\frac{dy}{dx} = \frac{1}{\dfrac{dx}{dy}} \tag{9}$$

if the conditions are met. The theorem and the general notion of inverse relations are illustrated in these examples.

Example (i)

Any number is equal to unity divided by the reciprocal of the number. For example,

$$5 = \frac{1}{\frac{1}{5}}; \qquad 2 = \frac{1}{\frac{1}{2}}; \qquad \frac{3}{2} = \frac{1}{\frac{2}{3}}$$

Thus, if $dy/dx = 3$, then $dx/dy = \frac{1}{3}$, since $3 = 1/\frac{1}{3}$.

Example (ii)

Consider the equation $y = x/2 + 3$, $dy/dx = \frac{1}{2}$, and $dx/dy = 2$.

Examine the graph of this equation (Figure 3–2). Note that the slope of y is $\frac{1}{2}$; i.e., y changes half as fast as x. Note that the slope of x relative to y is 2; i.e., x changes twice as fast as y.

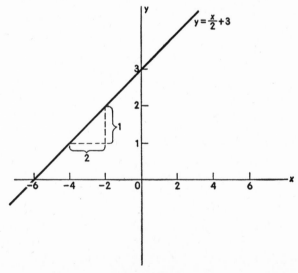

Figure 3–2

Example (*iii*)

Let $r = f(s) = 3s^2 + 5$. Then $dr/ds = 6s$.

If it were necessary to obtain ds/dr by methods learned prior to this section, it would be necessary, as before, to find the derivative of the two functions, $s = \pm\sqrt{r - 5/3}$. This could be done, but it is easier to take the reciprocal of dr/ds. By doing so, the derivative of s with respect to r is immediately found to be $1/6s$. Observe the point $(+2, 17)$ on the graph of this equation (Figure 3–3). By substituting $s = 2$ into the expressions for the derivatives, it is noted that $dr/ds = 12$ at this point, and that $ds/dr = 1/12$. This demonstrates that r is increasing 12 times as fast as s at this point, and that s increases only $1/12$ as fast as r. Examine the point $(-2, 17)$ on the same graph. Note that here the derivative of r with respect to s is -12, while the derivative of s with respect to r is $-1/12$.

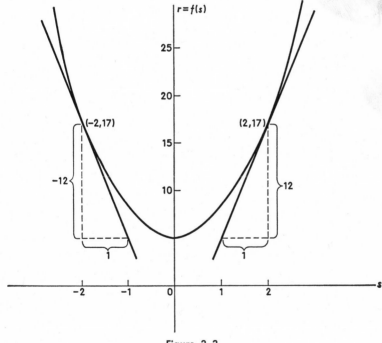

Figure 3–3

Example (*iv*)

If $y = x^6 - 5x^5 + 6/x$, find dx/dy.

Solution:

$$\frac{dy}{dx} = 6x^5 - 25x^4 - \frac{6}{x^2}$$

$$\frac{dx}{dy} = \frac{1}{6x^5 - 25x^4 - \dfrac{6}{x^2}}$$

EXERCISES, SECTION 1

1. Find
   a) $D_x(12)$
   b) $D_x(x)$
   c) $D_x(4x)$
   d) $\dfrac{d(3x^6)}{dx}$
   e) $\dfrac{d(2x^{-2})}{dx}$

2. Find the derivatives of the following:
   a) $x^2 - 2x + 3$
   b) $x + 2$
   c) $x^{-2} + 3x$
   d) $4x^4 - x^3 + 2x^2 - 6x + 11$

3. a) If $y = 2x^2 - 3x$, find dy/dx
   b) If $V = W^n - 6$, find dV/dW

4. Find the derivative of s with respect to t when $s = 2t^a + t^{a-1}$.

5. a) Find the derivative dy/dx if $y = 3x - 4$.
   b) What is the value of the derivative at the point $x = 6$?
      At $x = 10$? For all values of x?

6. Find dy/dx for $y = f(x) = x^2 + x - 3$. What is the value of the derivative at $x = 4$? At $x = 8$? At $x = a$? Is the value of the derivative constant?

7. If $C = a + bY$, what is dC/dY?

8. Suppose the relationship between a company's production volume and its profits is expressed by the following equation:

$$P = 6V - V^2$$

   where
      P = profits (in thousands of dollars) and
      V = production volume (in thousands of units of production)
   a) What is dP/dV?
   b) What is the value of dP/dV at $V = 1$? At $V = 2$? Is the value of the derivative increasing? What does this tell about the rate of change of P as V increases from 1 to 2?
   c) What is the value of dP/dV at $V = 3$? At $V = 4$? What is happening to total profits at volumes of V greater than 3?
   d) Graph the function $P = 6V - V^2$.
   e) Graph the function dP/dV. What happens to the sign of the value of dP/dV as V goes from 2 to 4?
   f) What do the above results suggest regarding the most desirable production volume for this company if it wishes to maximize its profits?

9. Suppose $f(x) = 8x^2 - 4x + 6$ and $g(x) = x^2 + 2$.
   a) Find $D_x f(x)$.
   b) Find $D_x g(x)$.
   c) Find $D_x[f(x) + g(x)]$.

10. Given: $f(x) = 7x - 8$
$$g(x) = x^2 + 3x - 3$$
   a) Find the derivative of $f(x)$.
   b) Find the derivative of $g(x)$.
   c) Find the derivative of $f(x) \cdot g(x)$.
   d) Multiply $f(x)$ by $g(x)$ and find the derivative of the product. Is it the same as the answer to part (c) above?

11. If $f(x) = (x + 3)(2 + x + 3x^2)$, find $f'(x)$.

12. If $g(u) = (u^3 - 2u^2 + u - 16)(u^6 + 4)$, find $g'(u)$.

13. If $g(u) = (u + 1)(u - 1)$, find $g'(u)$.

14. If $u = f(v) = (2v^{1/2})(v^{3/2} + 1)$, find du/dv.

15. If $f(x) = 3x - 2/x$, find $f'(x)$.

16. If $f(y) = y^2 + 2y + 1/y + 1$, find $f'(y)$. Express $f'(y)$ as a number.

17. Suppose $f(x) = x^5/x^2 + 1$. Find the derivative of $f(x)$.

18. Suppose $y = (x + 8)(x - 6)$. Find dy/dx.

19. If $u = 7/V^3$, find du/dV.

20. Company B's total sales revenue is equal to $3x$, where x is the num-- ber of units sold. Its total costs are equal to $500 + (x/20)^2$. Let R be revenue; C, cost; and P, profit. Then, define $P = R - C$.
   a) Give the equation of P as a function of x; graph the equation for values of x from $x = 0$ to $x = 1000$.
   b) Determine the derivative of P with respect to x.
   c) What is the rate of change of profits with respect to volume at the point $x = 600$?
   d) What is the total profit at $x = 600$?

EXERCISES, SECTION 2

21. If $u = f(v) = v^2 - 4$ and $v = g(x) = x + 3$, find
   a) du/dx by the chain rule.
   b) du/dx by substituting $(x + 3)$ for v in the first equation, and differentiating the result.

22. If $u = v^2 + 2v + 8$ and $v = w^3 - 2w$, find du/dw by the chain rule.

23. If $y = x^a$ and $x = z^2 + 2$, find dy/dz.

24. If $r = s^{3/2}$ and $s = t^2 + 2t + 1$, find dr/dt.

25. If $u = v^2 + v - 1$ and $v = 212 + x$, find du/dx.

26. If $y = (x^2 + 8)(1/x)$ and $x = z^2$, find dy/dz.

27. If $m = n^3$ and $n = p^2 + 4$, find dm/dp.

28. If $y = f(x) = 3x^2 - 9x + 15$ and $x = g(u) = u^2$, find dy/du.

EXERCISES, SECTION 3

29. Find the second derivative of y with respect to x, when $y = 9x^2 - 3x + 11$.

30. If $y = (x + 1)(x - 1)$, find d^2y/dx^2.

31. If $u = v^2/v + 1$, find the second derivative of u with respect to v.

32. If $r = 12s - 7$, find the second derivative of r with respect to s.

33. If $f(a) = 12$, what is $f'(a)$? What is $f^{[5]}(a)$?

34. Find the third derivative of $f(x) = x^3 - 2x^2 + 11x + 1$.

35. Find the second derivative of $g(u) = u^a + 5$ with respect to u.

36. In the above exercise, suppose that $a = 3$. Then $g(u) = u^3 + 5$. Find the second derivative.

37. If $f(y) = y/y + 1$, find $D_y^2 f(y)$.

38. If $y = (x^2 + 3x + 7)^7$, find dy/dx.

39. If $u = (2v^2 + 1/v)^3$, find du/dv.

40. If $s = \left(6t^5 - \dfrac{t + 1}{t^2} \right)^8$, find ds/dt.

EXERCISES, SECTION 4

41. Express y as an explicit function of x (if possible) in the following:
    a) $2y - 3x + 6 = 0$
    b) $y^2 - 4x^2 + 4x - 1 = 0$
    c) $4x + 2yx = 6$

42. Using the method of differentiation of implicit functions, find the derivative (of y with respect to x) for each equation in Exercise 41.

43. Find the derivative of y with respect to x when

$$y^2 = x^2 + 8x + 16$$

44. Find the derivative of y with respect to x if $y^2 - 3ax = 0$.

45. If $x^2/25 - y^2/9 = 1$, find dy/dx.

46. If $x^2 + 2xy + y^2 = 0$, find dy/dx.

47. If $(xy)^2 = x + y$, find dy/dx.

48. If $x^3 - y^3 + xy = 0$, find the derivative with respect to x.

49. If $x^2 + y^2 = 25$
    a) Find dy/dx.
    b) When $x = 3$ in the original equation, what does y equal? (*Two* values.)
    c) What is the value of dy/dx at this point?
    d) What does this mean in terms of the rate of change?
    e) What is the value of y in the original equation when $x = 0$?
    f) What is the value of the derivative at this point?
    g) Graph the original function and note the position of the two points identified above.

EXERCISES, SECTION 5

50. Find dy/dx and dx/dy for the following:
    a) $y = 3x^2 - 5$
    b) $2y = x + 3$
    c) $2x + 3y = 7$
    d) $x^2 + 3xy + 3y^2 = 4$

e) $y = \dfrac{x+3}{x-1}$

f) $x = y^5 + 7y^3 + y - 11$

g) $y^2 - 1/y = 2x^3 + 11$

h) $y^{1/2} - 3x = 7$

i) $2x/y - y^2 = x$

j) $y^3 - 2y^2 + 6y - 3/(y+1) - 5 = x$

k) $y^a/x = 1$

51. The Anderson Company has discovered empirically that its profit function can be approximated by the following:

$$P = 3x - 200 - \frac{x^2}{2500}$$

where

P = total profits, in hundreds of dollars,

x = total production volume (in thousands of units) (e.g., if $x = 20$, volume of production is 20,000 units—but do *not* use the 20,000 figure in solving the equation).

The company has also discovered that its total production is related to the size of its labor force by the following equation:

$$x = 4y + \frac{y^2}{100}$$

where

x = total production volume (in thousands of units),

y = number of men employed.

a) What are the company's profits if the labor force consists of 20 men?

b) What is the rate of change of profits with respect to the number of men employed at this point (i.e., find dP/dy)?

c) Is the rate of change increasing or decreasing? To determine this find d^2P/dy^2. To do this, it may be necessary to substitute in the first derivative.

d) Should more men be hired?

CHAPTER 4

OPTIMIZING FUNCTIONS OF ONE VARIABLE

The ESSENCE of many decision problems, especially in business applications, is the idea of optimizing—manipulating one or more decision variables until one outcome is settled upon as being "better" than the others. Most of the remainder of this text will be devoted to the problems of optimization and the mathematical techniques underlying various optimizing procedures. In this chapter the emphasis will be on using the concepts of the differential calculus to locate those values of the variables which will be optimum in some sense, i.e., which will maximize or minimize something. The relationship to a more traditional method of solution for this category of problems, the marginal analysis, will be described briefly in the next chapter.

1. MAXIMA AND MINIMA

A function is said to be at a *maximum* at some value of the independent variable if the value of the function at that point is greater than it is at any other point in the immediate neighborhood. There are several important aspects of this definition. First, it is a perfectly plausible, common-sense idea corresponding closely to the intuitive notion of a maximum. Second, the decision variable, the variable subject to direct control, is the independent variable, whereas the dependent variable, subject only to the indirect control that comes through manipulation of the independent variable, is the variable which may or may not assume a maximum value. Third, it may be that no maximum exists, that one and only one exists, or that many exist over the interval in question. Fourth, the definition serves perfectly well, with appropriate adjustments, for the concept of a *minimum*.

Consider an example. A commuter bus line finds that its present average charge of 20 cents a mile results in about 8000 passenger-miles of business a day in the area where this rate is in effect. The company's management believes that the number of daily passenger-miles will rise by about 400 for each one-cent decrease in this rate, and fall by about 400 for each one-cent increase. The question is whether or not the current rate is yielding the greatest possible gross revenue to the company.

Clearly, the company believes that its passenger volume (V passenger-miles per day) depends, other things unchanged, on the fare structure (r cents per mile). Equally obviously, the company's gross revenue (S dollars) depends on both the volume and the average rate charged. The problem can now be restated, first in general functional notation, then more specifically. First, then:

General Statement:
$$V = f(r) \qquad r \geq 0$$
$$S = g(V, r) \qquad V, r \geq 0$$
Find r^* which maximizes S.

(Note that r^* stands for some particular value, the optimizing value, of the variable r.)

Restatement in a more specific form requires that the functional notations f and g be replaced by specific expressions. The problem says that $V = 8000$ when $r = 20$, that $V = 8000 + 400 = 8400$ when $r = 19$, and, by similar reasoning, that $V = 16,000$ when $r = 0$. Thus, provided r is nonnegative and assuming continuity, $V = 16,000 - 400r$. Turning to the other function, S is clearly r times V. Thus

Specific Statement:
$$V = 16,000 - 400r \qquad r \geq 0$$
$$S = rV$$
$$= r(16,000 - 400r)$$
$$= 16,000r - 400r^2 \qquad r \geq 0$$
Find r^* which maximizes S.

One way to solve the problem is by trial and error, i.e., construction of a table showing the value of S associated with each of "a large number" of plausible values of r. Such a table might be:

r $\$$	0	.05	.10	.19	.20	.21	.30	.40	.50
S $\$$	0	700	1200	1596	1600	1596	1200	0	-2000

The table suggests that the current rate of 20 cents is indeed maximizing gross revenues for the company. But note that the table can never prove this inference since not all values of r were tested. Of course, in this and in most such situations a reasonable person would be willing to conclude that S is maximized when $r = 20$ cents, particularly if he were to plot the tabular values as is done in Figure 4–1. The function S, depending on r, achieves what seems to be a maximum when $r = 20$.

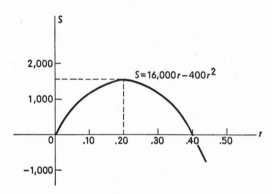

Figure 4–1

How could r^* have been identified analytically? After all, trial and error will usually be laborious, perhaps impossible, and always incomplete. The answer can be found in Figure 4–1 where it should be noted that the function S has its maximum where the graph becomes parallel to the horizontal axis. That is, the maximum occurs when *the slope of the graph of the equation is zero.* A moment's reflection confirms that the slope of the graph would also be zero where the function is at a minimum.

An analytic procedure for finding the maximum of the function S is now available, *for it is known from Chapter 3 that a slope of zero corresponds to a derivative of zero.* Thus, the problem of finding a maximum for S reduces to finding those values of r which make the derivative, S', zero. There are two steps:

1. Find S':

$$S = 16,000r - 400r^2$$

$$\frac{dS}{dr} = 16,000 - 800r$$

2. Find the value or values of r that will make $S' = 0$:

$$\frac{dS}{dr} = 0$$
$$16{,}000 - 800r = 0$$
$$800r = 16{,}000$$
$$r^* = \frac{16{,}000}{800} = 20$$

There are several traps here for the unwary, traps that will become apparent only when this procedure is justified by a formal
theorem setting forth the exact conditions under which a maximum
or minimum of a function can be found by the derivative test. One
dilemma is obvious: how does one know whether the procedure has
located a *maximum* or a *minimum?* After all, the intuitive justification simply related a horizontal slope to a zero first derivative.
Figure 4–2 shows the case of a minimum. If $y = x^2 - 4x$, $f'(x) =$
0 at $x = 2$, a minimum value of the function.

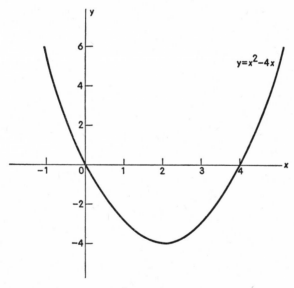

Figure 4–2

Figure 4–3, on the other hand, is an illustration of a function
which has a zero derivative at $x = 2$, but no maximum or minimum
there!

These difficulties mean a more rigorous analysis is in order.
After noting the convention that an open interval, denoted (a, b),
implies $a < c < b$, whereas a closed interval, denoted $[a, b]$, implies
$a \leqq c \leqq b$, an important theorem can be stated.

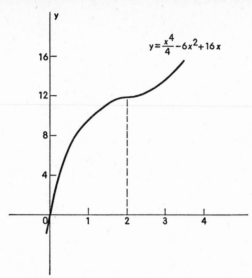

$$y = \frac{x^4}{4} - 6x^2 + 16x$$

Figure 4–3

Theorem

If $f'(c) = 0$ where c is some value of x, and if $f''(x)$ exists for every x in any open interval containing c, then

    i) $f(c)$ is a *maximum* value of f if $f''(c) < 0$; and

    ii) $f(c)$ is a *minimum* value of f if $f''(c) > 0$.

If the function f is continuous in the closed interval $[a, b]$ then it is certain that there exist numbers r and s in that interval such that $f(r)$ is *the* maximum and $f(s)$ is *the* minimum value of the function in the interval. Maxima and minima are also sometimes referred to as extrema or optima. A proof of the theorem may be found in most advanced calculus books.

Returning to the function relating bus revenues to fares, it can be seen that application of the theorem yields a maximum value of S at $r = 20$: first, $S' = 0$ if and only if $r = 20$; second, $S''(20) < 0$ since $S'' = -800$ for all r (in particular, for $r = 20$). Thus, S has one and only one maximum in the interval $(0, +\infty)$.

For the function of Figure 4–2, $y = x^2 - 4x$ so that $y' = 0$ at $x = 2$. Then, since $d^2y/dx^2 = 2$ for all x (and, in particular, for $x = 2$), $d^2y/dx^2 > 0$ and the extremum located by the first derivative test is a minimum.

It would be well to note several important aspects of this theory of extrema.

    1. A function may have an extreme point (i.e., either maximum or minimum) which cannot be identified by the theorem since f' may not exist at that point. (See Figure 4–4.)

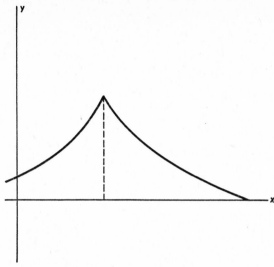

Figure 4–4

2. End points of the interval and other discontinuities must be examined independently of the theorem, a step not to be overlooked
since end points are often extrema. For instance, in Figure 4–5,
there are minima at points b and d, but the lowest value of the
function is at the end point $x = 0$. The theorem will *not* identify
such end-point extrema; separate examination of the behavior of
the function at the end points is necessary.
3. Except for the exceptions in (1) and (2), an extremum cannot
exist unless $f' = 0$. Having $f' = 0$ is therefore a necessary but not
a sufficient condition for the existence of an extremum.
4. A function may have a first derivative equal to zero at some
point which is not an extreme point. Such a point is an example
of an *inflection point* and may be identified by the fact that $f'' = $
zero. (An inflection point is any point where $f'' = $ zero.)
5. A function may have more than one maximum or minimum in an
interval. For example, if a function has two maxima as in Figure
4–5, application of the theorem will locate both. The value of f at

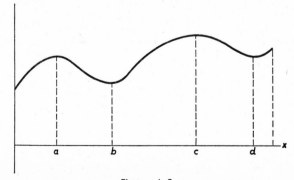

Figure 4–5

the two points will not necessarily be the same, and it may be desirable to distinguish between the *absolute maximum* within the interval—point *c* in the figure—and points which are only *relative maxima*—point *a*.

If the number $f(c)$ is a maximum value of f in an interval, it is called a *relative maximum* of f. It is also an *absolute maximum* if $f(c) \geqq f(x)$ for every x in the closed interval. Analogously, one speaks of *relative* and *absolute minima*. Sometimes "local" is used for "relative" and "global" for "absolute."

6. If the second derivative at the point in question either is itself zero or does not exist, then the second derivative test of the theorem cannot be used. (It still may be possible to identify the extrema, however.)

7. For other than simple functions the problem of solving the equation $f'(x) = 0$ is a substantial one, and indeed may be impossible. Example: If $f(x) = x^{10} - x^8 + x^5$, then $f'(x) = 10x^9 - 8x^7 + 5x^4$, and solution of $f'(x) = 0$ requires advanced numerical techniques.

With these qualifications in mind, two examples of the use of the theorem will be considered. Additional examples are in the exercises at the end of the chapter. Several illustrations of the application of the theorem to business and economic situations are in Chapter 5.

Example (i)

Suppose $f(x) = x^2 - 6x - 16$. Then $f'(x) = 2x - 6$. This derivative is zero when $2x - 6 = 0$, that is, when $x = 3$. See Figure 4–6. The second derivative $= 2$. At $x = 3$, $f''(x) = 2$

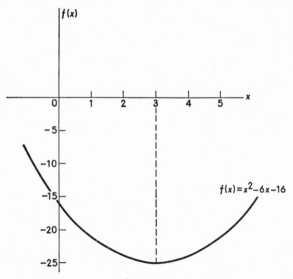

Figure 4–6

which is greater than zero. Thus, $f(x)$ is at an extreme point when $x = 3$, and it is known that this extremum is a minimum. It is, in fact, an absolute minimum in the interval $(-\infty, +\infty)$ because there is only one point at which $f'(x) = 0$, $f''(x)$ is positive at $x = 3$, and $f(x)$ is continuous over the interval $(-\infty, +\infty)$.

Example (ii)

Suppose $f(x) = x^3/3 - 9x + 50$. Thus, $f'(x) = x^2 - 9$ and $f'(x) = 0$ when $x^2 - 9 = 0$. Recognizing that $x^2 - 9 = (x+3)(x-3)$, it can be seen that $(x+3)(x-3) = 0$. Therefore, $f'(x) = 0$ either if $x = -3$ or if $x = +3$: there are two extrema as Figure 4–7 shows. The second derivative $(= 2x)$ reveals that the function f is at a *maximum* when $x = -3$ since $f''(-3) < 0$ and at a *minimum* when $x = +3$ since $f''(+3) > 0$.

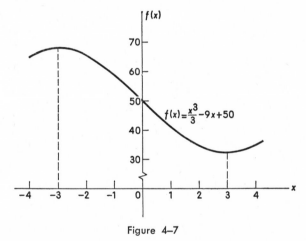

Figure 4–7

2. SOLVING EQUATIONS

A crucial step in applying the theory developed in the last section involves finding the solution of the equation, $dy/dx = 0$. "Solving" means finding the conditions under which the asserted statement is true. In the present context, this means finding all those values, if any, of x which will, when substituted, make $dy/dx = 0$.

Consider the equation

$$y' = 16{,}000 - 800r \qquad (1)$$

There is no question about this statement; it is true either by assumption or because previous work has shown it to be true. Consider the equation

$$y' = 0 \qquad (2)$$

where it is understood that this is the same y' as before. The statement $y' = 0$ may be true sometimes, always, or never. By substitution it is easy to see that the two statements together require that

$$16,000 - 800r = 0 \tag{3}$$

Application of certain properties of elementary algebra then reveals that for (3) to be true the variable r must be 20, i.e.,

$$r^* = 20 \tag{4}$$

Reviewing, it can be said that when (4) is true, (2) and (3) are true; (1), of course, is always true. Thus the condition $r = 20$ is the solution to the equations in (2) and (3). In fact, 20 is said to be the *root* of the equation in (3) because it makes (3) a true statement.

In many applications of mathematics it is necessary to solve individual equations, i.e., to find the roots of the equations. In general, this is a complex subject; the particular cases to be encountered in this book, however, will not be difficult.

The simplest case is where the highest power is one:

$$ax + b = 0 \tag{5}$$

Solution of (5) is a familiar process. Provided $a \neq 0$, the solution is, in fact,

$$x = \frac{-b}{a}$$

The second case is where the highest power is two. The general form, called the *quadratic equation* in one unknown is

$$ax^2 + bx + c = 0 \qquad a \neq 0 \tag{6}$$

The solution to (6) proceeds as follows:

$$ax^2 + bx + c = 0$$

$$x^2 + \frac{b}{a}x = -\frac{c}{a}$$

$$x^2 + \frac{b}{a}x + \left(\frac{b}{2a}\right)^2 = -\frac{c}{a} + \left(\frac{b}{2a}\right)^2$$

$$\left(x + \frac{b}{2a}\right)^2 = \frac{b^2}{4a^2} - \frac{c}{a}$$

$$\left(x + \frac{b}{2a}\right) = \pm\sqrt{\frac{b^2 - 4ac}{4a^2}}$$

$$x = \frac{-b}{2a} \pm \frac{\sqrt{b^2 - 4ac}}{2a}$$

$$x = \frac{-b \pm \sqrt{b^2 - 4ac}}{2a} \tag{7}$$

Clearly, (6) is true whenever (7) is. In other words, (7) is the solution to (6). But (7) is actually two equations,

$$x = \frac{-b - \sqrt{b^2 - 4ac}}{2a} \quad \text{and} \quad x = \frac{-b + \sqrt{b^2 - 4ac}}{2a} \tag{8}$$

Thus, there are two roots to (6). Either root will make (6) true.

Solving a functional equation of the form shown in (6) is now trivial with the use of (7). The following examples illustrate.

Example (i)

Find the values of x which satisfy

$$x^2 + 5x - 6 = 0$$

Solution:

$$x = \frac{-5 \pm \sqrt{(5)^2 - 4(1)(-6)}}{2}$$
$$= \frac{-5 \pm \sqrt{49}}{2}$$
$$= \frac{-5 \pm 7}{2}$$
$$= +1, -6$$

Example (ii)

Find the positive roots of

$$6x^2 - 4x - 2 = 0$$

Solution:

$$x = \frac{4 \pm \sqrt{16 + 48}}{12}$$
$$= \frac{4 \pm 8}{12}$$
$$= +1, -\frac{1}{3}$$

Hence, the solution is $x = +1$.

In addition to solving single equation systems such as (3) and (6), it is often necessary to solve systems with more than one equation. The situation of two equations will be explored here.

Suppose

$$2x + y - 11 = 0 \tag{9a}$$
$$3x + 5y - 27 = 0 \tag{9b}$$

is the system which must be solved. Rewrite the first equation as

$$y = 11 - 2x \tag{10}$$

Clearly, there are a number of pairs of values for x and y which will make (10) true: $(0, 11)$, $(1, 9)$, $(2, 7)$, $(\frac{3}{16}, 10\frac{5}{8})$, etc. In fact, there are an infinite number of solutions.

The same condition holds for the second equation, $3x + 5y - 27 = 0$. But the situation changes when the two equations are taken together as a system. The question now is: Do the equations have any solutions in common? That is, is there any pair of values for x and y which satisfy the requirements of *both* equations? The possibilities are (*i*) no solution, (*ii*) one and only one solution, (*iii*) two or more solutions, possibly even infinitely many solutions.

The rules of elementary algebra provide several ways of solving (9), one being that of substitution:

Solution of (9):

$y = 11 - 2x$	(from [9a])
$3x + 5(11 - 2x) - 27 = 0$	(substitute into [9b])
$-7x + 28 = 0$	(collecting terms)
$x = 4$	(simplification)
$2(4) + y - 11 = 0$	(substitute back into [9a])
$y = 3$	(simplification)

Answer:

$$x = 4, y = 3$$

Geometrically, solving a system such as (9) involves finding the common point(s) of the graphs of the individual equations. Figure 4–8 shows the graph of the system in (9). Manifestly, there

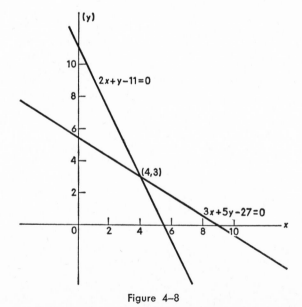

Figure 4–8

is only one solution—at $(4, 3)$—if it is first understood that the graph of each equation *is* the set of all solutions to that equation. In short, solving (9) involves finding the point of intersection of two nonparallel lines.

In general, systems of two linear equations can be written as

$$ax + by + c = 0$$
$$dx + ey + f = 0 \qquad (11)$$

or, more conveniently, as

$$y = \alpha x + \beta$$
$$y = \gamma x + \delta \qquad (12)$$

The system (12) will have a unique solution if $\alpha \neq \gamma$ (that is, if $d/e \neq a/b$). In geometric terms, this is equivalent to saying the system will have a solution if the lines are not parallel. There will be no solution if the lines are distinct but parallel. Finally, there will be infinitely many trivial solutions if the lines are coincident.

Other cases include systems of three or more linear equations, systems of nonlinear equations, systems of inequalities, and single equations which are neither linear nor quadratic. These cases are considered elsewhere as needed.

In spite of some difficulties, the use of the differential calculus for identifying extrema can be important in certain situations requiring optimization. Chapter 5 will explore the application of this powerful tool to a number of business and economic problems. Later chapters will present additional techniques; in particular, attention will be paid to the development of tools for handling problems where the theorem of this chapter is inapplicable.

EXERCISES

For each of the following functions (Exercises 1–13), determine dy/dx and find the value or values of x at which the first derivative is zero. Then find the corresponding extreme values of y by substituting the determined value or values of x into the original equations. Finally, indicate in each case whether the extrema which have been located are relative or absolute maxima or minima.

1. $y = \dfrac{x^2}{2} - 4x - 5$

2. $y = 12 + 3x - 3x^2$

3. $y = (x - 1)(x - 2)$

4. $y = \dfrac{1}{x + 1}(x^2 - x - 2)$

5. $y = 16 + 4x - x^2$

6. $y = 2x^3 - 3x^2 + 13$

7. $f(x) = x^3$

8. $y = 3x + 11$

9. $y = x^3 - 13x^2 + 4x - 721$

10. $y = \dfrac{x^2}{1 - x}$

11. $y = \dfrac{1}{x} + 4x$

12. $y = \dfrac{1 - x^2}{x}$

13. $y = \dfrac{3x + 4}{7}$

14. If $f(v) = v^4/4 - v^3 - v^2/2 + 3v + 6$,

    a) Find all maxima and minima in the interval $[-2, 6]$. (Suggestion: The first derivative will be a cubic expression; solve it by factoring.)

    b) Evaluate $f(v)$ at the end points of the interval $[-2, 6]$.

    c) What are the absolute extrema within the interval?

15. If $g(u) = u^3 - 7u^2 + 8u - 16$, find the maximum and minimum of $g(u)$.

16. If $r = s^2/(s - 1)$, find the extreme values of r, using the theorem in the foregoing section. Evaluate the function at $s = 1$. What can be said about the nature of the function at this point? Graph the function to verify your conclusions.

17. If $f(s) = s/(1 - s)$, find extrema, using the theorem in this chapter.

18. Sketch a graph of the function

$$y = \frac{x^4}{4} - 6x^2 + 16x - 100$$

(Hint: Use the theorem to determine extreme points.)

19. Sketch a graph of the function

$$y = x^4 - 24x^2 + 64x$$

CHAPTER 5

APPLICATIONS OF THE DERIVATIVE

Application of the theory of extrema for functions of one variable are considered in this chapter. The first section includes descriptions of three situations in which mathematics is useful in deriving policy conclusions, i.e., useful in the derivation of an action rule for a specific decision problem. Each of these descriptions is called a "case." Questions are asked at the end of some cases.

Section 2 investigates other areas of business and economics for which the theory of Chapter 4 is relevant. This section, particularly the part on marginalism, may be difficult for the reader not familiar with the language of elementary economics and accounting. Section 3 concludes the chapter with three cases which draw on the concepts of Section 2.

1. CASES

This section consists of three cases two of which illustrate the use of formal mathematical models in solving certain kinds of marketing and inventory problems. Each case demonstrates an application of the mathematics developed in Chapters 1 through 4.

Two of the cases are based on published accounts of how particular business problems have been analyzed. In some instances, mathematical notes have been appended or variables relabeled. The reader interested in additional details or background information should consult the original articles. In addition, the reader interested in the more general issue of the application of mathematics to marketing problems may wish to examine some of the more recent literature in this area.[1]

---

[1] In addition to the *Journal of Marketing*, and some of the operations research-management science journals, cf. Frank M. Bass, *et al, Mathematical*

Case No. 1. Optimum Lot Size

Suppose a retailer expects to sell some fixed amount of a certain commodity during the next year. Suppose further that the price is predetermined and that the demand for the commodity will be uniform throughout the year. The retailer wishes to determine how much inventory he should keep on hand in order to minimize the costs associated with holding inventory.

Let the total number of units to be sold be denoted by Q, and suppose that $Q = 100,000$ units. Then the retailer could, if he wished, order the entire 100,000 units delivered in January, store them in his warehouse, and use them up as needed. As a possible alternative, he could have 50,000 units delivered in January and the other 50,000 in July. Or he could have 25,000 units delivered every three months, and so on.

If he adopts the first alternative, he will have 100,000 units at the beginning of the year and zero at the end; since the rate of consumption is constant, his average inventory for the period will be 50,000 units. Similarly, the second alternative would begin with 50,000 and end with zero, so the average inventory would be 25,000. The third alternative would yield an average inventory of 12,500, and so on. Clearly, the more often he orders, the smaller will be the average inventory on hand.

Naturally a small inventory will save on carrying costs (storage, interest on cash used for purchase, etc.); however, carrying costs are not the only costs associated with the problem. If they were, the retailer would just order his goods every day, or even several times a day. But there will be other costs associated with *reordering* the merchandise, and since a smaller inventory involves more frequent orders, these costs will tend to rise as carrying costs fall. Determining the optimum inventory level involves balancing these two costs against one another.

Carrying Cost. The average inventory level, assuming constant demand, is half the amount received in a shipment, as was shown above. If x represents the number of units received in a ship-

Models and Methods in Marketing (Homewood, Ill.: Richard D. Irwin, Inc., 1961); "Applications to Marketing . . . ," Part IV in William J. Baumol, *Economic Theory and Operations Analysis* (New York: Prentice Hall, 1961); chaps. 18–21 in H. Bierman, L. Fouraker, and R. Jaedicke, *Quantitative Analysis for Business Decisions* (Homewood, Ill.: Richard D. Irwin, Inc., 1961); Robert D. Buzzell, *A Basic Bibliography on Mathematical Methods in Marketing* (American Marketing Association, 1961); and R. Fetter and W. Dalleck, *Decision Models for Inventory Management* (Homewood, Ill.: Richard D. Irwin, Inc., 1961).

ment, then $x/2$ will be the average inventory. Now, if k represents the interest and other carrying costs involved in holding one unit of inventory for one year, the total carrying cost will be equal to the annual carrying cost per unit (k) times the average number of units in inventory $(x/2)$; or,

$$\text{Carrying cost} = \frac{kx}{2}$$

Reorder Cost. It will be assumed that two kinds of costs are involved here:

1. A fixed cost for placing an order—a service charge—to cover such things as bookkeeping, processing the order, etc., which do not vary with the size of the order.
2. An additional cost which varies with the size of the order— shipping cost per item, packaging costs, etc.

Let the fixed cost be designated as a, and the unit variable cost as b; then total reorder cost per order will be $a + bx$; i.e., the fixed cost per order, a, plus b, the unit variable cost, times the number of units in the order. Total reorder cost is then $(a + bx)$ times the number of orders; or

$$\text{Reorder cost} = (a + bx)\left(\frac{Q}{x}\right)$$

since if Q units are demanded, and x units are ordered each time an order is placed, there must necessarily be Q/x orders placed during the year to meet the total demand. This means that it is necessary to multiply $a + bx$, the reorder cost per order, by Q/x, the number of orders which must be placed.

Total Cost. The total cost for buying and storing inventory will be the sum of the carrying costs and the ordering costs, or

$$TC = \frac{kx}{2} + (a + bx)\left(\frac{Q}{x}\right) \qquad (1)$$

Simplifying, (1) becomes

$$TC = \frac{kx}{2} + \frac{aQ}{x} + bQ \qquad (2)$$

There is only one unknown in the above equation—x. Q, the quantity demanded, is assumed to be known; a, b, and k are cost figures derived from the firm's books. The objective of minimizing TC may be accomplished by differentiating TC with respect to x and setting the derivative equal to zero—the normal optimization procedure.

Differentiating equation (2), it is found that

$$\frac{dTC}{dx} = \frac{k}{2} - \frac{aQ}{x^2} \tag{3}$$

Setting (3) equal to zero yields:

$$\frac{k}{2} - \frac{aQ}{x^2} = 0$$
$$\frac{k}{2} = \frac{aQ}{x^2}$$
$$x^2 = \frac{2aQ}{k}$$

and

$$x = \sqrt{\frac{2aQ}{k}} \tag{4}$$

It is relatively easy to show that a *minimum* rather than a *maximum* is obtained: the second derivative of TC with respect to x is equal to $2aQ/x^3$, which must necessarily be positive, since a, Q, and x are necessarily positive. Observe that the requirement that x be positive also eliminates the possibility of selecting the negative square root in expression (4).

The result of (4) is known as the "optimum lot size formula," "economic order quantity," or "Camp's Formula" and appears in management literature in a number of guises. Given the conditions stated at the beginning of the problem, application of this formula will yield the optimum lot size, x, at which total costs are minimized.

Questions

1. Show the three costs—reorder, carrying, and total—on a graph.
2. Suppose that shipping costs, b, per unit, decline as the size of the order increases. For instance, let $b = b_1/x$. Develop a formula incorporating this and then perform the differentiation to find the optimum x. What would be the effect on the size of x?
3. Comment on the difficulty of obtaining the parameters a, b, and k, assuming that "conventional" accounting and bookkeeping methods have been followed by the firm.
4. Comment on the validity and range of applicability of the model; could it be applied in a real-life situation? Cite an example to support the answer.

5. Suppose that demand for the product is not uniform but fluctuates above a known level; that is, the firm expects to sell, say, 50 units per week, but may sell an additional quantity ranging from 0 to 20. Could it still use this model? If so, how?

6. The results of this analysis could readily be applied to a production problem as well as a purchasing problem. For instance, if the firm manufactured its inventory instead of buying it, the decision would be expressed in terms of how many units to produce in a given production run, with due consideration being given to setup costs incurred at the beginning of each run (analogous to ordering costs) in relation to inventory handling costs.

However, an additional complicating factor might enter the situation; in some operations, the value of work in process and the cost of handling and storing it may be of more significance than the value of finished goods. To estimate the costs associated with handling and storing work in process, one must know (a) the average number of units in process; (b) the inventory handling costs per unit; and (c) the number of production runs per period—say, per year.

If t represents the time required to produce one item (t being expressed as a fraction of one working year), and n represents the number of units produced in a single production run, then nt is the "lead time" for the run; i.e., the total time required to complete the run, expressed as a fraction of one working year. Then $n(nt)$ is the number of units being produced times the fraction of a working year required to produce them.

From the above, develop a modification of the optimum lot size formula giving consideration to the cost of "work in process" inventory.

Case No. 2.   New England Warehouse Case[2]

A company located in the New England area had, over a period of years, acquired over a dozen warehouses in the five states served by its manufacturing plant. Acquisition had been carried out on a basis of subjective judgment, and seemed to have turned out reasonably well in most cases. The general manager, however, had begun to wonder whether these warehouses really represented the optimum arrangement; in particular, he was interested in finding out how large a territory should be served by each warehouse.

Management realized that warehousing costs per dollar's worth of goods tended to decrease as volume increased; that is, these costs varied inversely with volume, suggesting that a few large warehouses would be more efficient from a cost standpoint. However,

---

[2] Adapted with permission from "A Model for Scale of Operations" by E. H. Bowman and J. B. Stewart in *Journal of Marketing*, Vol. 20, No. 3 (January, 1956): pp. 242–47.

reducing the number of warehouses would result in increasing the costs associated with transportation and delivery of goods to purchasers since greater distances would have to be covered by the delivery trucks.

Since distance traveled would be the main factor in determining the level of costs associated with delivery, etc., it is reasonable to assume that such costs would vary with the area served by the warehouse. If the warehouse is regarded as the center of the circle which is the area served by the warehouse, the area served by the warehouse is given by πr^2, where r is the radius of the circle and π is approximately 3.14. If r increases by some amount, the area increases in proportion to the square of r; i.e., if distance from the warehouse (radius) increases, the area served increases in proportion to the square of this distance. Thus, if costs are directly related to distance, costs (or distance) can be said to vary in proportion to the square root of the area served.

With the foregoing in mind, a mathematical description of these cost factors can be constructed. First, let

> C = cost, within the warehouse district, per dollar's worth of goods distributed;
> V = volume of goods, in dollars, handled by the warehouse in a unit of time (could be a month, a year, etc.) ;
> A = area, in square miles, served by the warehouse;
> a = cost, per dollar's worth of goods, which is not affected either by volume handled or by area served;
> b = "fixed costs" associated with the warehouse operation, which when divided by V will yield the approximate cost per dollar's worth of goods distributed;
> c = costs which vary with the square root of the area, as described above (gasoline, truck repairs, driver time, etc.).

Then,

C = fixed costs + warehouse operating costs + transportation cost.

Or,

$$C = a + \frac{b}{V} + c\sqrt{A} \qquad (1)$$

Equation (1) contains two unknown factors—the volume of goods handled by the warehouse, V, and the area served by the warehouse, A. However, it is reasonable to assume that there will be some relationship between volume and area. In the states in which these warehouses were located, there was sufficient uniformity of population distribution to warrant the conclusion that a more or less uniform sales density could be assumed; i.e.,

$$K = \frac{V}{A}$$

where K = the constant dollar volume of sales per square mile of area. Then $V = KA$, which may be substituted for V in equation (1):

$$C = a + \frac{b}{KA} + c\sqrt{A} \qquad (2)$$

Since a, b, and c are specific cost figures (parameters) derived from company records, and since K is also a specific figure developed by analyzing maps and sales charts, there remains only one unknown in the expression, A. Thus, to minimize C, the expression is differentiated with respect to A and the derivative set equal to zero:

$$\frac{dC}{dA} = \frac{-b}{KA^2} + \frac{c}{2\sqrt{A}}$$

$$\frac{b}{KA^2} = \frac{c}{2\sqrt{A}}$$

$$2b = cKA^{3/2}$$

$$A^{3/2} = \frac{2b}{cK}$$

or

$$A = \left(\frac{2b}{cK}\right)^{2/3} \qquad (3)$$

It has now been learned that the optimal value of A is equal to $(2b/cK)^{2/3}$, that is, the area which yields a minimum cost is a function of b and c—constants calculated from company records—and K—sales density of the area under consideration.

Questions

1. Verify that (3) is actually a minimum.
2. There are two important assumptions underlying this model:
    a) That costs represented by a are not pertinent to the optimization procedure.
    b) That it is feasible to determine K.
    What other cost factors falling under a would have a bearing on a decision as to whether to open some warehouses?
3. Suppose the company operated warehouses in Kansas, Nebraska, Missouri, and Texas. How would the management go about computing K?

4. Is this model a complete "decision rule" for determining the number of warehouses which should be operated? Exactly what does it determine? What additional information would be necessary?

Case No. 3. Growth, Population, and Investment

The growth experience of any economy is the product of many forces and influences. Among these are the facts of the economy's rate of population change, its rate of saving and investment, and the technological consideration represented by the term, capital-output ratio. It is intuitively plausible that an economy's growth rate must depend in some logical fashion on these factors. The nature of this dependence is the subject of the result to be presented here.

Let the following variables be defined for an economy:

t,   time, usually measured in years

K,   capital stock

$I = \dfrac{dK}{dt}$,   net investment

S,   net saving

P,   population

$p = \dfrac{\dfrac{dP}{dt}}{P}$, percentage change in population

Y,   net national product ("income")

$\dfrac{Y}{P}$,   per capita income

$r = \dfrac{K}{Y}$,   the capital-output ratio

$\dfrac{I}{Y} = \dfrac{S}{Y}$,   the percent of its output which the economy is saving and investing

g,   the economy's growth rate, i.e., the percentage change in per capita income over time

It is understood that each of the variables (except the constant ratios) is a function of time. It will be shown that *the rate of saving and investment out of current output together with the capital-output ratio and the rate of population increase determine the economy's rate of growth according to the requirement that*

$$g = \frac{1}{r}\left(\frac{I}{Y}\right) - p \tag{1}$$

$$= \frac{1}{r}\left(\frac{S}{Y}\right) - p \quad \text{since } I = S \tag{2}$$

For any given I/Y, p, and r, it is possible to find the resulting g; or, for given p and r, it is possible to find the required $I/Y = S/Y$ for any target level of g. For example, suppose that $p = 2\%$ and $r = 3$. Then $I/Y = 3(g + 2)$ or $g = 1/3(I/Y) - 2$. The result of (1) generates the functional relationship:

g	0	1	2	3	5	6	10	
$\dfrac{I}{Y} = \dfrac{S}{Y}$	6	9	12	15	21	24	36	. . . .

Proof of (1):
By definition,

$$g = \frac{\dfrac{d\left(\dfrac{Y}{P}\right)}{dt}}{\dfrac{Y}{P}} \tag{3}$$

since the percentage change in per capita income is equal to the change in income (in dollars) over the time interval t, divided by the original per capita income. For instance, if $Y/P = \$2000$ at time t_0, but is changing at the rate of $\$200$ per year,

$$g = \frac{200}{2000} = 10\%$$

The relation in (3) may be rewritten as

$$g = \frac{d\left(\dfrac{Y}{P}\right)}{dt} \cdot \frac{P}{Y} \tag{4}$$

Noting that both Y and P are functions of t, and differentiating the quotient Y/P with respect to t as indicated yields

$$g = \frac{P\dfrac{dY}{dt} - Y\dfrac{dP}{dt}}{P^2} \cdot \frac{P}{Y}$$

which simplifies to

$$g = \frac{\dfrac{dY}{dt}}{Y} - \frac{\dfrac{dP}{dt}}{P} \tag{5}$$

Recognizing that

$$Y = \frac{K}{r} \text{ since } r = \frac{K}{Y} \text{ and that } \frac{\dfrac{dP}{dt}}{P} = p$$

(5) becomes

$$g = \frac{d\left(\frac{K}{r}\right)}{\frac{dt}{Y}} - p$$

and then

$$g = \frac{1}{r} \cdot \frac{\frac{dK}{dt}}{Y} - p \tag{6}$$

But $dK/dt = I$ by definition, so

$$g = \frac{1}{r} \cdot \frac{I}{Y} - p \tag{(1)=(7)}$$

or, since $I = S$,

$$g = \frac{1}{r}\left(\frac{S}{Y}\right) - p \tag{(2)=(8)}$$

2. BREAK-EVEN ANALYSIS, OPTIMIZATION, AND THE MARGINAL ANALYSIS

A widely used tool of management is *cost-volume-profit analysis,* sometimes referred to as *break-even analysis.* The technique, usually presented in the form of a diagram called a "break-even chart" (or "profit-graph"), compares the expected relationships of revenue, cost, and hence profits, to sales or production volume. To illustrate the major elements of this tool, consider the following simple example.

Suppose there is an activity which produces an output or a product, say X. Let x be the number of units produced of X, g the revenues received, h the costs incurred in the production, and π the profit which is equal to revenue less costs, or $g - h$. In general, g and h, and hence π, will be functions of x; i.e.,

$$g = g(x)$$
$$h = h(x)$$

The manager of the activity can ask the following questions:

> *Question 1:* At what value or values of x will the activity break even, i.e., have zero profits? Ans.: Find x_0 such that $\pi = 0$. This will be referred to as the *break-even problem.*

Question 2: At what value of x will the activity enjoy maximum profits? Ans.: Find x^* such that π is at a maximum. This will be referred to as *the optimizing problem.*

The answers to these questions will clearly depend on the form of the functions g and h, and hence π. First, suppose that g and h are linear functions:

$$g(x) = px$$

where p is unit price, assumed to be constant, and

$$h(x) = a + bx$$

where a and b are constants or parameters; a is fixed cost, and b is unit variable cost. Then

$$\pi(x) = g(x) - h(x)$$
$$= px - (a + bx)$$

The answer to Question 1, namely the value of x_0 such that $\pi(x_0) = 0$, can be found by determining the intersection of the two functions $g(x)$ and $h(x)$, since, if $\pi(x) = 0$,

$$g(x_0) = h(x_0)$$
$$px_0 = a + bx_0$$

and

$$x_0 = \frac{a}{p - b} = \frac{\text{Fixed costs}}{\text{Unit price} - \text{Unit variable cost}}$$

The point x_0 will be unique if $p \neq b$ and nontrivial if $p > b$. The graphical solution is shown in Figure 5–1, page 82.

The answer to the second question, i.e., finding x^*, is another matter. Common sense and the diagram in Figure 5–1 indicate clearly that there is no x^* at which $\pi(x^*)$ is a maximum except for the trivial one, $x^* = \infty$. Another conclusion is that if the original statement of the problem included the information that there was a fixed maximum level for the activity X, a capacity level, then, of course, that capacity value of X would be x^*.

If the theory of extrema is applied, the function π will be maximized when $\pi' = 0$, and $\pi'' < 0$. Thus

$$\pi(x) = px - (a + bx)$$
$$D_x\pi = p - b \text{ and } D_x\pi \text{ is a constant for all values}$$
$$\text{of } x \text{ and is equal to 0 when } p = b$$
$$D_x{}^2\pi = 0 \text{ for all values of } x$$

The two derivatives exist, and it is easy to see that $D_x\pi$ can be zero only if $p = b$, *but the theorem does not identify a maximum or*

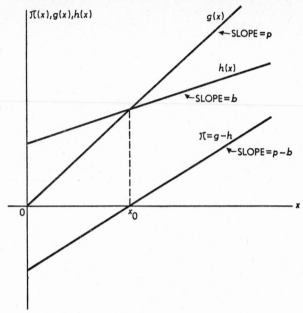

Figure 5–1

minimum because the second derivative test fails: D_x^2 is neither greater than nor less than zero as the theorem requires. The analysis thus confirms what is already known: profits cannot be maximized at some finite output—unless, of course, a maximum capacity level is introduced.

Suppose, and this is certainly both more realistic and interesting, that the cost or revenue functions or both are nonlinear. Consequently, as a rule, $\pi(x)$ is not linear.

The procedure used to answer the first question is the same, $\pi(x) = 0$ if $g(x) = h(x)$. The value of x_0 is the point at which the two curves intersect, or where $\pi(x) = 0$. Suppose (see Figure 5–2)

$$g(x) = 5x - \frac{x^2}{2000}$$
$$h(x) = 3x$$

The value of x_0 is the value at which $g(x_0) = h(x_0)$ or when

$$5x - \frac{x^2}{2000} = 3x$$
$$10{,}000x - x^2 = 6000x$$

Rearranging terms gives

$$x^2 - 4000x = x(x - 4000) = 0$$

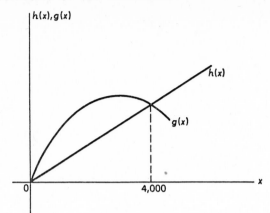

Figure 5–2

The two functions are equal when $x = 0$ and $x = 4000$, the roots of the quadratic; i.e., the break-even points are at 0 and 4000.

Another but equivalent way to find the break-even value is to compute $\pi(x)$ and solve $\pi(x_0) = 0$.

$$\pi(x) = g(x) - h(x)$$
$$= 5x - \frac{x^2}{2000} - 3x$$
$$= 2x - \frac{x^2}{2000}$$

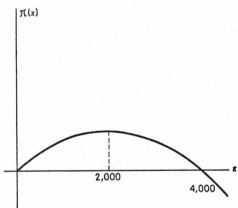

Figure 5–3

This function is shown in Figure 5–3. Setting

$$\pi(x_0) = 0$$

gives

$$2x_0 - \frac{x_0{}^2}{2000} = 0$$

or

$$4000x_0 - x_0{}^2 = (4000 - x_0)x_0 = 0$$

and again 0 and 4000 are the break-even values of x.

To answer the second question, the theory of extrema is applied to $\pi(x)$:

$$\pi'(x) = 2 - \frac{x}{1000} \text{ and } \pi'(x) = 0 \text{ implies } 2 - \frac{x}{1000} = 0$$

or $x^* = 2000$. Then,

$$\frac{d^2\pi}{dx^2} = -\frac{1}{1000}$$

which is negative for all x so that the point located is known to be a maximum. At the point $x = 2000$, $\pi = 5(2000) - 4,000,000/2000 - 3(2000) = \$2000$.

A third case will further illustrate. Suppose a firm's total cost function is

$$C = \frac{x^3}{3} - 3x^2 + 12x$$

where x represents the number of units produced (expressed in thousands). Suppose further that its revenue function is

$$R = 12x - x^2$$

Find the optimal production level. (Note that both functions are nonlinear. See Figure 5–4.)

Solution:
First,

$$\pi = 12x - x^2 - \frac{x^3}{3} + 3x^2 - 12x$$

$$= 2x^2 - \frac{x^3}{3}$$

Then

$$\frac{d\pi}{dx} = 4x - x^2 = 0 \text{ when } x = 0 \text{ and when } x = \mathbf{4}$$

Also

$$\frac{d^2\pi}{dx^2} = 4 - 2x$$

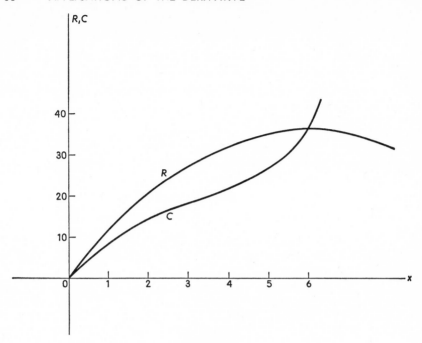

Figure 5–4

Clearly the second derivative is greater than zero when $x = 0$, and less than zero when $x = 4$. Therefore the former is a minimum and the latter a maximum. Consequently the solution is $x = 4$.

At this point total costs are

$$\frac{64}{3} - 48 + 48 = \frac{64}{3} = 21\frac{1}{3}$$

and total revenues are

$$48 - 16 = 32$$

Profit, π, is therefore $10\frac{2}{3}$, or approximately $10,667.

Marginalism. The break-even analysis is actually a part of a broader theory known in the economics literature as marginalism. The basic notion of marginalism involves the notion of an *optimum activity level.* One of the crucial decision problems in any economic situation is that of "level," or "scale": How many units to produce? How many operators to hire? How much of material x to order? How much money to invest in a given area of production? How much to spend on advertising in each of several media? Should more of product j be produced and less of k, or vice versa?

In general, the economist's answer to such questions is contained in the following axiom, the Optimum Activity Level rule:[3]

> The level or scale of an economic activity should be increased as long as the marginal net gain (i.e., the change in the difference between benefits and costs) is positive, thus expanding the activity until the marginal net gain is zero.

If put symbolically, this idea is a familiar one. It also will be seen to be an application of the theory of extrema. The marginalist axiom says that the "benefits" (revenue) and "costs" associated with any activity are both functions of the level of activity; hence, "net benefit" (= "profit" = benefit − costs) is a function of the activity level. The axiom then says that *total* net gain (total profit) will be at a maximum when activity level is such that *marginal* net benefit is zero. But marginal net benefit is exactly analogous to the derivative of net benefit with respect to the activity level. Thus the axiom simply restates in words the first part of the theorem. All that is missing is the sometimes important second derivative condition; there is an implicit assumption that the second derivative has the appropriate sign.

If the more conventional words of revenue and profit are used for benefit and net benefit, respectively, the marginalist axiom says the optimum level of an activity (i.e., that level where net benefits are maximized) is where marginal profit = 0. But this means, since marginal profit = marginal revenue − marginal cost, that marginal revenue = marginal cost. This latter is the more usual form of the marginalist axiom: profits are maximized when $MR = MC$ since MR is defined as D_x (revenues) and MC is D_x (*costs*). Again, all second-order conditions are assumed to be met.

It should be clear that the optimizing aspects of break-even analysis are simple marginalism. Figure 5–5 indicates clearly the geometry of the situation. It differs from Figure 5–4 only in that Figure 5–5 includes explicitly the function which is to be maximized, i.e., $\pi(x)$.

Since many discussions, applied and theoretical, are in terms of averages rather than totals or marginals, it is often necessary to inquire into the relation, one-to-another, of average, total, and marginal quantities.

Let $T = T(x)$ be some differentiable function; x can be interpreted as the level of an activity, and therefore nonnegative. $T(x)$

---

[3] Adapted from Baumol, *op. cit.*, p. 21.

could be total costs, total revenue, total production, total earnings, or some other "total" quantity associated with the activity level x.

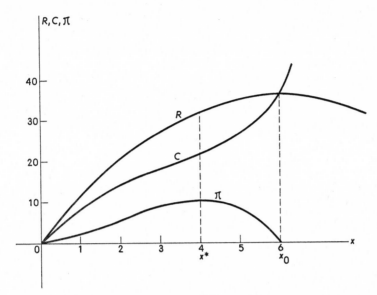

Figure 5–5

First, the marginal level of the activity (M) is, of course, dT/dx or T'. Second, the average value, denoted $A(x)$ or just A, is

$$\frac{T(x)}{x} \quad \text{or} \quad \frac{T}{x} \tag{1}$$

This can usefully be rewritten as

$$T = Ax \tag{2}$$

Differentiation of (2) with respect to x yields,

$$T' = A + xA' \tag{3}$$

A number of statements can now be made about the inter-relations of x, T, A, and T' (or M) on the basis of (3):

i) If $T' > A$, then A is increasing at that point because $(A + xA') > A$ from (3) which implies that $A' > 0$, and A' is the slope of A.

ii) If $T' < A$, then A is decreasing by the converse argument.

iii) If $T' = A$, then A is at a maximum or minimum or is constant, since A' is necessarily zero when $T' = A$.

iv) If A is a constant, $A' = 0$ and hence $T' = A$.

v) If T' is a constant, call it k, A may or may not be a constant, because $A = k - xA'$.

vi) If T' is used as an approximation of A, the error will be xA' which is clearly smaller the smaller x and the less steep is A.

The concept of *elasticity* is often used in economic and business literature as a measure of the responsiveness of one variable to changes in another. A common application of the idea is to the responsiveness of A to changes in x where both the changes are measured in relative terms; that is, using η ("eta") to denote elasticity,

$$\eta = \frac{\text{Percentage change in } x}{\text{Percentage change in } A} = \frac{\triangle x/x}{\triangle A/A} \qquad (4)$$
$$= \frac{A}{x}\frac{\triangle x}{\triangle A}$$

Or

$$\eta = \frac{A}{x}\frac{dx}{dA} \qquad (5)$$

in the continuous case as $\triangle A \to 0$.

Noting that $1/\eta$ is $(x/A)(dA/dx)$, and recalling (3), it is seen that

$$T' \text{ (or } M\text{)} = A\left[1 + \frac{x}{A}\frac{dA}{dx}\right]$$
$$= A\left[1 + \frac{1}{\eta}\right] \qquad (6)$$

Since η is sometimes defined with a negative sign, the relation in (6) occasionally appears as $T' = A(1 - 1/\eta)$.

Case No. 4.   An Advertising Decision[4]

Suppose that the Airow and Zande Companies, with advertising budgets of a dollars and b dollars, respectively, are selling in a market having a total sales potential of Q units, and that there are no other firms competing in the market.

The Airow Company's expected sales volume has been found to be

$$\left(\frac{aQ}{a+b}\right)$$

That is, the proportion of total possible sales which are obtained by the Airow Company is the ratio of the company's advertising expenditure to the total advertising expenditure by both firms.

[4] Suggested by an article by Lawrence Friedman, "Game-Theory Models in the Allocation of Advertising Expenditures," *Operations Research*, Vol. 6, No. 5 (September–October, 1958), pp. 699–709, and reprinted in Bass, *et al., op. cit.,* pp. 230 ff.

The cost to the Airow Company of producing and selling N units (exclusive of advertising costs) is

$$C_1 + C_2 N$$

where C_1 represents fixed costs, and C_2 represents variable costs per unit. Therefore, if an expenditure of a dollars on advertising results in sales of $aQ/(a + b)$, the Airow Company's total costs are

$$C_1 + C_2 \left[\frac{aQ}{(a + b)} \right] + a$$

1. Let P be the selling price per unit, which is assumed fixed and equal for both companies. Develop the expression for the profit of Airow as a function of its advertising expenditures.
2. Determine the optimum level of advertising by
   a) Maximizing earnings.
   b) Equating marginal revenue to marginal cost. Are the two values equal? Explain.
3. How does Airow's optimum action depend on Zande's decisions?
4. Find a^* when $b = \$1,000,000$, $Q = 40,000$, $P = \$200$, $C_2 = \$100$, and $C_1 = \$500,000$.

Case No. 5. National Motors Case[5]

The National Motors Corporation makes and sells one million cars annually. At a price of $3000 per car, the total sales revenue is therefore $3000 million. Total costs are $2500 million, or $2500 per car, and thus total profits are $500 million. Total costs are split between fixed costs ($500 million) and variable costs ($2000 per car).

The firm is considering a price reduction to $2700 per car in the belief that increased sales volume, with a subsequently favorable impact on profit, may result from the price decrease. It has been encouraged in this opinion by the results of a study which indicated that the elasticity of demand for automobiles with respect to price is 1.5; i.e., a 1% change in price will result in a 1.5% change in the number of cars sold, the changes being in opposite directions, of course.

Since the contemplated price reduction is 10%, the firm expects to increase unit sales by 15%. Furthermore, it believes that it can meet the increased demand without increasing fixed costs or unit variable costs.

The problems are these: What will revenue be if the price reduction is adopted? What will total costs be? What will happen to profits?

---

[5] Suggested by an article, "When Is Price Reduction Profitable?" by Clare E. Griffin in *Harvard Business Review*, September–October, 1960, pp. 125–32.

The arithmetic of the situation is simple:

	At Price of $3000	At Price of $2700
Expected sales......	1,000,000	1,150,000
Total revenues.......	$3,000,000,000	$3,105,000,000
Total costs..........	$2,500,000,000	$2,800,000,000
Expected profits.......	$ 500,000,000	$ 305,000,000

Thus, even though sales are stimulated by the price reduction, profits can be expected to fall.

Questions

1. On the surface, it seems logical to assume that if a 10% price reduction will generate a 15% increase in sales, a firm would be well advised to reduce prices. This is not the case, however, in the example presented here. What are the fallacies of the logic in the argument for price reduction? How big would the elasticity have to be for price reduction to be profitable for National?

2. From the data given, and recalling that elasticity can be defined as:

$$\frac{p}{x}\ \frac{dx}{dp}$$

where p is price and x unit sales, what is the optimum price policy for National if its goal is to maximize profits? (Hint: Keep clearly in mind that there is a fixed relationship between x and p.)

Case No. 6. Pricing the 707[6]

In 1955 the Boeing Airplane Company was faced with the problem of determining the selling price for the 707 jet airliner. The situation in which the company found itself was rather unusual; it had only one competitor—Douglas and its DC-8. It was realized that price would be only one variable affecting demand for its aircraft; with a single competitor and a very few potential customers political and financial considerations beyond the control of the operating divisions of the firm would assume substantial importance. For instance, United Air Lines had purchased propeller-type aircraft from Douglas for many years, and appeared willing to wait for the DC-8 even though the 707 was operational first. In spite of these factors, however, it was felt that an attempt to determine an optimal price on the basis of explicit economic considerations would be useful.

The company realized that the two airplanes were sufficiently

---

[6] Adapted with permission from Georges Brigham, "Pricing Investment and Games of Strategy," C. W. Churchman and M. Verhulst (eds.), *Management Sciences, Models and Techniques,* Vol. 1 (New York: Pergamon Press, 1960). pp. 271–87.

similiar that one firm would have to meet the other's price, more or less. If either firm lowered the price, the other would have to follow suit, but if one raised its price, the other might not do so—with consequent effect on the proportion of sales which each would make.

Boeing had an advantage over Douglas in that its fixed costs were less because of an arrangement with the military to share certain costs. But this same arrangement involved the payment of a kind of rent to the military, thus making Boeing's operating costs somewhat higher than those of Douglas—all other things being considered equal.

Due to the high initial investment necessary to undertake production of the aircraft, one plausible strategy was to set as high a price as possible in order to reach the break-even date quickly. This attitude met with resistance from the salespeople, who naturally wanted a lower price. If, however, the primary objective was to maximize profits over the production period for the plane, still a different strategy, outlined below, was necessary.

If π represents profit, x the number of planes sold, p the price at which they are sold, and C the total cost of producing x planes, then obviously

$$\pi = px(p) - C(x) \tag{1}$$

treating x as a function of p and C as a function of x.

Then, if N is the total number of aircraft which can be sold in the market at price p, and h is Boeing's share of the market,

$$x = h \cdot N(p) \tag{2}$$

N now being a function of p. Since it is assumed that both competitors are charging the same price, it can be said that h, the share of the market, is independent of p. (This means that Boeing's share doesn't depend on the price it charges—a strange conclusion on the face of it, but perhaps reasonable if Douglas charges the same.)

It is necessary now to estimate the industry's demand-price relationship, or market demand curve. The procedure is outside the scope of the discussion; however, suppose that in the price range under consideration one can approximate the market curve by the function

$$N = -78p^2 + 655p - 1125 \tag{3}$$

Note that p is very much greater than zero, and that the function describes part of a parabola. It is a purely arbitrary function; let it be noted only that it in fact fitted the point-by-point estimates of sales volume at varying prices. Substituting this value of N into the original expression for profit gives the result that

$$\pi = hp(-78p^2 + 655p - 1125) - C(x) \tag{4}$$

To complete the process of stating π in terms of one variable only, the cost function, $C(x)$, must be developed in terms of p. Again using empirical data, Boeing's cost function might look something like this:

$$C = 50 + 1.5x + 8x^{.75} \tag{5}$$

Observe that this total cost function is, as might be expected, monotonically increasing (increases continually as x increases) but at a decreasing rate. From an accounting point of view, this function includes fixed costs of $50 million, plus variable costs represented by $(1.5x + 8x^{.75})$. One might observe that the variable costs themselves include a "fixed" cost of $1.5 million per airplane, plus a second factor which reflects decreasing costs per unit as larger numbers of planes are manufactured. The function is an example of what is sometimes called a "learning curve"—reflecting not only "learning" with consequent increased efficiency but also, probably, cheaper costs associated with larger purchases of parts, materials, etc.

It is now possible to describe π as a function of p only; although the expression could be written out in this manner, it is more convenient to leave it in the form

$$\pi = hp\,N(p) - C(x) \tag{6}$$

and proceed to optimize with respect to p, using the "chain rule" and the relationships developed in equations (2), (3), and (5) above. Since the goal is to find that value of p which will optimize π, the appropriate precedure is to differentiate π with respect to p and set the derivative equal to zero:

$$\frac{d\pi}{dp} = hp\frac{dN}{dp} + hN - \frac{dC}{dx} \cdot h \cdot \frac{dN}{dp} \tag{7}$$

Denoting the derivatives by primes, (7) can be written

$$\frac{d\pi}{dp} = hpN' + hN - hN'C' \tag{8}$$

Setting (8) equal to zero, yields

$$hpN' + hN = hN'C' \tag{9}$$

Then, dividing through by the common coefficient h shows that

$$pN' + N = N'C'$$

or

$$p + \frac{N}{N'} = C'$$

or

$$p^* = C' - \frac{N}{N'} \tag{10}$$

C', of course, refers to the derivative of C with respect to x; that is, the derivative of $50 + 1.5x + 8x^{.75}$, which, from (5), is $1.5 + 6x^{-.25}$. Since it has already been ascertained that N is equal to $-78p^2 + 655p - 1125$, N', the derivative of N with respect to p, is $-156p + 655$. Thus (10) becomes

$$p = 1.5 + 6x^{-.25} - \frac{-78p^2 + 655p - 1125}{-156p + 655} \tag{11}$$

Recall that x, the number of planes sold by Boeing, is equal to hN, where h, the share of the market, is assumed to be independent of p but N, the total market, is a known function of p. Because of (2), the expression $h(-78p^2 + 655p - 1125)$ could be substituted for x in (11) in order to solve explicitly for p, but the algebra would become complex.

It is, however, a relatively simple matter to perform a number of trial numerical calculations on a computer. The several relations underlying (11) were programmed on a computer. The machine was

Table I

h	p	$N(p)$	$x = hN(p)$	π	$\dfrac{d\pi}{dp}$	$\dfrac{d^2\pi}{dp^2}$
0.25	5.09	188.12	47.03	-24.83	1.88	-105.46
0.25	5.10	186.72	46.68	-24.82	0.83	-105.99
0.25	5.11	185.31	46.33	-24.82	-0.24	-106.50
0.25	5.12	183.88	45.97	-24.83	-1.30	-107.00
0.50	4.98	202.47	101.23	46.97	4.43	-228.43
0.50	4.99	201.24	100.62	47.01	2.14	-229.96
0.50	5.00	200.00	100.00	47.02	-0.16	-231.48
0.50	5.01	198.74	99.37	47.00	-2.49	-232.97
0.75	4.94	207.22	155.41	132.49	4.45	-356.56
0.75	4.95	206.06	154.54	132.52	0.87	-359.08
0.75	4.96	204.88	153.66	132.51	-2.74	-361.57
0.75	4.97	203.68	152.76	132.46	-6.36	-364.05
1.00	4.91	210.62	210.62	225.91	7.01	-485.16
1.00	4.92	209.50	209.50	225.96	2.14	-488.71
1.00	4.93	208.37	208.37	225.96	-2.77	-492.22
1.00	4.94	207.22	207.22	225.90	-7.71	-495.71

instructed to compute π, $\pi'(p)$ and $\pi''(p)$ for a variety of values of p ranging from \$3 to \$6 million for $h = 25\%$. It then repeated for other h values, i.e., for 50%, 75%, and 100%. The programming took less than half an hour, the calculations less than two minutes. Certain of the results of the machine's work are shown in Table I.

Note that a glance at the column $d\pi/dp$ shows, for each tested h value, that value of p which will maximize π. When $h = .25$, the optimal p is approximately \$5.1 million since at that price $\pi'(p)$ is approximately zero and $\pi''(p) < 0$. Similarly, for the other values of h: e.g., if $h = 50\%$, $p^* = 5.01$ since $\pi'(5.01) \doteq 0$ and $\pi''(5.01) < 0$.

A second table summarizing the relevant results of Table I can be prepared to show the optimal price policy for several alternative assumptions about market share.

Table II

h	p^*	x	$\pi(p)$
0.25	5.11	46.33	−24.81
0.50	5.00	100.00	47.02
0.75	4.95	154.54	132.52
1.00	4.92	209.50	225.96

Those responsible for pricing the airplane can now proceed to weigh the likelihood of various market share situations, seeing as they do the price-production-profit implications of each possibility. At the same time, a decision can be made about the magnitude of the selling effort which should be undertaken.

CHAPTER 6

ALGEBRAIC AND TRANSCENDENTAL FUNCTIONS

THE POLYNOMIAL has played a prominent role in the previous chapters. The nth degree polynomial is a function of the form

$$f_n(x) = a_n x^n + a_{n-1} x^{n-1} \cdots + a_1 x + a_0 \tag{1}$$

where the a_i are constants, $a_n \neq 0$, and n is an integer. Another class of function that has been used is one which consists of the ratio of two polynomials. This class of functions is known as rational; e.g.,

$$H(x) = \frac{a_0 + a_1 x}{b_0 + b_1 x + b_2 x^2}$$

is a rational function.

Occasionally functions of the form

$$g(x) = x^m$$

where m is the ratio of two integers, have also been used, as for example in $\sqrt{x}$ $(= x^{1/2})$.

These three classes of functions, while being extremely important in practice, represent only a part of all possible types of functions. In this chapter another class of functions—the exponential, logarithmic, and algebraic functions—will be presented.

1. EXPONENTS AND EXPONENTIALS

Before introducing the exponential function, recall what has been said about the power function

$$g(x) = x^n \tag{2}$$

where n is an integer. An example of this type of function is shown

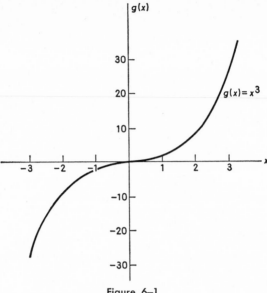

Figure 6–1

in Figure 6–1, where $n = 3$. Figure 6–2 is an illustration of a case where $n = 4$. Power functions are subject to the operations of mul-

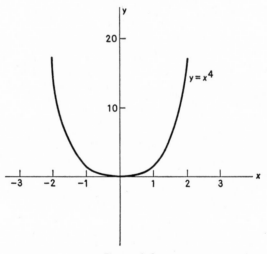

Figure 6–2

tiplication and division according to the properties of exponents, some of which are given in Appendix 4. Power functions may also be added or subtracted to form polynomials.

Consider now a function of the form

$$f(x) = a^x$$

where a is constant, greater than zero and different from one. Suppose as an example that $a = 3$. Then

$$f(x) = 3^x \qquad (3)$$

It is a straightforward task to compute $f(x)$ for integral values of x; e.g.,

x	-10	-5	-3	-2	-1	0	1	2	3	5	10
$f(x)$	$\frac{1}{59,049}$	$\frac{1}{243}$	$\frac{1}{27}$	$\frac{1}{9}$	$\frac{1}{3}$	1	3	9	27	243	59,049

The values of $f(x)$ have been plotted in Figure 6–3 and a smooth

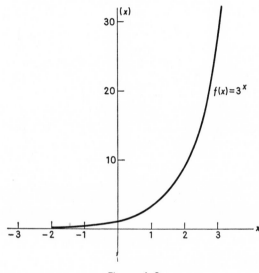

Figure 6–3

curve has been drawn through the points. This implies that (3) is a function for any value of x, in particular, that a numerical value can be ascribed to quantities such as

$$3^{6.735}$$

This is in fact true and the function so created,

$$f(x) = a^x \quad a > 0 \text{ and } a \neq 1,\ -\infty \le x \le \infty \qquad (4)$$

is called an *exponential function*.

Certain elementary properties of the exponential function are immediately apparent:

1. $f(x) > 0$ since $a > 0$.
2. $f(0) = 1$ since $a^0 = 1$.
3. $f(x)$ increases as x increases if $a > 1$. Figure 6–3 shows the particular case $a = 3$.

4. $f(x)$ decreases as x increases if $0 < a < 1$. An example is shown in Figure 6–4 for $a = \frac{1}{2}$.

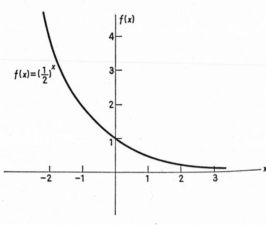

Figure 6–4

The rate of change of an exponential function is, as with other functions, nothing more or less than the derivative function. That derivative, when it exists, is given by the same definition as before, i.e.,

$$D_x a^x = D_x f(x) = \lim_{\Delta x \to 0} \frac{f(x + \Delta x) - f(x)}{\Delta x}$$

$$= \lim_{\Delta x \to 0} \frac{a^{x+\Delta x} - a^x}{\Delta x} \tag{5}$$

Notice, however, in this case how the numerator of the right-hand side of the definition can be factored so that

$$D_x a^x = \lim_{\Delta x \to 0} \frac{a^x(a^{\Delta x} - 1)}{\Delta x}$$

$$= a^x \lim_{\Delta x \to 0} \frac{(a^{\Delta x} - 1)}{\Delta x}$$

Thus it is seen that the derivative of the exponential function is the product of the function itself and some number which can be called L; that is,

$$f'(x) = f(x) \cdot L \tag{6}$$

where $L = \lim_{\Delta x \to 0} \dfrac{a^{\Delta x} - 1}{\Delta x}$.

Note that L depends only on the constant a. Now it is true that there is one particular value of a for which $L = 1$. Let that special value of the number a which causes $L = 1$ be labeled e. That is, the number e is the numerical value of a which causes $f'(x) = f(x)$.

By advanced methods it can be shown that e does in fact exist and that it is an irrational number (one which cannot be written as the ratio of two integers, i.e., a "never-ending decimal") which is approximately $2\frac{5}{7}$, 2.718, or, more accurately, 2.718 281 828.

The number e often disturbs the newcomer just as the similarly irrational number π (approximately 3.14) is sometimes distressing when first encountered. Thus it may help to give an alternative definition of e, one which can be derived from the first:

$$e = \lim_{n \to \infty} \left(1 + \frac{1}{n}\right)^n \tag{7}$$

This definition of e is useful because it illustrates how a numerical approximation can be obtained. Consider the term $F(n) = (1 + 1/n)^n$ for a few selected values of n (rounded to three decimals in all but the first two instances):

$$
\begin{aligned}
F(1) &= (1 + \tfrac{1}{1})^1 & &= 2 \\
F(2) &= (1 + \tfrac{1}{2})^2 & &= 2.25 \\
F(3) &= (1 + \tfrac{1}{3})^3 & &= 2.370 \\
F(4) &= (1 + \tfrac{1}{4})^4 & &= 2.441 \\
F(10) &= (1 + \tfrac{1}{10})^{10} & &= 2.594 \\
F(50) &= (1 + \tfrac{1}{50})^{50} & &= 2.692 \\
F(1000) &= (1 + \tfrac{1}{1000})^{1000} & &= 2.717
\end{aligned}
$$

Although this is certainly no proof that e is approximately 2.718, it should make the unsupported statement somewhat more credible.

Since e is that special value of a which causes the exponential function to be its own derivative, another differentiation formula can now be added to those of Chapter 3:

Theorem 1

$$
\begin{aligned}
&\text{If } f(x) = e^x \\
&\quad f'(x) = e^x
\end{aligned} \tag{8}
$$

And, following the procedure of Chapter 3, (8) can be generalized as this useful theorem:

Theorem 2

$$
\begin{aligned}
&\text{If } f(x) = e^{g(x)}, \text{ and if } g(x) \text{ is differentiable,} \\
&\quad f'(x) = e^{g(x)} \cdot g'(x)
\end{aligned} \tag{9}
$$

The properties which have been shown for the exponential function make the function a natural one to apply in practical problems where a quantity changes at a rate which is proportional to the value of the quantity itself. Several examples of the use of this function and of the differentiation formulas are given below.

Example (i)

Suppose $f(x) = e^{2x}$. Then

$$f'(x) = 2e^{2x}$$

Example (ii)

Suppose $f(x) = e^{x^2}$. Then

$$f'(x) = e^{x^2} \cdot 2x = 2xe^{x^2}$$

This function is illustrated in Figure 6–5 in order to show that an exponential function may be both decreasing and increasing.

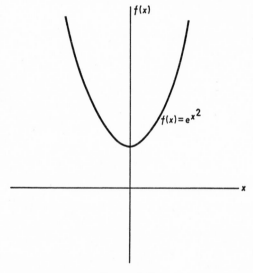

Figure 6–5

Example (iii)

Suppose $f(x) = e^{3x} + e^{-2x}$. Then

$$f'(x) = 3e^{3x} - 2e^{-2x}$$

Example (iv)

Suppose $f(x) = xe^{3x}$. Finding $f'(x)$ involves a differentiation of the product $(x)(e^{3x})$. Therefore,

$$f'(x) = (x)(3e^{3x}) + (e^{3x})(1)$$
$$= 3xe^{3x} + e^{3x}$$
$$= (3x + 1)e^{3x}$$

Example (v). Efficiency Improvement in Petroleum

In the petroleum industry one study showed that capital costs per barrel of raw material for thermal cracking, expressed in constant dollars, were reduced 78% between 1913 and 1946. The relation between improved efficiency and time, shown in Figure 6–6, is obviously not linear, since improvement was great-

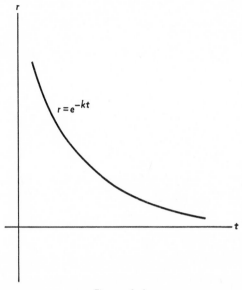

Figure 6–6

est in the first few years and then became smaller as some sort of "limit of efficiency" was approached over a long period of time.

Thus the relationship can be described as being roughly exponential, i.e.,

$$r = e^{-kt}$$

where

r = fraction of capital cost of improved cracking unit to that of original unit,

t = time, in years,

k = constant reflecting improvement rate in per cent.

Example (vi). Constant Sales Decay

Sales of a product which is not advertised or promoted actively may tend to decrease over time because of competing advertising, product obsolescence, lack of knowledge of the product by the public, etc. When market conditions are relatively constant, the rate of sales decrease will also be constant; that is, a constant percentage of sales will be lost each year. This constant rate of decline may be called the sales decay constant.

Letting S represent sales, s represent the sales decay constant, and t represent time, then the sales rate at time t of such a product will be

$$S(t) = S(0)e^{-st}$$

where $S(0)$ represents sales level at $t = 0$, that is, at the beginning of the period under study.

For a product such as a soap or a soft drink, where product differentiation is slight and promotional activity among competitors is very pronounced, the sales decay constant would be high. For a noncompetitive, well-established product, the sales decay constant might be almost zero.

2. Logarithmic Functions

In the previous section the exponential function f with base a has been defined as

$$y = f(x) = a^x \qquad a > 0 \text{ and } a \neq 1 \qquad (10)$$

For the case where $a > 1$ the form of the exponential function is as shown in Figure 6–3. The function is always increasing, and therefore it is possible to find a unique value of x for any given value of y. In Figure 6–7, y has been plotted as the independent variable

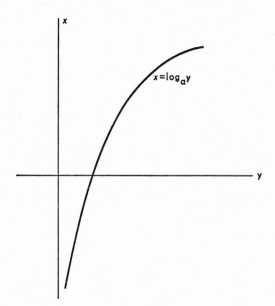

Figure 6–7

and x as the dependent variable. This function is given by

$$x = g(y)$$

and is an inverse function in the sense described in Chapter 3. The common name for this function is the *logarithmic function*. This notion of a "log" function as an inverse of an exponential can be formalized as follows:

Given some positive number, a, not equal to one, the unique number x associated with each positive number y such that

$$y = f(x) = a^x$$

is called the logarithm of y. That x is a function of y is indicated by writing the *logarithmic function:*

$$x = g(y) = \log_a y$$

The standard notation is $\log_a y$ for $g(y)$. If

$$y = a^x \tag{11}$$

then

$$x = \log_a y \tag{12}$$

What is being said here is essentially this: if x is the "log" of y to the base a, then x is the power to which the number a must be raised so that a^x equals y, i.e., a logarithm is an exponent.

Several elementary properties of the logarithmic functions which are analogous to the properties of the exponential function can be deduced directly from the definition of a logarithmic function. The first is that $\log_a a = 1$ since the power to which a must be raised for it to be equal to a is indeed one ($a^1 = a$). Similarly, $\log_a 1$ must be zero since $a^0 = 1$. These and a number of other properties of logarithms are listed in Appendix 4.

Logarithms in one base can be expressed in logarithms to another base by the relation

$$\log_a x = (\log_b x) \log_a b \tag{13}$$

The most important cases of log functions for present purposes will be the *natural logarithms*, i.e., logarithms to the base e. The term "natural" is used because of the simplicity and convenience of this base. This function is usually written $\log_e x$ or $\ln x$ with the understanding that the base of the logarithm is e. If another base is used, it is stated explicitly.

The derivative of the logarithm function can be obtained from the derivative of the exponential function. If

$$y = f(x)$$

then

$$\frac{dx}{dy} = \frac{1}{\dfrac{dy}{dx}}$$

where dy/dx is expressed in terms of y. In this case

$$y = e^x \quad \text{and} \quad \frac{dy}{dx} = e^x = y$$

But

$$x = \log_e y = \ln y$$

Therefore, since

$$\frac{dx}{dy} = \frac{1}{\dfrac{dy}{dx}} = \frac{1}{y}$$

it follows that

$$\frac{d(\ln y)}{dy} = \frac{1}{y} \quad \text{or} \quad \frac{d(\ln x)}{dx} = \frac{1}{x}$$

This proves Theorem 3:

Theorem 3

$$\text{If } y = \ln x \quad \text{then} \quad y' = \frac{1}{x} \tag{14}$$

This theorem together with (13) and (9) gives a theorem for differentiating the general exponential function

$$y = a^x \tag{15}$$

Using (13) the function may be written as

$$y = e^{x \, \log_e a} \tag{16}$$

and therefore

$$\frac{dy}{dx} = (\log_e a) e^{x \, \log_e a} \tag{17}$$
$$= (a^x) \log_e a$$

The inverse function is $x = \log_a y$ and

$$\frac{dx}{dy} = \frac{1}{a^x \log_e a} \tag{18}$$
$$= \frac{1}{y} \log_a e$$

from (13). This proves another theorem:

Theorem 4

$$\text{If } f(x) = \log_a x \text{ then } f'(x) = \frac{1}{x} \log_a e \tag{19}$$

It will be recalled that the function a^x was differentiated by the use of the difference quotient with the result that

$$\frac{da^x}{dx} = a^x \cdot L \tag{6} = (20)$$

It follows from the above result that

$$L = \lim_{\Delta x \to 0} \frac{a^{\Delta x} - 1}{\Delta x} = \log_e a \tag{21}$$

Application of the chain rule yields these generalizations:

Theorem 5

If $f(x) = \ln g(x)$ then $f'(x) = g'(x)/g(x)$ provided $g(x) > 0$

Theorem 6

$$\text{If } f(x) = a^{g(x)}, \text{ then } f'(x) = g'(x)a^{g(x)} \ln a. \tag{22}$$

These concepts are illustrated by the following examples and by the exercises at the end of the chapter. Some business applications will be presented later.

Example (i)

If $y = \ln (x + 3)$

$$\frac{dy}{dx} = \frac{1}{x + 3}$$

Example (ii)

If $y = \ln (x^2 - 2x + 6)$,

$$\frac{dy}{dx} = \frac{2x - 2}{x^2 - 2x + 6}$$

Example (iii)

Suppose $\beta(u) = 3^u/(u - 1)$.

This may be differentiated like any quotient, i.e.,

$$\beta'(u) = \frac{(u - 1)(3^u) \ln 3 - 3^u}{(u - 1)^2}$$

A table of natural logarithms can be consulted to obtain the value of log 3, approximately 1.099, so that

$$\beta'(u) = \frac{1.099(u - 1)3^u - 3^u}{(u - 1)^2}$$

This last example raises the question of computing numbers such as e^5 or log 6.1. Although there are direct methods, the usual procedure is to use prepared tables. Tables, of course, provide only approximations. But the accuracy of tabular approximations usually is satisfactory for real problem situations.

The common tables show e^n, e^{-n}, and log n for various values of n. For illustration and for use in solving exercises in this book, limited versions of each of these three tables are collected in the appendix at the back of the book. Published tables of greater detail should be consulted if greater accuracy or range is needed. Instructions for use accompany each table.

3. ALGEBRAIC FUNCTIONS

Until the introduction of the transcendental functions in this chapter, the analysis had been restricted to some simple functions—in fact, primarily to a particular type of algebraic function, the *polynomial*. Polynomials were introduced in Chapter 1 without a rigorous definition, on the assumption that the reader would find them familiar. Whether or not this assumption was warranted, it is unlikely that a careful definition of a polynomial or a classification of functions would have added anything to those early sections. Now, however, it is desirable to consider number systems and functions more systematically.

Originally a function was defined as a rule for associating a variable y to another variable x. It has been implicitly assumed that both y and x represented numbers, "number" not being defined. The purpose of this section is to present a systematic though intuitive development of number systems and to show the relationship between types of mathematical operations and number systems.

The simplest set of numbers is that of the positive integers, 1, 2, 3, · · ·. The simplest arithmetic operation is that of addition. Suppose this operation is applied to the positive integers. The sum of any two positive integers is itself a positive integer. If an arithmetic operation is applied to any pair of a set of numbers and the result is again a member of the set, then the set is said to be *closed* under this operation.

Consider next the operation of subtraction. Clearly, the set of positive integers is not closed under subtraction; for example, 7 subtracted from 5 does not yield a positive integer. An equivalent way of saying this is that the equation

$$x = 5 - 7$$

cannot be solved if x is restricted to the set of positive integers. Equations of this type can be solved if the set of numbers is enlarged to include the negative integers and the number 0. This enlarged set is called the set of *integers*.

The next operation is that of multiplication. Let

$$x = ab$$

where a and b are any integers, then x will also be an integer and hence the set of integers is closed under multiplication.

Suppose the product is

$$a = bx$$

where a and b are any integers and x is unknown ($b \neq 0$). This equation in general will not be true if x is restricted to the set of integers. Formally,

$$x = \frac{a}{b}$$

and hence the equation can always be solved if the set of numbers is enlarged to include *rational numbers*. Rational numbers are numbers which can be expressed as the ratio of two integers. The set of rational numbers includes the set of integers.

It should be noted that the computation

$$x = a + b \quad \text{and} \quad x = ab$$

could be solved within a certain set of numbers, but the solution of equations

$$a = b + x \quad \text{and} \quad a = bx$$

requires extension of the original number system.

The next logical operation, after addition, subtraction, multiplication, and division, is that of exponentiation. Consider the power function

$$y = x^n$$

where x is a rational number and n is an integer. Clearly, y can be computed and will be a rational number.

The inverse problem is to find x when y is a rational number and n is an integer. It is true, but not so obvious, that this problem cannot be solved in general if x is restricted to the set of rational numbers. For example, let $y = 2$ and $n = 2$, then

$$2 = x^2$$

The formal solution is $x = \sqrt{2}$. Suppose that the "number" $\sqrt{2}$ can be expressed as the ratio of two integers,

$$\sqrt{2} = \frac{a}{b}$$

where a and b are integers and all common factors have been canceled; then squaring both sides and simplifying gives

$$2 = \frac{a^2}{b^2} \quad \text{or} \quad 2b^2 = a^2$$

From this it follows that a^2 is an even integer since it can be written as twice some integer. Since the square of any odd integer is odd, it follows that a itself must be an even integer. Therefore, it can be written in the form

$$a = 2c$$

where c is an integer. Substituting gives

$$2b^2 = a^2 = (2c)^2 = 4c^2$$

or

$$b^2 = 2c^2$$

Reasoning as before, b must be an even integer and therefore a and b have the common factor 2. But this contradicts the assumption that a and b have no common factors. This proves that $\sqrt{2}$ cannot be written as the ratio of two integers, for to assume the contrary leads to a logical contradiction.

To solve equations of the form

$$y = x^n$$

for x when y and n are given requires the extension of the set of rational numbers to include *real numbers*. Real numbers include those which cannot be written as the ratio of two integers. This definition states what these numbers are not; it does not give any help in determining what the numbers are. Some examples of real numbers have been used, e.g., $5e$, $\sqrt{2}$, π, 631, etc., but the problem of constructing and defining real numbers is complicated and requires advanced mathematical techniques and concepts.

The class of real numbers is sufficient for the computation of algebraic and transcendental functions. The power function has been defined as

$$y = x^n$$

If x and n are any real numbers, y is also a real number. Two inverse functions can be defined:

1. If y and x are any real numbers ($y > 0$; $x > 0$; $x \neq 1$), then $n = \log_x y$ is the logarithmic function and n will be a real number.
2. If y and n are real numbers, then

$$x = \sqrt[n]{y}$$

   is also a real number.

The results apply to more general algebraic and transcendental functions.

A "monomial" or *term* in x is an expression involving the product of a constant, call it k, and a power of x: e.g., $3x$, $15x^2$, $-318x^9$, $\cdots$. A *polynomial* in x can be defined as the sum of any number of monomials in x: e.g., $3x^2 - 4x - 6$. Note that polynomials, or polynomial functions, involve only the algebraic operations of addition, subtraction, and multiplication.

A second type of function is the algebraic. An *algebraic* function is one which involves quotients, powers, and roots of polynomials: e.g.,

$$\frac{6x - 5}{x^3 + 9}, \; \frac{(x^2 - 1)^3}{(2x - 1)^2}, \; \sqrt{5x - 2}, \; \frac{4\sqrt{x^2 - 2}}{(1 - x^3)^2}$$

Note that polynomials are simply special kinds of algebraic functions, just as linear and quadratic expressions are special cases of polynomials.

The theorems of Chapters 1–5 were stated and proven for polynomials only. Some of the illustrations, however, involved algebraic functions which were not polynomials. Thus, it is necessary to state for the record that all of the theorems stated in those chapters are valid for algebraic functions generally. For example, $f'(x) = ng^{n-1}g'$, when $f(x) = [g(x)]^n$ regardless of whether n is 3 or $\frac{1}{3}$, and regardless of whether g is a polynomial or a more complex function such as

$$\frac{(x^3 - 15)^{3/2}}{(x - 1)}$$

The only class of nonalgebraic functions of concern here is the transcendental, and only the exponential and logarithmic functions within that class are discussed. The major exclusion is that subclass of transcendental functions known as the trigonometric functions (e.g., sin x, cos x, etc.). They are excluded for the simple reason that they are rarely important in business applications.

The several functions mentioned in this section are summarized in the following schematic table:

Algebraic Functions				Transcendental Functions		
Polynomial Functions			Other Algebraic Functions	Exponential Functions	Logarithmic Functions	Other Transcendental Functions
Linear Functions	Quadratic Functions	Other Polynomial Functions				

As general as the set of real numbers is, it is not so general as to include the solutions of all polynomials. Let $f(x)$ be a general second degree polynomial,

$$f(x) = ax^2 + bx + c$$

and consider the problem of finding the value of x, say x^*, which satisfies

$$f(x^*) = 0$$

By the result given in Chapter 4,

$$x^* = \frac{-b \pm \sqrt{b^2 - 4ac}}{2a}$$

If $b^2 - 4ac$ is negative, then x^* will not be a real number because the square root of a negative number has been given no meaning in the real number system. There is no real number whose square is a negative number. Numbers which do have this property are called "imaginary" numbers; their study is beyond the scope of this text.

The types of numbers included in the hierarchy of number systems is summarized in the following table:

Complex Numbers					
Imaginary Numbers	Real Numbers				
	Irrational Numbers	Rational Numbers			
		Other Rationals	Integers		
			Negative Integers	Zero	Positive Integers

EXERCISES, SECTION 1

In exercises 1 to 6, find the derivative of the general function.

1. $f(x) = e^{2x^2}$

2. $f(y) = ye^y$

3. $f(x) = x^2 e^{x^2}$

4. $f(x) = (x - 1)e^{x-1}$

5. $f(x) = \dfrac{x}{e^x}$

6. $f(x) = \dfrac{x}{1 + e^x}$

7. Given $y = (x^2 + 1)e^x$, find the point(s) at which $y' = 0$. Determine whether maxima, minima, or inflection point(s) have been located.

8. Suppose $y = (1 - e^x)^2$. Determine whether there are any extreme points; if so, are they maxima, minima, or inflection points?

9. Suppose $f(x) = e^{-x^2}$. Locate extrema, if any, and determine whether they are maxima or minima, as above.

10. Suppose $f(x) = xe^{-x}$. Determine maxima, minima, or inflection points, as above.

11. Sketch the function e^x using the table in Appendix 5.

12. A promoter, who is staging a circus, advertises the fact by distributing handbills. Let

   x = number of handbills distributed,
   N = total number of people in the geographical area,
   r = admission price,
   c = the fixed cost of staging the circus—there are no variable costs,
   b = cost per handbill distributed.

   Assume that the response, i.e., the number of people paying the admission price is given by

$$N(1 - e^{-x/3N})$$

   Determine the optimum number of handbills that should be distributed. Compute the optimum for $N = 76,385$, $r = \$3.00$, $c = \$10,000$, $b = .25$.

13. A method of depreciation called double declining balance, DDB, or accelerated depreciation, is widely used in business. It differs from the regular straight-line method in that it reduces the book value of an asset by a constant ratio each year instead of by a constant amount.

   For example, suppose an asset is worth \$10,000; under the straight-line method, if the asset had an estimated life of ten years, the amount of depreciation would be \$1000 a year, or 10% of the initial value of the asset. After ten years the book value of the asset would be zero. Under the DDB method, the percentage reduction would be 20% instead of 10%, but would be applied each year to the book value of the asset at the beginning of the year. Thus, depreciation during the first year would be

$$(\$10,000)(.20) = \$2000$$

Then the book value of the asset at the beginning of the second year would be $10,000 − $2000, or $8000. Depreciation during the second year would be

$$(8000)\,(.20) = \$1600$$

a) Develop a formula for the amount of depreciation in the tth year of an asset purchased for A which has a useful life of n years.

b) Develop a formula for the book value of this asset after t years.

c) The federal tax law permits the DDB method to be used in the early years and the straight-line method in later years of an asset's life. Determine the optimum point in time to make the change so as to accelerate the depreciation as much as possible.

EXERCISES, SECTION 2

Find the derivatives of the first-mentioned variable with respect to the second variable in Exercises 14–23.

14. $y = \ln\,(2 - 5x)$
15. $y = \ln x^2$
16. $f(x) = a^{x^2-2x}$
17. $a = \ln\,[\,(s^2 + 2)^3]$
18. $y = \ln\,(2x + 2)$
19. $u = \ln\,(v^2 - 2v)$
20. $u = \ln \dfrac{x}{(x + 3)}$ (Recall that this is the same as $u = \ln\ x - \ln$ $(x + 3)$.
21. $y = 3 \ln\,(x^2 + 1)$
22. $f(v) = \ln \sqrt{v^2 - 2}$
    (Hint: Remember that the above can be written as $f(v) = \tfrac{1}{2} \cdot \ln$ $(v^2 - 2)$.)
23. $y = \ln\,(x^2 - 1)/(x^2 + 1)$
24. Sketch a graph of the function $\ln x$ using the graph prepared in Exercise 11.
25. Assume, in Exercise 12, that the response is given by

$$N\!\left(.1 \ln \frac{x}{N} + .5\right)$$

Determine the optimum number of handbills.

26. A firm has $N(0)$ employees at time $t = 0$ and grows at the rate R so that the number of employees at time t, $N(t)$, is $N(0) \cdot R^t$. Determine $dN(t)/dt$ as a function of $N(t)$.
27. Prove the result given in the chapter as equation (13). (Hint: Note that $a^{\log_a b} = b$ and then take logarithms of both sides.)
28. Develop the result of Case No. 3 using logarithms and Theorem 3 of this chapter.

REVIEW EXERCISES: EXPONENTS

1. Show the cube root of x in exponential form.

2. Show $1/2x^2$ in exponential form.

3. Show $1/(2x)^2$ in exponential form.

4. Write the cube root of x^2 as a power of x.

5. Write the square root of $x^{1/2}$ as a power of x.

6. What is the value of $2x^a + 3x^{a-1} + x^{a-2} + 6$ when $a = 2$?

7. $a)$ Find the value of x^{-3} when $x = 3$.

   $b)$ Find the value of $1/x^3$ when $x = 3$.

8. Express $(x + 1)^{-1}$ as a fraction.

9. Express $(\sqrt[3]{y})^{-2}$ as a power of y.

10. $u = h(y) = y^a - y^{a-1} + y^{a-2}$.

    Give the equation of u as $h(y)$ when $a = 1$.

CHAPTER 7

MULTIVARIATE FUNCTIONS

SINCE Chapter 1, only functions of a single variable, i.e., $y = f(x)$, have been discussed. Now it is time to consider again functions of two, three, or more variables. For example, $y = f(x_1, x_2)$; $z = g(x, y)$; $w = h(r, s, t)$; and $y = F(x_i)$, $i = 1, 2,$ $\cdots$, n, are functions of two or more variables.

Clearly, functions of several variables are of prime importance empirically. A person's height is not a function of age alone, intellectual achievement depends on more than IQ, and so on for many other phenomena. Multivariate functions are particularly important in business and economics: sales depend on many factors in addition to advertising; costs depend on more than production level; etc.

1. FUNCTIONS OF SEVERAL VARIABLES

A function of two variables is a correspondence, say f, that associates with each pair of possible values of the independent variables (x_1, x_2) one and only one value for the dependent variable $f(x_1, x_2)$. Similarly, a function of three variables is a correspondence f that associates with each triplet of values of the independent variables (x_1, x_2, x_3) one and only one value for the dependent variable $f(x_1, x_2, x_3)$, and so on for any number of independent variables. Notice, however, that regardless of the number of independent variables there is still only one dependent variable.

Functions of several variables can be manipulated just as functions of one variable can. The sum, difference, product, and quotient of two such functions are defined as expected. For example, if $f(x, y) = x + xy + y^2$ and $g(x, y) = 3x + 2y^2$, then

$$f + g = 4x + xy + 3y^2$$
$$f - g = -2x + xy - y^2$$
$$f \cdot g = (x + xy + y^2) \cdot (3x + 2y^2)$$

and

$$\frac{f}{g} = \frac{x + xy + y^2}{3x + 2y^2}$$

Composite functions are handled just as before except that the greater complexity in the present case makes operations seem more difficult and increases the opportunities for confusion. There are two guidelines: first, remember that a function is a *rule* for "doing something to something"; second, remember that the labels for the variables are simple placeholders, and that quite complicated-appearing expressions may be substituted for a simple placeholder such as x. A few examples will illustrate these remarks.

Example (i)

If $f(x, y) = x + xy + y^2$
and $g(u) = u^2$
then $g(f) = g(x, y) = f^2 = (x + xy + y^2)^2$

Example (ii)

If $f(x, y) = x + xy + y^2$ as before
and $h(w) = aw + b$
then $h(f) = h(x, y) = a(x + xy + y^2) + b$

Example (iii)

If $f(t) = 5 + t^2$, $F(t) = \dfrac{1}{t}$, $g(t) = t^3 - 2$

and $h(x, y, z) = xy^2z$

then $h(f, F, g) = H(t) = (f)(F)^2 g = (5 + t^2)\dfrac{1}{t^2}(t^3 - 2)$

$$= t^3 + 5t - 2 - \frac{10}{t^2}$$

if f replaces x, F replaces y, and g replaces z in the function $h(x, y, z)$. It would be just as reasonable, however, to let g replace x, F replace z, and f replace y, etc. The order of replacement would depend on the problem under consideration.

Example (iv)

Suppose C = total costs, x = sales volume, A = advertising expenditure, R = total revenues from sales, P = unit price, and π = profits, and suppose further that $\pi = f(C, R)$, $C = F(x, A)$, $R = x \cdot P$, and $P = G(x, A)$. Then a composite profits function $\pi = \pi(x, A)$ can be formed:

$$\pi(x, A) = f(F[x, A], x \cdot P) = f(F[x, A], x \cdot G[x, A])$$

2. PARTIAL DIFFERENTIATION

In a function of two variables, $z = f(x, y)$, for example, each of the variables x and y can be varied independently of the other. In particular, one variable, say x, can be fixed, and y varied in order to see the "net" effect of changes in y on the dependent variable, z. The function, in a manner of speaking, has been reduced to one independent variable, $z = \psi(y)$, since x is being treated as a constant. Thus one can speak of the derivative of $f(x, y)$ with respect to y and mean essentially what has been understood all along by the term derivative, just as one can speak of the derivative of f with respect to x.

These new derivatives are called *partial derivatives* and are symbolized in a number of ways:

$$\frac{\partial z}{\partial x}, \ \frac{\partial f}{\partial x}, \ \frac{\partial f(x, y)}{\partial x}, \ z_x, \ f_x(x, y), \ f_x$$

The symbol "∂" replaces the previous "d" so as to distinguish partial derivatives unambiguously from the derivatives defined in Chapter 3. The partial derivatives of a function are defined in a familiar way:

$$\frac{\partial f(x, y)}{\partial x} = \lim_{\Delta x \to 0} \frac{f(x + \Delta x, y) - f(x, y)}{\Delta x}$$

$$\frac{\partial f(x, y)}{\partial y} = \lim_{\Delta y \to 0} \frac{f(x, y + \Delta y) - f(x, y)}{\Delta y} \tag{1}$$

The limit operation used in (1) is the same as that which was introduced and used in Chapter 3 since in each case the function depends on only one variable when the limit is taken.

As before, it is convenient to avoid the use of the definition when actually differentiating functions, relying instead on special rules which follow from the definition. The rules are essentially the ones developed in Chapter 3 except that the "other" variable is temporarily treated as a constant; that is, when finding $\partial f/\partial x$, y is treated as a constant, and similarly for x when finding $\partial f/\partial y$.

If $f(x, y) = 3x + 2y$, the partial derivative $\partial f/\partial x$ is the derivative of $3x$ with respect to x plus the derivative of $2y$ with respect to x, i.e., $3 + 0$. By the same reasoning, $\partial f/\partial y = 0 + 2 = 2$. The following examples will illustrate this further:

Example (i)

If $g(s, t) = s^3 + 3st + 5t^2$, then $g_s = 3s^2 + 3t$ and $g_t = 3s + 10t$

Example (ii)

If $w = u^2 + uv$, then $\dfrac{\partial w}{\partial u} = 2u + v$ and $\dfrac{dw}{\partial v} = u$

Example (iii)

$$\text{If } R = 3x^2 + 2yx + y^5 - 3xz^2, \text{ then}$$

$$R_x = 6x + 2y - 3z^2$$
$$R_y = 2x + 5y^4$$
$$R_z = -6xz$$

Example (iv)

$$\text{If } f(x, y) = \frac{x - y}{x + y}, \text{ then } \frac{\partial f}{\partial x} = \frac{2y}{(x + y)^2}$$

$$\text{and} \quad \frac{\partial f}{\partial y} = \frac{-2x}{(x + y)^2}$$

Each partial derivative might in turn have partial derivatives, just as there may be first, second, and higher derivatives of a function of one variable. A function $f(x, y)$ may have *four* second partial derivatives as follows:

$$f(x, y) \Big\langle \begin{array}{l} f_x(x, y) = \dfrac{\partial f(x, y)}{\partial x} \Big\langle \begin{array}{l} \dfrac{\partial[f_x(x, y)]}{\partial x} = \dfrac{\partial^2 f}{\partial x^2} \\[2ex] \dfrac{\partial[f_x(x, y)]}{\partial y} = \dfrac{\partial^2 f}{\partial x \partial y} \end{array} \\[6ex] f_y(x, y) = \dfrac{\partial f(x, y)}{\partial y} \Big\langle \begin{array}{l} \dfrac{\partial[f_y(x, y)]}{\partial x} = \dfrac{\partial^2 f}{\partial y \partial x} \\[2ex] \dfrac{\partial[f_y(x, y)]}{\partial y} = \dfrac{\partial^2 f}{\partial y^2} \end{array} \end{array}$$

The derivatives $\partial^2 f/\partial x \partial y$ and $\partial^2 f/\partial y \partial x$ are called the "cross" partials and are the subject of this interesting and important theorem:

Theorem 1

If the "cross" partial derivatives of a function of two variables are continuous in some region, they are equal in that region:

$$\frac{\partial^2 f}{\partial x \partial y} = \frac{\partial^2 f}{\partial y \partial x}$$

The theorem simply means that the order of the partial differentiation is immaterial when the continuity condition is satisfied, as it is for essentially all functions in this book.

The theorem and the notation can be extended to higher-order partial derivatives. Thus, if the conditions of the theorem are satisfied for a function $u = f(x, y, z)$,

$$\frac{\partial^3 u}{\partial x \partial y \partial z} = \frac{\partial^3 u}{\partial z \partial y \partial x} = \frac{\partial^3 u}{\partial x \partial z \partial y}, \text{ etc.}$$

The rapid increase in the number of higher-order partials that a function may have is shown in this table:

Function	First-Order Partials	Second-Order Partials	Third-Order Partials	Nth-Order Partials
$f(x)$	1	1	1	1
$f(x, y)$	2	4	8	2^N
$f(x, y, z)$	3	9	27	3^N
$f(w, x, y, z)$	4	16	64	4^N
$f(x_i), i = 1, 2, \cdots, n$	n	n^2	n^3	n^N

Many of the higher-order cross partials will not be distinct, however, because of the extension of Theorem 1. For example, $f(x, y)$ usually will have only three distinct second-order partials and four distinct third-order partials.

To illustrate some of these concepts, suppose $f(x, y) = 5x^2 + 2xy + 4y^2$. The first-order partial derivatives are

$$\frac{\partial f}{\partial x} = 10x + 2y \quad \text{and} \quad \frac{\partial f}{\partial y} = 2x + 8y$$

The second-order partials can then be found:

$$\frac{\partial^2 f}{\partial x^2} = 10 \qquad \frac{\partial^2 f}{\partial y^2} = 8$$

$$\frac{\partial^2 f}{\partial x \partial y} = 2 \qquad \frac{\partial^2 f}{\partial y \partial x} = 2$$

Note that the cross partials are equal just as Theorem 1 promised. Also note that all of the third- and higher-order partials are zero.

This brief discussion of the theory of partial differentiation can be concluded with mention of one additional theorem, the analogue to the "chain rule" in Chapter 3 for differentiating composite functions. It was found in Chapter 3 that the derivative of a composite function of two differentiable functions, say $y = f(u)$ and $u = g(x)$, could be found by the rule that

$$\frac{dy}{dx} = \frac{dy}{du} \cdot \frac{du}{dx} \quad \text{(equivalently, } D_x y = D_u y \cdot D_x u) \tag{2}$$

The analogous "chain rule" for a composite function $z = F(x, y)$, where $x = f(u, v)$, and $y = g(u, v)$ is that the composite function can be differentiated as follows:

Theorem 2

$$\frac{\partial z}{\partial u} = \frac{\partial z}{\partial x}\frac{\partial x}{\partial u} + \frac{\partial z}{\partial y}\frac{\partial y}{\partial u}, \quad \text{and} \quad \frac{\partial z}{\partial v} = \frac{\partial z}{\partial x}\frac{\partial x}{\partial v} + \frac{\partial z}{\partial y}\frac{\partial y}{\partial v} \tag{3}$$

A generalization for the case where $z = F$ is a differentiable function of n variables, x_i, and each x_i is a differentiable function of m variables u_j, is:

$$\frac{\partial F}{\partial u_j} = \sum_{i=1}^{n} \frac{\partial F}{\partial x_i} \frac{\partial x_i}{\partial u_j} \quad j = 1, 2, \cdots, m$$

The most interesting use of the derivatives of composite functions involves the special case where f and g are functions of one variable. Suppose there is a function $F(x, y)$ where $x = f(t)$ and $y = g(t)$. Then the function-of-a-function, F, can be differentiated as follows:

$$\frac{\partial F}{\partial t} = \frac{\partial F}{\partial x} \frac{\partial x}{\partial t} + \frac{\partial F}{\partial y} \frac{\partial y}{\partial t} \tag{4}$$

But since f and g (or x and y) are each functions of a single variable, t, $\frac{\partial x}{\partial t} \left(\text{or } \frac{\partial f}{\partial t} \right)$ and $\frac{\partial y}{\partial t} \left(\text{or } \frac{\partial g}{\partial t} \right)$ are the "total" derivatives $\frac{dx}{dt}$ and $\frac{dy}{dt}$. Thus, Theorem 2 has the useful corollary that

$$\frac{\partial F}{\partial t} = \frac{\partial F}{\partial x} \frac{dx}{dt} + \frac{\partial F}{\partial y} \frac{dy}{dt} \tag{5}$$

These additional examples and the exercises at the end of the chapter offer further illustrations of the definitions and theorems of this section.

Example (i)

Suppose $x = f(t) = \frac{1}{t}$, $y = g(t) = t^2$, and $F(x, y) = x^2 y^2$.

Then

$$\frac{\partial F}{\partial t} = \frac{\partial F}{\partial x} \cdot \frac{dx}{dt} + \frac{\partial F}{\partial y} \cdot \frac{dy}{dt}$$

$$= 2xy^2 \left(\frac{-1}{t^2} \right) + (2x^2 y)(2t)$$

$$= \frac{-2t^4}{t^3} + \frac{2t^2}{t^2} (2t)$$

$$= -2t + \frac{4t^3}{t^2}$$

$$= -2t + 4t = 2t$$

Example (ii)

Suppose $f(u, v) = u^3 - uv + 2v^2$. Then

$$\frac{\partial f}{\partial u} = 3u^2 - v \qquad\qquad \frac{\partial f}{\partial v} = -u + 4v$$

$$\frac{\partial^2 f}{\partial u^2} = 6u, \quad \frac{\partial^2 f}{\partial v^2} = 4, \quad \frac{\partial^2 f}{\partial u \partial v} = -1, \quad \frac{\partial^2 f}{\partial v \partial u} = -1$$

$$\frac{\partial^3 f}{du^3} = 6 \quad \text{(all other third partial derivatives are zero)}$$

Example (iii)

Suppose $f(x, y) = \dfrac{1}{x} + xy^2$. Then

$$\frac{\partial f}{\partial x} = \frac{-1}{x^2} + y^2 \qquad\qquad \frac{\partial f}{\partial y} = 2xy$$

$$\frac{\partial^2 f}{\partial x^2} = \frac{2}{x^3}, \quad \frac{\partial^2 f}{\partial y^2} = 2x, \quad \frac{\partial^2 f}{\partial x \partial y} = 2y, \quad \frac{\partial^2 f}{\partial y \partial x} = 2y$$

Partial differentiation may be used instead of the implicit differentiation described in Chapter 3 to solve for the derivative dy/dx of a function such as

$$3x^2 + xy + y^2 = 6 \tag{6}$$

where it is not easy to solve the function explicitly for y.

Rearrange (6) to read

$$3x^2 + xy + y^2 - 6 = 0 \tag{7}$$

Letting $z = f(x, y) = 3x^2 + xy + y^2 - 6$, it can be seen that z is zero for all x, y satisfying (6). But since $z = f(x, y)$ and $y = g(x)$,

$$z = f[x, g(x)]$$

Then the partial derivative of z with respect to x is

$$\frac{\partial z}{\partial x} = \frac{\partial f}{\partial x} \cdot \frac{\partial x}{\partial x} + \frac{\partial f}{\partial g(x)} \cdot \frac{\partial g(x)}{\partial x} \tag{8}$$

by (3). But (8) defines the total derivative of z with respect to x, since the whole expression is now defined in terms of x. Therefore the expression is equal to zero, since dz/dx must be zero. (Since $z = 0$ for all x, y, the total derivative of z must also be zero since the rate of change of z is zero.) Thus,

$$\frac{\partial f}{\partial x} \cdot \frac{\partial x}{\partial x} + \frac{\partial f}{\partial g(x)} \cdot \frac{\partial g(x)}{\partial x} = 0 \tag{9}$$

Since $\partial x/\partial x = dx/dx = 1$, and substituting y back into (9), it is seen that

$$\frac{\partial f}{\partial x} + \frac{\partial f}{\partial y} \cdot \frac{dy}{dx} = 0 \tag{10}$$

and, finally,

$$\frac{dy}{dx} = -\frac{\dfrac{\partial f}{\partial x}}{\dfrac{\partial f}{\partial y}} \tag{11}$$

This latter expression can be used for finding dy/dx of $3x^2 + xy + y^2 = 6$ since $\partial f/\partial x = 6x + y$ and $\partial f/\partial y = x + 2y$,

$$\frac{dy}{dx} = -\frac{(6x + y)}{x + 2y} \tag{12}$$

by substitution. This is exactly the same result as was obtained in Chapter 3 by the method of implicit differentiation. Though there is little difference in ease of computation in this particular case, there are many occasions when it is easier to use the partial differentiation method outlined here than to attempt implicit differentiation. Both methods are important.

Two examples illustrate the method further.

Example (i)

Consider $x^3 + x^2y + y^2 + 2 = 0$. Find dy/dx by the implicit differentiation method.

Solution:

$$3x^2 + x^2\frac{dy}{dx} + 2xy + 2y\frac{dy}{dx} = 0$$

$$(x^2 + 2y)\frac{dy}{dx} = -(3x^2 + 2xy)$$

$$\frac{dy}{dx} = -\frac{(3x^2 + 2xy)}{x^2 + 2y}$$

Now find dy/dx using partial differentiation.

Solution:

$$\frac{\partial f}{\partial x} = 3x^2 + 2xy$$

$$\frac{\partial f}{\partial y} = x^2 + 2y$$

$$\frac{dy}{dx} = -\frac{\dfrac{\partial f}{\partial x}}{\dfrac{\partial f}{\partial y}} = -\frac{(3x^2 + 2xy)}{x^2 + 2y}$$

Example (ii)

Find dy/dx by using partial differentiation if

$$3x^2 + 3xy + \frac{y^2}{2} - 6 = 0$$

Solution:

$$\frac{dy}{dx} = -\frac{\dfrac{\partial f}{\partial x}}{\dfrac{\partial f}{\partial y}} = -\frac{(6x + 3y)}{3x + y}$$

3. THEORY OF EXTREMA FOR MULTIVARIATE FUNCTIONS

The graph of a function of two variables is, of course, a three-dimensional surface as in Figure 7–1. The function in that figure has

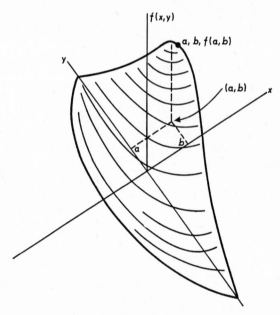

Figure 7–1

an extremum, a maximum, value at the point (a, b); changing either x or y from the point $x = a$, $y = b$ will reduce the value of the function. The analytical way of describing (a, b) is to say that the rate of change of the function in both dimensions, x and y, is zero; that is, the partial derivatives f_x and f_y are zero.

More precisely, to test for an extremum, maximum, or minimum of a function of two variables, it is necessary to determine whether or not, at any point (a, b) for which the function $f(x, y)$ is defined, both $\partial f(a, b)/\partial x$ and $\partial f(a, b)/\partial y$ are zero. The second condition is that

$$\frac{\partial^2 f(a, b)}{\partial x^2} \cdot \frac{\partial^2 f(a, b)}{\partial y^2} > \left(\frac{\partial^2 f(a, b)}{\partial x \partial y}\right)^2 \tag{13}$$

i.e., that the product of the two "pure" second partials be greater than the product of the two "cross" partials, f_{xy} and f_{yx} (written as

"f_{xy} squared" since $f_{xy} = f_{yx}$ in most cases). Finally, the theorem says a maximum value of f has been found if $f_{xx}(a, b)$ is negative, a minimum value if it is positive.

The theorem is as follows:

Theorem 3

If f is a function of two variables and if it has continuous second-order partial derivatives in some region, then at a point (a, b) in that region the function is at an extreme point if

$$f_x(a, b) = 0 = f_y(a, b)$$

and if

$$f_{xx}(a, b) \cdot f_{yy}(a, b) > [f_{xy}(a, b)]^2$$

The extremum is a maximum if $f_{xx}(a, b) < 0$ and a minimum if $f_{xx}(a, b) > 0$.

Two aspects of this theorem should be noted immediately. First, $f(a, b)$ is not an extremum if the sign in the second derivative test is reversed, i.e., if $f_{xx} \cdot f_{yy} < (f_{xy})^2$ at (a, b). Second, if $f_{xx} \cdot f_{yy} = (f_{xy})^2$ at (a, b) the theorem yields no information about f: it is not known whether $f(a, b)$ represents an extremum or not, much less whether it is a maximum or a minimum. Note also that the first part of the test involves the solution of two simultaneous equations,

$$f_x(a, b) = 0$$
$$f_y(a, b) = 0 \tag{14}$$

The analogy between the theory of extrema for a function of two variables and that presented in Chapter 4 for functions of one variable merits emphasis. For a continuous function $g(x)$ to have an extremum at point c, it is necessary that $g'(c) = 0$; for the continuous function $f(x, y)$ to have an extremum at the point (a, b), it is necessary that

$$f_x(a, b) = 0 \quad \text{and} \quad f_y(a, b) = 0$$

Figure 7–2 shows the single-variable case: the extremum occurs where the slope (the derivative) is zero. Figures 7–1 and 7–3 illustrate the two-variable case: the extremum occurs where the "slope in both directions" is zero.

In Figure 7–1 the value of $f(x, y)$ is represented by a surface. Starting from the point $(0, 0)$, where, incidentally, the function is positive, it is possible to increase $f(x, y)$ by increasing x, that is, by moving along the x-axis in a positive direction. Or, $f(x, y)$ can be increased by increasing y. Or, $f(x, y)$ can be increased by increasing

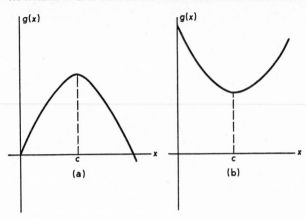

Figure 7–2

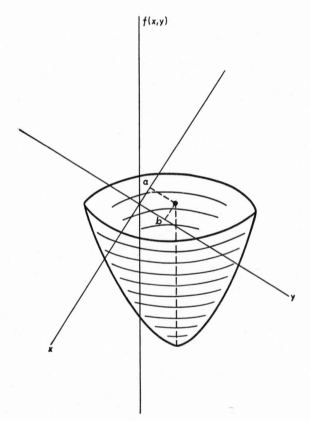

Figure 7–3

both x and y. Eventually, a point is reached where f decreases with further increases in x or y or both. The reader should satisfy himself by studying Figures 7–1 and 7–3 that at the extreme points both f_x and f_y are indeed zero.

Having $g'(c) = 0$ when g is a continuous function is a *necessary* condition for an extremum, but it is not a *sufficient* condition. The analysis of Chapter 4 showed that if $g''(c) < 0$ the extremum exists and is a maximum (Figure 7–2a), if $g''(c) > 0$ it exists and is a minimum (Figure 7–2b), and if $g''(c) = 0$ there may be an inflection point rather than an extremum (Figure 7–4).

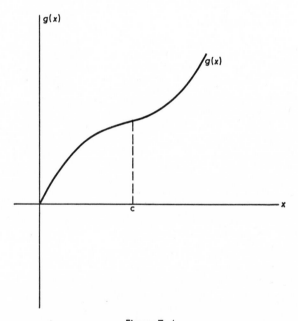

Figure 7–4

The function of two variables can be analyzed analogously: having $f_x = 0 = f_y$ is a *necessary* condition for an extremum, but it is not *sufficient*. As the theorem states, it must also be true that the product of the "pure" second partials (f_{xx} and f_{yy}) be greater than the product of the "cross" partials (or the square of one of them since they are equal by Theorem 1). It should be intuitively clear that if $f(x, y)$ is to have an extremum at a point (a, b), then the rate of change of the slope in any direction must have the same sign (positive for a minimum and negative for a maximum). However, the derivative f_{xx} measures the rate of change of the slope only in the x-direction, while f_{yy} measures the rate of change of the slope

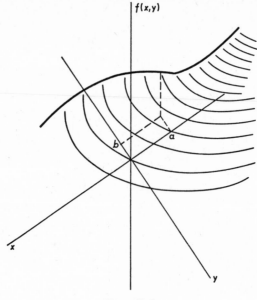

Figure 7–5a

only in the y-direction. The effect of the second derivative condition is to insure that the rate of change of the slope has the same sign in any direction from the extremum, $f(a, b)$.

The second derivative, as before, distinguishes maxima from minima: $f_{xx} < 0$ denoting a maximum; $f_{xx} > 0$ a minimum, assuming, of course, that the necessary conditions for an extremum have already been met.

Figures 7–5a and 7–5b show functions which meet the first derivative condition—both partials zero—but not the second derivative condition. In Figure 7–5a, just as in the analogous case of the inflection point in the theory of functions of one variable, the point (a, b) is not unique and there is no extremum. The point (a, b) in Figure 7–5b, called a "saddle point," is characterized by the fact that although the first partials are zero, the inequality sign in the second derivative condition is reversed.

Figure 7–6 shows a single-valued function which clearly has an extremum at $f(c)$, yet $f'(c)$ does not exist. The reason, of course, is that the function is not differentiable at the point c. The analogous situation in three dimensions is shown in Figure 7–7: an extremum exists at (a, b), but the conditions of the theorem are not met. The reason again is the nondifferentiability of the function. The warning given in Chapter 4 must therefore be repeated here: The theory of

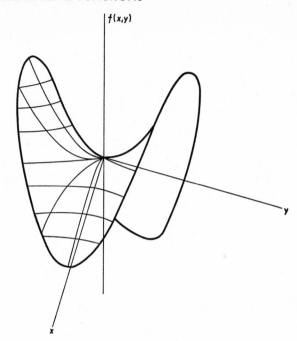

Figure 7–5b

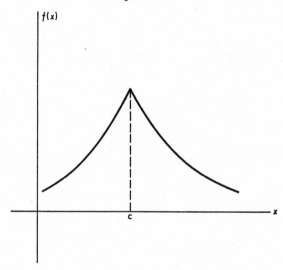

Figure 7–6

extrema will locate and identify only those extrema which occur in areas in which the function in question is differentiable. End points and points of discontinuity and nondifferentiability must be examined separately. Three examples will help clarify the use of the theorem.

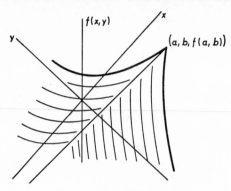

Figure 7–7

Example (i)

Suppose $f(x, y) = 2x^3 - 2xy + y^2$. Does $f(x, y)$ have any extrema? If so, where are they and are they maxima or minima?

Solution:

Step 1: Find those points, if any, which satisfy the necessary condition that $f_x = 0 = f_y$. Thus, it is necessary to find the first partial derivatives:

$$f_x = 6x^2 - 2y \quad \text{and} \quad f_y = -2x + 2y$$

Setting these two partials equal to zero and solving simultaneously yields two points,

$$(0, 0) \quad \text{and} \quad (\tfrac{1}{3}, \tfrac{1}{3})$$

at which this first condition is met. These points may represent extrema.

Step 2: Verify that the points meeting the first condition also meet the second one. Thus, find the second partial derivatives,

$$f_{xx} = 12x, \quad f_{xy} = -2 = f_{yx}, \quad f_{yy} = +2$$

The requirement is that

$$f_{xx} \cdot f_{yy} > (f_{xy})^2$$

at the points in question. For $(0, 0)$ this becomes the condition that

$$(12 \cdot 0) \cdot (2) > (-2)^2$$

or $$0 > 4$$

a condition which is obviously not met. Hence, $(0, 0)$ is not an extremum. For $(\tfrac{1}{3}, \tfrac{1}{3})$ the condition implies that

$$(12) \cdot (\tfrac{1}{3})(2) > (-2)^2$$

or

$$\mathbf{8 > 4}$$

a condition which is met. The conclusion is that there is one extremum and it is at the point ($\frac{1}{3}$, $\frac{1}{3}$).

Step 3: Discover whether the identified extremum is a minimum or a maximum. This involves only the sign of f_{xx} at the point in question. Since

$$f_{xx}(\tfrac{1}{3}, \tfrac{1}{3}) = 12(\tfrac{1}{3})$$
$$= 4 > 0$$

the extremum located is a minimum.

Example (ii)

Suppose $f(x, y) = x^2 + xy + y^2 + 24$. Then, the relevant partials are as follows:

$$f_x = 2x + y, \quad f_{xx} = 2, \quad f_{xy} = 1$$
$$f_y = x + 2y, \quad f_{yy} = 2, \quad (f_{xy})^2 = 1$$

Solving

$$2x + y = 0 \quad \text{and} \quad x + 2y = 0$$

simultaneously generates only one solution, $(0, 0)$. The second necessary condition is met at $(0, 0)$ since $(2)(2) > 1$. The function is known to assume a minimum at $(0\cdot, 0)$ since

$$f_{xx} = 2 > 0$$

In retrospect, these results are plausible since direct inspection of $f(x, y)$ shows clearly that f is at a minimum if and only if $x = 0 = y$.

Example (iii)

A department store has two departments. The earnings (gross revenue minus cost of goods sold) are given by:

$$E_1(x_1, y_1) = 4x_1 + 5y_1 + x_1y_1 - x_1^2 - y_1^2$$

for department 1, and   (15)

$$E_2(x_2, y_2) = 4x_2 + 2y_2 + 2x_2y_2 - 2x_2^2 - y_2^2 - 5$$

for department 2, where

E_i = earnings of department i in millions of dollars,
x_i = investment in inventory by department i in millions of dollars,
y_i = floor space used by department i in units of 10,000 square feet.

The store's management wishes to determine the allocation of capital and floor space to the departments in order to optimize the total earnings for the store. The total earnings are given by:

$$E(x_1, y_1, x_2, y_2) = E_1(x_1, y_1) + E_2(x_2, y_2)$$ (16)

The optimum values of the four variables, x_1, x_2, y_1, y_2, may be determined by solving the four equations

$$\frac{\partial E}{\partial x_1} = 0 \; ; \quad \frac{\partial E}{\partial y_1} = 0 \; ; \quad \frac{\partial E}{\partial x_2} = 0 \; ; \quad \frac{\partial E}{\partial y_2} = 0 \tag{17}$$

Since the first two equations do not involve x_2 and y_2, and the last two do not involve x_1 and y_1, the two sets of equations can be solved separately. The optimum values for the store are, in this case, the optimum values for the individual departments. The problem, which at first appeared to require the optimization of a function of four variables, turns out to require only the optimization of two functions of two variables.

The equations for department 1 are, from (15),

$$\frac{\partial E}{\partial x_1} = 4 + y_1 - 2x_1 = 0$$

and $\qquad \frac{\partial E}{\partial y_1} = 5 + x_1 - 2y_1 = 0 \tag{18}$

The solution is

$$x_1 = \frac{13}{3} \quad \text{and} \quad y_1 = \frac{14}{3}$$

Since

$$\frac{\partial^2 E}{\partial x_1{}^2} = -2 \, , \quad \frac{\partial^2 E}{\partial y_1{}^2} = -2 \, , \quad \frac{\partial^2 E}{\partial x_1 \partial y_1} = \frac{\partial^2 E}{\partial y_1 \partial x_1} = 1$$

and

$$\left(\frac{\partial^2 E}{\partial x_1{}^2}\right)\left(\frac{\partial^2 E}{\partial y_1{}^2}\right) - \left(\frac{\partial^2 E}{\partial x_1 \partial y_1}\right)^2 = 4 - 1 = 3$$

An optimum exists for E_1, and it is a maximum as required. Similarly, the equations for the second department are

$$\frac{\partial E}{\partial x_2} = 4 + 2y_2 - 4x_2 = 0$$

and $\tag{19}$

$$\frac{\partial E}{\partial y_2} = 2 + 2x_2 - 2y_2 = 0$$

The solution is

$$x_2 = 3 \cdot \text{ and } \quad y_2 = 4$$

The second-order conditions for a maximum are satisfied since

$$\frac{\partial^2 E}{\partial x_2{}^2} = -4 \, , \quad \frac{\partial^2 E}{\partial y_2{}^2} = -2 \, , \quad \frac{\partial^2 E}{\partial x_2 \partial y_2} = \frac{\partial^2 E}{\partial y_2 \partial x_2} = 2$$

and

$$\left(\frac{\partial^2 E}{\partial x_2{}^2}\right)\left(\frac{\partial^2 E}{\partial y_2{}^2}\right) - \left(\frac{\partial^2 E}{\partial x_2 \partial y_2}\right)^2 = 8 - 4 = 4$$

The store's total earnings at the optimum are determined by substitution into (15):

$$
\begin{aligned}
E^* &= E^*{}_1 + E^*{}_2 \\
&= E_1(\tfrac{13}{3}, \tfrac{14}{3}) + E_2(3, 4) \\
&= \tfrac{61}{3} + 5 \\
&= 25\tfrac{1}{3}
\end{aligned}
\tag{20}
$$

An optimum allocation thus requires that \$7.3 million be invested in inventory since

$$
\begin{aligned}
x^*{}_1 + x^*{}_2 &= \tfrac{13}{3} + 3 \\
&= 7\tfrac{1}{3}
\end{aligned}
\tag{21}
$$

and that the departments together be allocated about 87,000 square feet of floor space since

$$
\begin{aligned}
y^*{}_1 + y^*{}_2 &= \tfrac{14}{3} + 4 \\
&= 8\tfrac{2}{3}
\end{aligned}
\tag{22}
$$

This section has extended the optimizing techniques of Chapter 5 to functions of two variables. The next logical step would be to inquire into the theory of extrema for functions of n variables, n larger than two. Such a theory exists but is beyond the scope of this book. The reader may be interested in knowing, however, that the theory is a direct extension of the theorems presented here and in Chapter 5—or, more accurately, these theorems are special cases of the more general theory.

The present chapter does introduce an additional optimizing technique, however. This is the theory of Lagrangian multipliers.

4. LAGRANGIAN MULTIPLIERS

Frequently the situations for which optimum decisions are required have physical restrictions of various kinds. For example, the department store described in Section 3 might have a limitation on the amount of money available for investment in inventory and on the amount of floor space available. Suppose, in particular, that exactly \$8,000,000 and 70,000 square feet of floor space are available. Then, *if both these resources are to be fully utilized,* the variables would have to satisfy the conditions

$$
\begin{aligned}
x_1 + x_2 &= 8 \quad \text{or} \quad x_2 = 8 - x_1 \\
y_1 + y_2 &= 7 \quad \text{or} \quad y_2 = 7 - y_1
\end{aligned}
\tag{23}
$$

This particular problem could be solved by substitution. The relations of (23) could be substituted into (16).

$$E(x_1, x_2, y_1, y_2) = E_1(x_1, y_1) + E_2(x_2, y_2)$$

in order to eliminate the two variables, x_2 and y_2. The problem would then be to maximize

$$E(x_1, y_1) = E_1(x_1, y_1) + E_2(x_1, y_1)$$

in the usual manner.

Fortunately, there is an alternative technique which permits the optimization of functions subject to restrictions without eliminating any of the variables; it also provides a measure of how restrictive a restriction actually is. This remarkable technique was discovered by Lagrange in the eighteenth century and is known as "Lagrange's method of multipliers" or the "method of undetermined multipliers." A statement of the technique for a simple case is as follows:

The optimum of a function $f(x_1, x_2)$, subject to the condition that $g(x_1, x_2) = 0$, can be obtained by forming the function

$$F(x_1, x_2, \lambda) = f(x_1, x_2) + \lambda g(x_1, x_2)$$

and optimizing it with respect to x_1, x_2, and λ as indicated by Theorem 3. In particular, the necessary conditions are

$$\frac{\partial F}{\partial x_1} = 0 , \ \frac{\partial F}{\partial x_2} = 0 , \ \frac{\partial F}{\partial \lambda} = 0$$

If there is more than one restriction, additional λ's are defined, one for each equation.

The proof of this result and a statement of the second-order conditions (omitted here) are somewhat complex and reference should be made to an advanced text in mathematics.

The Lagrangian technique may be applied to the department store problem as modified. The function to be maximized then becomes

$$F(x_1, x_2, y_1, y_2, \lambda_1, \lambda_2) = E_1(x_1, y_1) + E_2(x_2, y_2) + \lambda_1 g_1(x_1, y_1) + \lambda_2 g_2(x_2, y_2) =$$
$$[4x_1 + 5y_1 + x_1 y_1 - x_1^2 - y_1^2] + [4x_2 + 2y_2 + 2x_2 y_2 - 2x_2^2 - y_2^2 - 5]$$
$$+ \lambda_1(x_1 + x_2 - 8) + \lambda_2(y_1 + y_2 - 7) \quad (24)$$

and the necessary conditions are:

$$\frac{\partial F}{\partial x_1} = 4 + y_1 - 2x_1 + \lambda_1 = 0$$

$$\frac{\partial F}{\partial x_2} = 4 + 2y_2 - 4x_2 + \lambda_1 = 0$$

$$\frac{\partial F}{\partial y_1} = 5 + x_1 - 2y_1 + \lambda_2 = 0 \quad (25)$$

$$\frac{\partial F}{\partial y_2} = 2 + 2x_2 - 2y_2 + \lambda_2 = 0$$

$$\frac{\partial F}{\partial \lambda_1} = x_1 + x_2 - 8 = 0$$

$$\frac{\partial F}{\partial \lambda_2} = y_1 + y_2 - 7 = 0$$

From the last two equations it is seen that

$$x_2 = 8 - x_1 \qquad \text{and} \qquad y_2 = 7 - y_1$$

Thus the system with six unknowns and six equations in (25) can be reduced, by eliminating x_2 and y_2, to a system with four unknowns and four equations as in (26):

$$\begin{aligned}
4 + y_1 - 2x_1 + \lambda_1 &= 0 \\
5 + x_1 - 2y_1 + \lambda_2 &= 0 \\
-14 + 4x_1 - 2y_1 + \lambda_1 &= 0 \\
4 - 2x_1 + 2y_1 + \lambda_2 &= 0
\end{aligned} \qquad (26)$$

Solving this set of equations by elimination gives:

$$\begin{aligned}
x_1 &= 5 & x_2 &= 3 \\
y_1 &= 4 & y_2 &= 3 \\
\lambda_1 &= 2 & \lambda_2 &= -2
\end{aligned} \qquad (27)$$

The analysis is completed by substitution into the earnings function (24) to obtain E^*. The calculation is as follows:

$$\begin{aligned}
E^* &= E_1 + E_2 \\
&= (4x_1 + 5y_1 + x_1 y_1 - x_1^2 - y_1^2) + (4x_2 + 2y_2 + 2x_2 y_2 - 2x_2^2 - y_2^2 - 5) \\
&= (4 \cdot 5 + 5 \cdot 4 + 5 \cdot 4 - 5^2 - 4^2) + \\
&\qquad\qquad (4 \cdot 3 + 2 \cdot 3 + 2 \cdot 3 \cdot 3 - 2 \cdot 3^2 - 3^2 - 5) \quad (28) \\
&= 23
\end{aligned}$$

Therefore, investing \$8 million instead of \$7.3 million and using 70,000 square feet of floor space instead of 87,000 reduces the total earnings from \$25⅓ million to \$23 million.

The function (24) may be considered a generalized earnings function consisting of three parts:

Unrestricted earnings in the two departments
+ Change in earnings due to investment restriction
+ Change in earnings due to space restriction

The interpretation of the parameters is that λ_1 is the decrease in earnings due to a small change in the amount available for investment, and similarly, λ_2 is the decrease in earnings due to a small change in floor space. The signs of λ_1 and λ_2 then indicate the effect of the restriction. If λ_1 is positive, the earnings will decrease as

$(x_1 + x_2)$ become larger than 8, and if λ_1 is negative, the earnings will increase.

In the example, the Lagrange multiplier for the inventory investment, λ_1, is positive; this indicates that total earnings can be increased by investing *less* money in inventory. The optimum solution can be obtained by solving the same problem without the inventory restriction.

The function to be optimized in this case is

$$F(x_1, x_2, y_1, y_2, \lambda_2) = E_1(x_1, y_1) + E_2(x_2, y_2) + \lambda_2(y_1 + y_2 - 7)$$

The solution becomes

$$x_1 = 4 , \qquad x_2 = 2.5 , \qquad y_1 = 4 , \qquad y_2 = 3 , \qquad \lambda_2 = -1$$

and

$$E_1(4, 4) = 20 , \qquad E_2(2.5, 3) = 4.5 , \qquad E = 20 + 4.5 = 24.5$$

Since λ_2 is negative, the restriction on space limits the earnings to $24.5 million; however, only $6.5 million is required for inventory. By relaxing the inventory restriction, earnings have actually been increased from $23 to $24.5 million.

Lagrangian multipliers are applicable to situations in which the function to be optimized is nonlinear, and subject to restrictions which are equations. In situations where the function, sometimes called the objective function, is *linear* and the restrictions are inequalities, a method known as linear programming must be used. A discussion of optimizing techniques for this situation will be given in Chapters 13 and 14.

Case No. 7. Advertising and Product Improvement Decisions

The Diomed Cutting Tools Corporation is considering the question of whether to invest more heavily in advertising, or to concentrate on product improvements in order to increase profits. Market studies have indicated that, with no changes or improvements in the product line, the relationship of profits to advertising expenditures can be approximated by a simple quadratic function; i.e., as advertising increases, profits also increase until the heavy advertising outlays begin to cut into profit in spite of increasing sales. The relationship between product improvement expenditures and profits is also expressible in terms of a quadratic—or inverted parabola. Small-scale expenditures, unaccompanied by advertising, would raise profits a little, since knowledgeable customers would observe the improvements and be more ready to buy—but large-scale expenditures without advertising would merely tend to reduce profits.

A third relationship to be considered is the joint effect of advertising plus product improvements, over and above the individual effect of each. This joint effect arises from the increased effectiveness of advertising when it has something new or unique as subject matter, plus the increased effectiveness of product improvement when such improvement is brought to the attention of consumers by appropriate advertising.

Presently the firm is spending $30,000 per year on advertising, and nothing on product improvement. Company officers feel that expenditures on product improvement would yield immediate results. Such expenditures would consist of the use of more high-quality material, which would present an attractive aspect to potential buyers. Thus there would be no need for additional capital investment, and no time lag to wait for results of research and development.

Under present conditions, with no product improvement contemplated, the profit-advertising relationship may be expressed as follows:

$$P_1(x) = \left[10 + 20x - \frac{7x^2}{2}\right] \cdot \frac{1}{50} \tag{1}$$

where

$P_1(x)$ = profit, expressed in units of $10,000,
$\quad x$ = advertising expenditures, expressed in units of $10,000.

Thus, at the present time, $x = 3$, and profits are $7700.

The effect of introducing product improvements has been estimated to be:

$$P_2(y) = [10y - 3.75y^2] \cdot \tfrac{1}{50} \tag{2}$$

where

y = expenditures on product improvement, expressed in units of $10,000.

The joint effect of advertising plus product improvements, exclusive of individual effects described above, is

$$P_3(xy) = \frac{x^2y}{100} \tag{3}$$

The company wants to know what its maximum profit would be if optimum decisions on the amount of advertising and the amount of product improvement were made simultaneously. The profit function is:

$$P(x, y) = P_1(x) + P_2(y) + P_3(xy)$$

$$= \left[10 + 20x - \frac{7x^2}{2} + 10y - 3.75y^2 + \frac{x^2y}{2} \right] \cdot \frac{1}{50} \qquad (4)$$

The procedure for optimizing is:

1. Determine the partial derivatives

$$\frac{\partial P(x, y)}{\partial x} = \frac{20 - 7x + xy}{50} \qquad (5)$$

$$\frac{\partial P(x, y)}{\partial y} = \frac{10 - 7.5y + \dfrac{x^2}{2}}{50} \qquad (6)$$

2. Set the derivatives equal to zero and solve: From (6)

$$y = \frac{10 + \dfrac{x^2}{2}}{7.5} = \frac{4}{3} + \frac{x^2}{15}$$

Substituting in (5) and rearranging gives

$$x^3 - 85x + 300 = 0 \qquad (7)$$

The general formula for the solution of a cubic equation is rather cumbersome. Fortunately in this case a little reflection will show that one of the roots of x is 5. The other two roots may then be readily obtained by application of the simple quadratic formula, since knowledge of one of the roots enables the equation to be written as:

$$(x - 5)(x^2 + 5x - 60) = 0$$

The remaining two roots are $x = +5.64$ and $x = -10.64$. Clearly -10.64 is not an admissible value, since x cannot be negative. Therefore this value may be disregarded and consideration limited to the other two values of x at which the function may be at an optimum. Consider first the associated value of y: when $x = 5$, then

$$y = \frac{4}{3} + \frac{25}{15} = \frac{45}{15} = 3$$

and when $x = 5.64$, then

$$y = \frac{4}{3} + \frac{31.81}{15} = \frac{51.81}{15} = 3.46$$

Consider the point $(5, 3)$. To determine whether it is an extremum, the "pure" second partial derivatives with respect to x and y, and also the cross partials are computed:

$$\frac{\partial^2 P}{\partial x^2} = \frac{-7 + y}{50}, \frac{\partial^2 P}{\partial y^2} = \frac{-7.5}{50}, \frac{\partial^2 P}{\partial x \partial y} = \frac{x}{50}$$

At $(5, 3)$

$$\frac{\partial^2 P}{\partial x^2} = \frac{-4}{50}, \frac{\partial^2 P}{\partial y^2} = \frac{-7.5}{50}, \frac{\partial^2 P}{\partial x \partial y} = \frac{5}{50}$$

$$(-4)(-7.5) > 5^2$$

Thus the point is an extremum, and since the pure partials are negative, the point locates a maximum value of the function. Now consider the other possible extremum:

At $(5.64, 3.46)$

$$\frac{\partial^2 P}{\partial x^2} = \frac{-3.54}{50}, \frac{\partial^2 P}{\partial y^2} = \frac{-7.5}{50}, \frac{\partial^2 P}{\partial x \partial y} = \frac{5.64}{50}$$

$$(-3.54)(-7.5) < 5.64^2$$

Therefore this point is not an extremum. The function has a single maximum, at $(x = 5; y = 3)$, and if the firm spends $50,000 on advertising and $30,000 on product improvement it will achieve a profit of $11,250 instead of the current profit level of $7700.

Questions

1. Suppose management allocated $100,000 to be spent on advertising and product improvement combined, with the stipulation that all of the money was to be spent. Use Lagrange multipliers to find the optimum allocation. (Assume second-order conditions are met.) What is profit? Compare the answer with that shown in the problem for an $80,000 expenditure. Comment.

2. Suppose the firm decided to maintain its advertising-product improvement budget at the original level of $30,000. Could it improve its profits?

3. Would the function be reasonable for values beyond $100,000? Explain.

EXERCISES, SECTION 1

1. $f(x, y) = 3xy + 2$ and $g(x, y) = x^2 + xy + y^2$, find
   a) $f \cdot g$
   b) $\dfrac{g}{f}$
   c) $f + g$
   d) $g - f$

2. If $h(u, v) = au + bv^2$ and $g(u, v) = cu + dv^2$, find
   a) $h - g$
   b) $h \cdot g$
   c) $\dfrac{g}{h}$
   d) $g + h$

3. If $f(x, y) = xy - 1$, and $g(x, y) = x^2 + y$, find the composite function $H = f \cdot g$.

4. If $f(x, y) = x^2 - y^2$ and $g(x) = x^2$, find the composite function $G(x, y) = g(f)$.

5. Suppose $f(x, y) = x - y^2 + 1$; $g(x, y) = 1/(x^2 + 1)$; and $h(x, y) = 2x^2 + y$. Find $H(x, y) = h(f, g)$

6. Suppose $f(u) = u^2 - 1$; $g(u) = u + 3$; $h(u) = 1/u$; and $k(x, y, z) = \dfrac{1}{x} + (y - 1)/z + z^2$. Find the composite function $K(u) = k(f, g, h)$.

7. Suppose $u(t) = 1/t$; $v(t) = 2t^2 - t + 2$; and $w(t) = w(x, y) = x^2 - y^2$. Find the composite function $W(t) = w(u, v)$.

8. If $f(x) = x^2 + 2x + 3$, $g(y) = 3y^3 - y^{-3}$, and $h(x, y) = x^4 - y^3$, find $H(x, y) = h(f, g)$

EXERCISES, SECTION 2

9. If $x = u^2 - v^2$, $y = 2u + v$, and $z = x + y$, find the partial derivatives of z with respect to u and with respect to v; express these in terms of u and v.

10. If $p = st^2$ and $q = 1/st$, and if $R = p^2q - 1/q$, find the partial derivatives of R with respect to s and t. Eliminate p and q from the expressions for the partial derivatives and express them in terms of s and t.

11. If $x = t^2 - 4$ and $y = 2t + 1$, and if $Z = y^2/x$, find the derivative of Z with respect to t.

12. If $u = t^2 + 1$, $v = 1 - t^3$, and $w = u^2 - v$, find the derivative of w with respect to t by substituting the values of u and t in terms of t into the expression for w. Find the derivative of w with respect to t by using partial differentiation, as described in the foregoing section, thus verifying that the results are the same.

13. Suppose $f(x, y) = 2x^2 + 3xy + y^2$.
    a) Find the first and second partial derivatives.
    b) Ascertain whether the cross partials are equal.
    c) How many distinct third-order partials are there?

14. Suppose $f(u, v) = u + 1/uv + v - 1/u$. Find the cross-partial derivatives. Are they equal?

15. Find the cross-partial derivatives of

$$R(x, y) = \frac{1}{x - y} + \frac{1}{x + y}$$

Are they equal?

16. Suppose $u^3 + u^2v + uv^2 + v^3 = 0$. Find dv/du, using partial differentiation.

17. Suppose $\dfrac{1}{r} + 2rs + 3s^2 = 0$. Find dr/ds and ds/dr.

18. Suppose $x^2 + y^2 - 16 = 0$.
    a) Find the first-order partials and the cross partials.
    b) Find the point(s) at which $dy/dx = 0$, and the point(s) at which $dx/dy = 0$. What figure does this expression describe?

EXERCISES, SECTION 3

In the following five exercises, find extrema, if any, and determine whether they are maxima or minima.

19. $g(x, y) = 3x^2 + 3xy + y^2$

20. $h(x, y) = x^2 - xy^2$

21. $H(x, y) = \dfrac{4x^3}{3} - \dfrac{1}{y}$

22. $f(s, t) = s^3 + s^2t - t^3$

23. $B(x, y) = 2x^2 - 2xy - y + \dfrac{3y^2}{2}$

24. The total profit per acre on a wheat ranch has been found to be related to the expenditure per acre for (a) labor, and (b) soil conditioners and fertilizers. If x represents the dollars per acre spent on labor, and y represents the dollars per acre spent on soil improvement, the following relationship holds:

$$\text{Profit, } P, = 48x + 60y + 10xy - 10x^2 - 6y^2$$

Determine the optimum expenditure levels.

25. A firm has two plants with the following revenue and cost functions:

$$TR_1 = 10x - x^2$$
$$TR_2 = 6x - \frac{x^2}{2}$$
$$TC_1 = \frac{x^3}{4} - 3x^2 + 4x + 8$$
$$TC_2 = 2x$$

A total of ten units must be produced. Determine how many should be produced in each plant in order to optimize total profit.

EXERCISES, SECTION 4

Using the method of Lagrange multipliers and assuming second-order conditions are met, find the extreme values of the following functions, subject to constraints as indicated:

26. $f(u, v) = u^2 - uv + v$, subject to: $u + v = 2$.

27. $f(x, y) = x^2 + 2xy + y^2$, subject to: $x - y = 3$.

28. $f(x, y) = x^2 - 2x + xy + 2y^2$, subject to: $x - 2y + 1 = 0$.

29. In a situation such as is described in the foregoing exercises, the constraint may be regarded as a straight line on a two-dimensional surface. Thus any value can be assigned to x, for instance, and a corresponding value is automatically determined for y. If one assigns a number of values to x, determines the related values of y as defined by the constraint, and then computes the value of $f(x, y)$ for each pair of values, it is possible to graph $f(x, y)$ as a function of either variable. Perform this operation for Exercise 27 above and indicate whether the optimum value obtained from the Lagrange process is a maximum or a minimum.

30. Refer to Exercise 24. Suppose that, due to financial constraints, it had been decided that a maximum of $15 per acre would be spent on labor and soil improvement combined. What would be the optimum allocation of expenditure? Interpret the significance of the sign of the Lagrange multiplier, and its magnitude.

CHAPTER 8

SUMMATION AND INTEGRATION

IT IS A common practice to speak of the "differential calculus" and the "integral calculus." The former has been presented in the preceding chapters; it is now time to introduce the integral calculus. It will be seen that these two bodies of concepts are intimately linked by the "fundamental theorem of the calculus" presented in Section 2.

1. THE DEFINITE INTEGRAL AS A SUM

The concept of *area* as representing the "size" of a figure is a familiar one. The area of the rectangle in Figure 8–1, for example, is

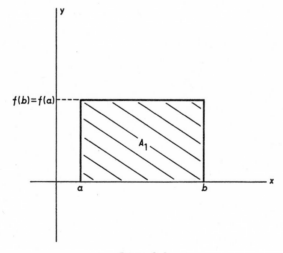

Figure 8–1

easily computed even though it may appear strange by reason of having been superimposed on a coordinate system. The base of the figure is the distance, or quantity, $(b - a)$. The height is either $f(b)$ or $f(a)$ since, obviously, $f(b) = f(a)$. Thus, by the familiar formula that the area of a rectangle is the base times the height, where A_1 is the area of the rectangle in Figure 8–1,

$$A_1 = f(b)(b - a)$$

Partly for tidiness and partly for later convenience, let the base be relabeled Δx, for certainly that is what it is. Thus,

$$A_1 = f(b)\Delta x$$

The second figure (Figure 8–2), the triangle, is also easily handled. The base of the figure is $(b - a)$ or Δx. The height is $f(b)$.

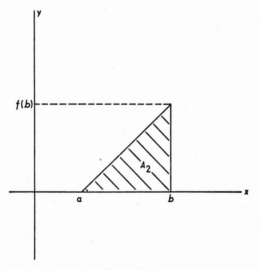

Figure 8–2

Thus, since the area of a triangle is one half the base times the height, it is possible to write

$$A_2 = \tfrac{1}{2}f(b)\Delta x$$

Consider now the polygons in Figure 8–3. Clearly, any polygon can be subdivided into triangles. Thus, the area of any polygon can be defined as the sum of the areas of its constituent triangles. In case the polygon can be subdivided into rectangles (Figure 8–3a), the area of a polygon is the sum of the areas of the rectangles into which it is subdivided.

Figure 8–4 obviously poses some new problems. It is not clear how to define its area, even though it seems intuitively plausible to

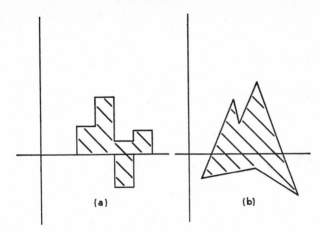

Figure 8–3

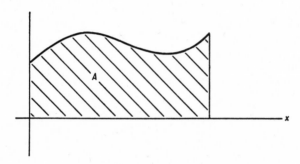

Figure 8–4

call the shaded portion "the area under the curve." Finding the area in such cases is the subject of this chapter.

As a preliminary to finding the shaded area for Figure 8–4 it is necessary to introduce the idea of a *partition of an interval*. Consider the line shown and the interval $[a, b]$ thereon:

$$a \quad \cdot \quad \cdot \quad \cdot \quad \cdot \quad \cdot \quad b$$
$$\overline{\quad x_0 \quad x_1 \quad x_2 \quad x_3 \quad x_4 \quad x_5 \quad x_6 \quad} x$$

The interval $[a, b]$ has been subdivided into smaller intervals—six of them in this case: $[x_0, x_1]$, $[x_1, x_2]$ . . . , $[x_5, x_6]$. Note that the intervals are of equal length: for example, $(x_1 - x_0)$, the length of the first interval, is equal to $(x_4 - x_3)$. A partition which has subintervals of equal length is called a *regular partition*. By calling each interval Δx, the regular partition of $[a, b]$ can be relabeled as follows:

$$a \quad \cdot \quad \cdot \quad \cdot \quad \cdot \quad \cdot \quad b$$

x_0		$x_0 + 2\Delta x$		$x_0 + 4\Delta x$		$x_0 + 6\Delta x$
	$x_0 + \Delta x$		$x_0 + 3\Delta x$		$x_0 + 5\Delta x$	

Now consider a regular partition of the interval $[a, b]$ such that there are n subintervals with the "typical" interval having length Δx_n. A moment's reflection should confirm the fact that

$$\Delta x_n = \frac{b - a}{n} \tag{1}$$

where the subscript n is a reminder that the interval $[a, b]$ has been divided into n subintervals.

Returning to the problem of finding "the area under a curve," begin by approximating the area under the curve in Figure 8–5 by a

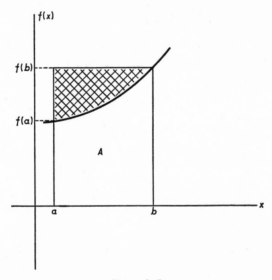

Figure 8–5

rectangle whose base is $(b - a)$ and whose altitude is $f(b)$:

$$A \doteq f(b)(b - a) \tag{2}$$

(The symbol $\doteq$ means "approximately equal to.") Or, since $\Delta x_1 = (b - a)/1 = b - a$,

$$A \doteq f(b)\Delta x_1 \tag{3}$$

The subscript 1 on Δx simply means that $n = 1$.

Clearly, an approximation to the desired area has been obtained. Equally clearly, the approximation of (3) is in error by an amount represented by the shaded portion in Figure 8–5.

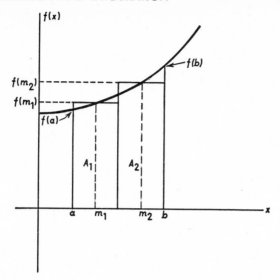

Figure 8–6

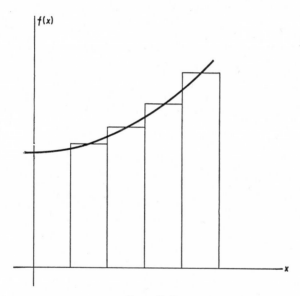

Figure 8–7

One improvement in the closeness of the approximation would be to divide the interval $[a, b]$ in half, construct two rectangles, and then let the approximation be the *sum* of the areas of the two rectangles (Figure 8–6). The base of each rectangle, Δx_2, is $(b - a)/2$. Although there are a variety of altitudes that could be used, let the height of the curve over the centerpoint of the subinterval be the present choice. Labeling these centerpoints m_1 and m_2, the respective heights become $f(m_1)$ and $f(m_2)$. Thus,

$$A \doteq f(m_1)\Delta x_2 + f(m_2)\Delta x_2 \tag{4}$$

Now consider, as in Figure 8–7, a regular partition of $[a, b]$ into n intervals instead of two. There would be n rectangles whose areas would have to be summed to obtain the approximation

$$A \doteq f(m_1)\Delta x_n + f(m_2)\Delta x_n + \cdots + f(m_n)\Delta x_n \tag{5}$$

This can be rewritten using the summation notation, as

$$A \doteq \sum_{i=1}^{n} f(m_i)\Delta x_n \tag{6}$$

Expression (6) could also be written with $(b - a)/n$ substituted for Δx_n.

It can be seen from the figures that the approximation of (6) improves as the number of rectangles increases, i.e., as n increases. See Figure 8–7. Thus, it is intuitively plausible to claim that as n increases, $\sum_{i=1}^{n} f(m_i)\Delta x_n$ gets closer and closer to the "true" area, the area under the continuous function f over the interval $[a, b]$.

Recalling the earlier discussion on limits, the area A is now defined as the limit of the sum in (6) as n becomes infinitely large:

$$A = \lim_{n \to \infty} \sum_{i=1}^{n} f(m_i)\Delta x_n \tag{7}$$

This limit A is called the *definite integral* and is commonly designated by the symbol

$$\int_a^b f(x)dx \tag{8}$$

Thus the definite integral is defined as the limit of a sum,

$$\int_a^b f(x)dx = \lim_{n \to \infty} \sum_{i=1}^{n} f(m_i)\Delta x_n \tag{9}$$

and is intimately associated with the notion of the area under the function f.

Before proceeding to the problem of computing the definite integral—(9) is certainly not computationally convenient—examine the symbol $\int_a^b f(x)dx$. The several parts of this symbol, which should, incidentally, be viewed as a single entity, are clearly related to the elements of the definition

$$\sum_{i=1}^{n} f(m_i)\Delta x$$

Sigma, $\sum$, is the upper-case Greek letter for s, and stands for "sum." It is thus no coincidence that $\int$ is an elongated S. The finite notation Δx is replaced, as in the case of the derivative notation, by dx, sometimes called the differential. The functional notation f remains the same for, of course, it refers to some particular function: F, g, β, etc. The elimination of the m_i is understandable as $\Delta x \to 0$

$$f(x) \doteq f(m_i)$$

where x is in the ith subinterval and x replaces m_i.

The integral notation uses x in two places: $f(x)$ and dx. This is certainly customary; it is also unnecessary except as a reminder or placeholder. Any symbol could be used: w, v, t, α, ψ, and so on. Or, the integral can be written as $\int_a^b f$ since this contains the necessary information.

The subscript and superscript a and b are obviously the endpoints of the interval in question and are called the limits of integration. Sometimes they are more complicated than implied here. In particular, one or both may involve ∞; e.g., it may be necessary to find the area under a curve over the interval $(-\infty, +\infty)$. Finally, there is a case, *the indefinite integral,* in which the a and b are omitted because no particular interval is specified. The definite integral $\int_a^b f$ can be formed from the indefinite form by addition of the limits of integration as described in Section 3.

As frequently happens in mathematics, the definition of an operation, in this case given by (9), is inconvenient to apply. Fortunately, there is a better way of evaluating integrals than through (9). It will be considered in the next section. The definition is sufficient, however, to establish certain elementary properties of the integral. The following are obvious:

$$\int_a^a f(x)dx = 0 \tag{10}$$

$$\int_a^c f(x)dx = \int_a^b f(x)dx + \int_b^c f(x)dx \tag{11}$$

where $a \leqq b \leqq c$

The next result is not as obvious, but can easily be verified.

$$\text{If } G(t) = \int_a^t f(x)dx, \quad \text{then} \quad G'(t) = f(t) \tag{12}$$

since by definition

$$G'(t) = \lim_{\Delta t \to 0} \frac{G(t + \Delta t) - G(t)}{\Delta t}$$

$$= \lim_{\Delta t \to 0} \frac{1}{\Delta t}\left[\int_a^{t+\Delta t} f(x)dx - \int_a^t f(x)dx\right] \text{ since } G(t + \Delta t) = \int_a^{t+\Delta t} f(x)dx$$

$$= \lim_{\Delta t \to 0} \frac{1}{\Delta t}\left[\int_a^t f(x)dx + \int_t^{t+\Delta t} f(x)dx - \int_a^t f(x)dx\right]$$

$$= \lim_{\Delta t \to 0} \frac{1}{\Delta t}\left[\int_t^{t+\Delta t} f(x)dx\right]$$

$$= f(t) \quad \text{since} \quad \int_t^{t+\Delta t} f(x)dx \doteq f(t) \cdot \Delta t$$

This shows that when a definite integral is considered as a function of its upper limit, the derivative of the definite integral is the value of the integrand at the upper limit.

2. THE FUNDAMENTAL THEOREM OF THE CALCULUS

Sir Isaac Newton and Gottfried Leibniz are each credited with the independent discovery, in the seventeenth century, of the calculus. Neither discovered the concept of the derivative of a function, nor did either discover the definite integral; both ideas antedated Newton and Leibniz. But each man did discover that there was an important and intimate relationship between the derivative and the integral. This discovery is called the fundamental theorem of the calculus.

Before stating the theorem, however, it is necessary to introduce the idea of an *antiderivative*. For any differentiable function f a derivative function f' exists. Suppose $f(x) = 5x^4 - 2x^2 + 36$. Then

$f'(x) = 20x^3 - 4x$. Now consider the opposite statement: for a function, call it $h(x)$, does there exist a function $f(x)$ such that the given function h is the derivative function of f? Clearly, if $h(x)$ happened to be defined as $20x^3 - 4x$, the answer would have to be yes, since if $5x^4 - 2x^2 + 36$ is differentiated the result is h. In this case, f would be an antiderivative of $h(x)$. Thus, the function f is an antiderivative of the function h if $h = f'$.

Two important characteristics of antiderivatives should be noted. First, h has an antiderivative if the function h is continuous. Second, if h has an antiderivative, f, then it has many antiderivatives. The latter follows from the fact that if f is an antiderivative of h, then so is the function $(f + c)$ where c is any constant. For example, if $h(x) = 20x^3 - 4x$, $f(x) = 5x^4 - 2x^2$ is an antiderivative since $f' = h$. But so are $5x^4 - 2x^2 + 36$, $5x^4 - 2x^2 + 37$, $5x^4 - 2x^2 - 156389105$, etc. Thus $5x^4 - 2x^2$ is *an* antiderivative of h, not *the* antiderivative. Only $5x^4 - 2x^2 + C$, C a constant, is *the* antiderivative of h.

Antiderivatives can be found by applying the theorems of Chapter 3 "in reverse." These two examples and the exercises at the end of the chapter illustrate the technique of finding antiderivatives.

Example (i)

If $u = (v^2 + 2v + 1)^4$, and $w = 4(v^2 + 2v + 1)^3(2v + 2)$, then u is *one* antiderivative of w, since $u' = 4(v^2 + 2v + 1)^3(2v + 2)$; i.e., $u' = w$.

Example (ii)

If $r = s^3/3 - 7s + 12$; then $r' = 3s^2/3 - 7 = s^2 - 7$. Suppose $t = s^2 - 7$; then r is an antiderivative of t, since $r' = t$. Now suppose that $u = s^3/3 - 7s - 28$; then $u' = s^2 - 7$. u is also an antiderivative of t, since $u' = t$. Observe that although r and u are not the same, both are antiderivatives of t.

Now it is possible to return to Newton and Leibniz, who discovered for a function f that, under certain conditions,

$$\int_a^b f = F(b) - F(a) \tag{13}$$

where F is an antiderivative of f (i.e., $F' = f$). Nothing done thus far has suggested this amazing theorem relating the definite integral representing area to the process of differentiation. Hence a formal statement and proof of the theorem is presented. In the next section the theorem will be used to evaluate integrals.

Theorem 1

If $f(x)$ is continuous in a closed interval containing the numbers a and b and if F is an antiderivative of f in that interval, then

$$\int_a^b f(x)dx = F(b) - F(a)$$

Proof:

Let

$$\phi(x) = \int_a^x f(u)du$$

Then $\phi'(x) = f(x)$ by result (12), above.

Since $F'(x) = f(x)$; $F'(x) = \phi'(x)$.

Then there exists a constant C such that $\phi(x) = F(x) + C$, or, since $F(x)$ and $\phi(x)$ are both antiderivatives of $f(x)$,

$$\int_a^x f(u)du = F(x) + C$$

If $x = a$, $\displaystyle\int_a^x f(u)du = 0 = F(a) + C;\ C = -F(a)$ and

$$\int_a^x f(u)du = F(x) - F(a)$$

If $x = b$, $\displaystyle\int_a^b F(u)du = F(b) - F(a)$

3. INTEGRATION

The theorem of Section 2 makes it feasible to evaluate definite integrals. This is the operation known as *integration*. Integration can also be viewed as the inverse operation to differentiation—and vice versa. Or, because of the definitions of Section 1, integration may be viewed as the process of finding the area under a given function over some interval.

In this section some integration formulas analogous to the differentiation formulas of Chapters 3 and 6 will be developed. Integration is more difficult than differentiation; only a few formulas will be developed. The reader is referred to a standard calculus text or to one of the many handbook lists of integration formulas for information about integrating more complicated functions. Such lists usually show the indefinite integral of the particular function, the indefinite integral being an antiderivative of the function.

Consider first the power function, x^n. An antiderivative of $f(x) = x^n$ is $\dfrac{x^{n+1}}{n+1}$. Thus, according to the Fundamental Theorem,

$$\int_a^b x^n\, dx = \frac{b^{n+1}}{n+1} - \frac{a^{n+1}}{n+1}$$ after the substitution of the limits of integration in the expression for antiderivatives. It will be convenient to accept the notational device of writing $F(x)\Big|_a^b = F(b) - F(a)$.

Then $\dfrac{b^{n+1}}{n+1} - \dfrac{a^{n+1}}{n+1}$ becomes $\dfrac{x^{n+1}}{n+1}\Big|_a^b$, read ". . . evaluated at $x = b$ and $x = a$." The first evaluation formula can now be stated, taking for granted the conditions and definitions of the Fundamental Theorem:

Theorem 2

If $f(x) = x^n$, $n \neq -1$, then

$$\int_a^b f(x)dx = \frac{x^{n+1}}{n+1}\Big|_a^b \tag{14}$$

The next two theorems are straightforward extensions of properties previously encountered. First, the integral of the product of a constant and a function is the product of the constant and the integral of the function, i.e.,

Theorem 3

If $f(x) = kg(x)$, k a constant, then $\displaystyle\int_a^b f dx = k \int_a^b g dy.$ (15)

Second, the integral of a sum or difference of functions is the sum or difference of the integrals of the functions:

Theorem 4

$$\int_a^b [f(x) + g(x)]dx = \int_a^b f(x)dx + \int_a^b g(x)dx \tag{16}$$

Several examples will illustrate the applications of these theorems.

Example (i)

Find $\displaystyle\int_{4}^{10} f(x)dx$ if $f(x) = x^2$.

Solution:

$$\int_{4}^{10} x^2\,dx = \frac{x^3}{3}\Bigg|_{4}^{10} = \frac{10^3 - 4^3}{3} = \frac{1000 - 64}{3} = 312\cdot$$

Example (ii)

Find $\displaystyle\int_{2}^{8} \alpha(t)dt$ if $\alpha(t) = t$.

Solution:

$$\int_{2}^{8} t\,dt = \frac{t^2}{2}\Bigg|_{2}^{8} = \frac{8^2 - 2^2}{2} = 30\cdot$$

Example (iii)

Evaluate $\displaystyle\int_{0}^{20} (6y^2 - 3y + 4)dy$.

Solution:

$$6\int_{0}^{20} y^2 - 3\int_{0}^{20} y + 4\int_{0}^{20} 1 = 6\left(\frac{y^3}{3}\Bigg|_{0}^{20}\right) - 3\left(\frac{y^2}{2}\Bigg|_{0}^{20}\right) + 4\left(y\Bigg|_{0}^{20}\right) =$$

$$6\left(\frac{20^3 - 0^3}{3}\right) - 3\left(\frac{20^2}{2} - 0^3\right) + 4(20 - 0) = 15{,}480$$

Example (iv)

Evaluate $\displaystyle\int_{\alpha}^{2\alpha} 15\beta\, Z^4\, dZ$.

Solution:

$$\int_{\alpha}^{2\alpha} 15\beta\, Z^4\, dZ = 15\beta \int_{\alpha}^{2\alpha} Z^4\, dZ = 15\beta\left(\frac{Z^5}{5}\Bigg|_{\alpha}^{2\alpha}\right) =$$

$$15\beta\,\frac{(2\alpha)^5 - \alpha^5}{5} = 93\beta\alpha^5$$

Note that the *variable of integration,* Z in the last example, is a "dummy" variable: it does not appear in the final result due to the substitution denoted by the symbol "$\Big|_{a}^{b}$." Thus, no importance should be attached to the particular label; Z in the last example could have been x, s, σ, ϕ, w, or anything else.

The next three theorems are analogous to and follow from the formulas presented in Chapter 6 for differentiating log and exponential functions.

Theorem 5

$$\text{If } f(x) = \frac{1}{x} [= x^{-1}], \quad \int_a^b f(x)dx = \ln |x| \; \Big|_a^b \qquad (17)$$

Proof:

See Chapter 6, Section 2.

Theorem 6

$$\text{If } f(x) = \ln |x|, \quad \int_a^b f(x)dx = (x \ln |x| - x) \; \Big|_a^b \qquad (18)$$

Proof:

See Chapter 6, Section 2.

Theorem 7

$$\text{If } f(x) = e^{kx}, \quad \int_a^b f(x)dx = \frac{e^{kx}}{k} \; \Big|_a^b \qquad (19)$$

Proof:

Differentiating e^{kx}/k yields $ke^{kx}/k = e^{kx}$. Hence e^{kx}/k is an antiderivative of $f(x)$. Now apply Theorem 1 to obtain the desired result.

Examples of each of these theorems follow:
Example (i)

$$\int_0^3 e^{4u} \, du = \frac{e^{4u}}{4} \Big|_0^3 = \frac{e^{12} - 1}{4}$$

Example (ii)

$$\int_0^1 e^{v/2} = 2e^{v/2} \Big|_0^1 = 2e^{1/2} - 2 = 2(e^{1/2} - 1)$$

Example (iii)

$$\int_1^5 y^{-1} \, dy = \ln |y| \Big|_1^5 = \ln 5 - \ln 1 = \ln \frac{5}{1} = \ln 5$$

Example (iv)

$$\int_3^6 2 \ln |t| \, dt = 2 \int_3^6 \ln |t| \, dt = 2(t \ln |t| - t) \Big|_3^6$$
$$= 2(6 \ln 6 - 6 - 3 \ln 3 + 3)$$
$$= 12 \ln 6 - 6 \ln 3 - 6.$$

4. AREA

In Section 1 the definite integral was defined in terms of area. The subsequent discussion laid the basis for using this relationship in the determination of the "areas under certain curves." This section will consider a few curves and show how their areas can be computed by integration of the corresponding functions.

Consider first the curve of Figure 8–5, repeated here as Figure 8–8. The area of the shaded region is

$$\int_a^b f(x)dx$$

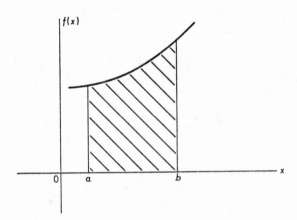

Figure 8–8

where $f(x)$ is the (unknown) analytical representation of the curve. The area of the region from $x = 0$ to $x = a$ is

$$\int_0^a f$$

Similarly, the area of the region to the right of $x = b$ is

$$\int_b^\infty f$$

and the area of the region under the curve and to the right of $x = 0$ is

$$\int_0^\infty f$$

Suppose $f(t) = \sqrt[3]{t}$. See Figure 8–9. The area under f from

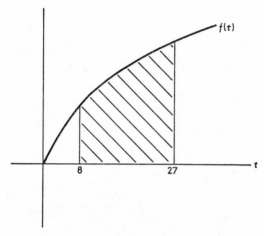

Figure 8–9

(say) $t = 8$ to $t = 27$ is

$$\int_8^{27} \sqrt[3]{t}\, dt = \int_8^{27} t^{1/3}\, dt$$

$$= \frac{3t^{4/3}}{4}\Big|_8^{27}$$

$$= \frac{3}{4}(27^{4/3} - 8^{4/3})$$

$$= \frac{3}{4}(27 \cdot 3 - 8 \cdot 2) = 48.75$$

Suppose now that there is a function $g(t) = -\sqrt[3]{t}$ as in Figure 8–10 and that it is necessary to find the area of the shaded region. Use of the formula

$$\int_8^{27} -\sqrt[3]{t}\, dt$$

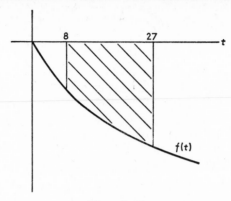

Figure 8–10

yields −48.75. But this is nonsensical since area must be nonnegative. Since it seems reasonable to view $g(t)$, which equals $-f(t)$, as being a "reflection" in some sense of $f(t)$, an integration procedure which will yield an area of +48.75 for the given interval is needed. The formula

$$-\int_{8}^{27} g(t)dt$$

will do exactly that and suggests this definition:

If $f(x)$ is a continuous nonnegative function over the interval $[a, b]$, its area is given by $\int_{a}^{b} f(x)dx$. If $g(x)$ is a continuous nonpositive function over the interval $[c, d]$, its area is given by $-\int_{c}^{d} g(x)dx$.

Another situation is one in which it is necessary to find the area between two curves. As expected, this involves the integration of a difference over an interval:

$$\int_{a}^{b} (f - g) = \int_{a}^{b} f - \int_{a}^{b} g \tag{20}$$

Although the correct integration is

$$\int_{b}^{a} [f(t) - g(t)]dt \tag{21}$$

not

$$\int_b^a [g(t) - f(t)]dt \qquad (22)$$

simply changing the sign in the latter case is an easy remedy if the "incorrect" integration is performed. In the previous example, since $g(t) = -f(t)$, the area is

$$\int_8^{27} [f - (-f)] = \int_8^{27} 2f = 2\int_8^{27} f = 2(48.75)$$

exactly as expected.

A common instance of finding the area between the two functions occurs when one is a straight line. Suppose $\psi(r) = r - 3$ and $\phi(r) = 3r - r^2$ as in Figure 8–11. The area between them is

$$\int_a^b [\phi(r) - \psi(r)]dr \qquad (23)$$

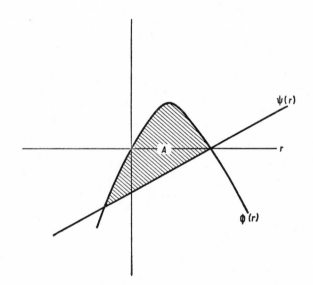

Figure 8–11

The difficulty comes in determining the limits of integration. It is necessary to find the two points of intersection by solving two equations simultaneously.

Solution:

$$r - 3 = \psi(r)$$
$$3r - r^2 = \phi(r)$$

At the intersection $\psi = \phi$. Thus,

$$r - 3 = 3r - r^2$$
$$r^2 - 2r - 3 = 0$$

and

$$r = \frac{-(-2) \pm \sqrt{(-2)^2 - 4(-3)}}{2} = \frac{2 \pm \sqrt{(4) + (12)}}{2}$$
$$= 1 \pm \tfrac{1}{2}\sqrt{16} = -1, 3$$

$$\psi(-1) = -1 - 3 = -4$$
$$\phi(-1) = -3 - (-1)^2 = -4$$
$$\psi(3) = 3 - 3 = 0$$
$$\phi(3) = 3(3) - (3^2) = 0$$

Thus, since $a = -1$ and $b = 3$,

$$A = \int_{-1}^{3} (\phi - \psi)dr$$

$$= \int_{-1}^{3} (3r - r^2) - (r - 3)dr$$

$$= \int_{-1}^{3} (3 + 2r - r^2)dr$$

$$= \left(3r + r^2 - \frac{r^3}{3}\right)\Big|_{-1}^{3}$$

$$= \left(9 + 9 - \frac{27}{3}\right) - \left(-3 + 1 - \frac{-1}{3}\right)$$

$$= 9 - (-1\tfrac{2}{3})$$
$$= 10\tfrac{2}{3}$$

Direct application of the definitions of this section would suggest that

$$A = -\int_{-1}^{0} (\psi - \phi) + \int_{0}^{3} (\phi - \psi) \tag{24}$$

This can, however, be simplified before integration:

$$A = -\int_{-1}^{0} (\psi - \phi) + \int_{0}^{3} (\phi - \psi)$$

$$= \int_{-1}^{0} (\phi - \psi) + \int_{0}^{3} (\phi - \psi)$$

$$= \int_{-1}^{3} (\phi - \psi) \tag{25}$$

Integration of (24) would, of course, also yield $A = 10\tfrac{2}{3}$.

Case No. 8. Learning Curves

It is generally recognized that individuals tend to require less time to perform a task successfully after they have practiced it a number of times. After a while, however, as the limit of efficiency is approached, the amount of time required will begin to level off.

A similar phenomenon is encountered in industry. Manufacturing industries, for example, have found that earlier prototype models take longer to build, in terms of man-hours, than do later models, since it takes progressively less time for employees to perform their tasks as they familiarize themselves with the requirements and have had an opportunity to practice.

The total number of man-hours required to produce a given quantity of units must sometimes be determined in advance in order to establish a suitable selling price, determine a delivery date, or bid on a contract. Frequently the only data on which to base the forecast will be that setting forth the time requirements for a preliminary production run, or for a few prototypes. Thus some sort of forecasting technique is needed. In this section some forecasting models will be developed and the process of integration will be used to solve the models and estimate production time requirements.

Model 1. Suppose, contrary to what was just said, there is no real limit to efficiency, and that the workers simply work faster and faster as the production run continues. Suppose further that the increase in efficiency—i.e., the learning effect—is constant. This means that the decrease in man-hours between the 4th unit and the 5th unit is the same as the decrease between the 100th unit and the 101st unit. A model can be defined as follows: let

n = the total number of units to be produced,
$T(x)$ = the number of man-hours needed to produce the xth unit,
k = the number of man-hours needed to build the 1st unit,
a = the reduction in man-hours achieved as the result of building one unit.

Then the times required for producing each unit in turn are:

$$T(1) = k$$
$$T(2) = k - a$$
$$T(3) = k - 2a$$
$$T(4) = k - 3a$$
$$\dotfill$$
$$T(n) = k - (n - 1)a$$

Apparently the time requirement for producing each unit $T(x)$ is $k - (x - 1)a$; i.e., $T(x) = k - (x - 1)a$. $T(x)$ is therefore a straight line which is illustrated in Figure 8–12. The derivative of $T(x)$—the rate of change of $T(x)$—must be equal to $-a$. The function $T(x)$ can be integrated to obtain the number of hours needed to produce all n units:

$$\int_0^n [k - (x - 1)a]dx = \left[\left(kx - \frac{ax^2}{2}\right) + ax\right]\Big|_0^n = kn - \frac{an^2}{2} + an$$

$$= (k + a)n - \frac{an^2}{2}$$

A few figures will illustrate the example. Suppose that $n = 1000$, $k = 80$ hours, and $a = .05$ hours. That is, 1000 units are to be produced, the first one will take eighty hours to build, and each sub-

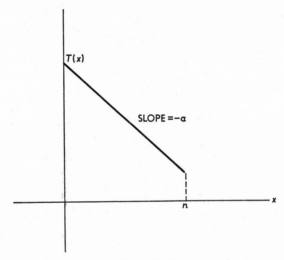

Figure 8–12

sequent unit will require .05 hours less than the previous one. Using the formula derived by integration, the total time required to build 1000 units is 55,050 hours.

Model 2. Suppose that instead of learning proceeding at a constant rate, the conditions described in the first paragraph of the section were fulfilled—i.e., learning is fairly rapid at first, but tends to "level off" or slow down as a limit is approached (Figure 8–13). The model might be

$$T(x) = kx^b \text{ where } -1 \leq b \leq 0$$

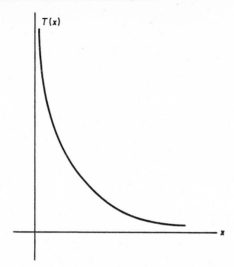

Figure 8–13

In order to compute the total time required to produce n units, $T(x)$ must be integrated over the interval $[0, n]$:

$$\int_0^n kx^b dx = \frac{kx^{b+1}}{b+1} \bigg|_0^n = \frac{kn^{b+1}}{b+1}$$

The function $T(x) = kx^b$ is well adapted for practical application since it can be transformed into a straight-line function by taking the logarithm of both sides of the expression so that

$$\log T = \log k + b \log x$$

Clearly this is an equation of a straight line having slope b. This greatly facilitates graphical interpretation of data. It might also be noted that the function involves a constant *percentage* reduction in time requirements rather than a constant absolute reduction, as was the case in Model 1.

The particular curve described when $b = -.322$ is called the "80% airframe curve" because it depicts a curve which shows a 20% improvement every time production doubles; i.e., the fourth unit requires 80% as much time as the second unit, the tenth unit requires 80% as much time as the fifth unit, etc. Studies of the aircraft industry suggested that this rate of improvement seems to prevail consistently over the range of production under study—hence the name applied to the curve.

If this airframe curve is drawn on ordinary graph paper, it describes a curved line, of course. However, if the logarithm of both sides of the expression is obtained, or the original function is plotted on special graph paper known as "log-log" paper, the straight line

$$\log T(x) = \log k + b \log x$$

will be obtained. It will be observed that b is the slope of this straight-line function. If a curve which shows a 20% improvement every time production doubles is desired, any two values of x such that the second x is twice the first, that is, the ratio of the second to the first is 2, are selected. Since b is the improvement rate

$$2^b = .8$$

Therefore $b \log 2 = \log .8$ and

$$b = \frac{\log .8}{\log 2} = -.322$$

To design an 80% curve requires b to be $-.322$ as indicated above.

Some firms habitually use this 80% model for estimating costs, basing the model on the cost of the initial prototype and *assuming* that b is $-.322$. However, the majority prefer to develop their own learning curves from empirical data. It should also be noted that a firm can frequently influence the shape of its learning curve to some extent by improving efficiency; for instance, an 80% curve might be reduced to a 78% curve if the firm could develop improved

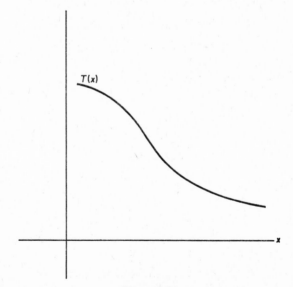

Figure 8–14

methods, etc. Many factors other than simple "learning" enter into the nature of the curve.[1]

Curve fitting is difficult, and frequently the resulting mathematical expressions are complex. For example, the learning curve may assume something resembling a flattened **S** shape. (See Figure 8–14). This reflects slow, trial-and-error improvement at first, followed by rapid improvement as the right combinations are developed and, finally, by a slowing down as the limit of efficiency is approached. Mathematical handling of such a function is not simple, and frequently a firm will depend heavily on graphical interpretation.

Questions

1. Suppose that a firm is using Model 1 in order to estimate the total time requirement for producing 500 units of a certain item. The first item requires 50 man-hours; each item thereafter could be produced in three minutes less than the preceding one.

   a) Find the total time requirement by integrating $[k - (x - 1)a]$.

   b) Suppose the production run had involved 5000 units instead of 500. Would the solution be meaningful? Comment.

2. Consider again the firm in Question 1 above. Suppose that it now decides to use Model 2; it has adopted the 80% airframe curve as an estimate. Thus

$$k = 50 \text{ man-hours, as before}$$
$$b = -.322$$

   Find the time required to produce 500 units; 5000 units. Use a table of logarithms in order to express the answer in numerical terms.

EXERCISES, SECTION 1

1. Use the definition of the definite integral to estimate

$$\int_0^1 f(x)dx$$

where

a) $f(x) = 3 + 4x$
b) $f(x) = 4x^2$

---

[1] See Frank J. Andress, "The Learning Curve as a Production Tool," *Harvard Business Review,* January–February, 1954, pp. 87–97; Paul F. Williams, "The Application of Manufacturing Improvement Curves in Multi-Product Industries," *Journal of Industrial Engineering,* March–April, 1961; and A. Alchian, *Reliability of Progress Curves in Airframe Production,* Rand Corporation Research Memorandum RM260–1, 1950.

2. Use the definition of the definite integral to estimate

$$\int_a^b f(x)dx$$

where

    a) $f(x) = m + nx$
    b) $f(x) = cx^2$

EXERCISES, SECTION 2

3. If $y = 2x^2 + 12$, determine whether y is an antiderivative of s, when $s = 4x$.

4. Find an antiderivative of u, if $u = 3v^2$.

5. Find an antiderivative of y, if $y = 4$. Express the antiderivative in terms of x.

6. If $w = 2z/(z - 1)$, determine whether w is an antiderivative of u, when $u = -(z - 1)^{-2}$.

7. If $y = e^x$, find an antiderivative of y.

8. If $u = 1/v$, find an antiderivative of u.

9. Given the function $F(x) = (x - 1)^5$, indicate whether $F(x)$ is an anti-derivative of $g(x) = 5(x^2 - 2x + 1)^3$.

10. If $T(x)$ is a company's total cost function where x is production volume, $T(x)$ is the antiderivative of what? (Give "practical" answer.)

11. A worker's time requirement for completing a routine task x times is given by $t = 4x^{1/2} + x$. t is an antiderivative of $s = 2x^{-1/2} + 1$. In practical terms, what is the significance of s?

EXERCISES, SECTION 3

12. Find $\displaystyle\int_0^6 (3x^2 + 2x)dx$.

13. Find $\displaystyle\int_c^d \left(\frac{u^2}{2} + 6\right)du$.

14. Evaluate $\displaystyle\int_0^x u\,du$.

15. a) Evaluate $\displaystyle\int_0^1 3x^2\,dx$.

    b) What percentage of the total area of the above curve, evaluated between 0 and 1, lies beyond the interval $(0, \tfrac{2}{3})$?

16. Find $\displaystyle\int_{-1}^1 e^{2y}\,dy$.

17. If $f(v) = 2/v$, find the value of the integral of $f(v)$ between 2 and 5.

18. If $g(x) = x^2 + 2$, and $h(x) = e^x$, find the value of the integral of $g(x) + h(x)$ between 0 and 1.

EXERCISES, SECTION 4

19. If $f(x) = 3x^2 - 2x + 10$, find the area under $f(x)$ from $x = 0$ to $x = 4$.

20. If $f(v) = e^{-v}$, find the area under $f(v)$ from $v = 0$ to $v = 1$.

21. If $f(x) = x^{-1}$, find the area under $f(x)$ from $x = 2$ to $x = 5$.

22. If $f(s) = 5s - s^2 - 3$, and $g(s) = s^2 - 1$, find the area between $f(s)$ and $g(s)$.

CHAPTER 9

PROBABILISTIC MODELS

PROBABILITY theory is concerned with the study of random phenomena and the methods which have arisen to deal with such phenomena. The theory, unlike statistics, is a branch of mathematics: certain propositions are established by a process of deduction from accepted axioms without any appeal to experience. Nonetheless, the application of probability theory is of great importance in the "real world."

No attempt will be made here to give a comprehensive outline of probability theory. Rather, a few probability concepts will be introduced, partly for their own value, partly to show the roles that the mathematics developed thus far in this book play in the theory, and partly to permit the consideration of more realistic cases in Chapter 11.

1. RANDOM VARIABLES AND DISTRIBUTION FUNCTIONS

Consider a measurement situation where the variable being measured is the length of telephone calls coming into a switchboard. Suppose that it is sufficient to approximate the variable length, call it L, to the nearest minute. Then the allowable values of L might be the set of numbers, , 1, 2, 3, 4, 5, $\cdot$ $\cdot$ $\cdot$, 60. If a call of more than an hour's duration is encountered, or if it is desired to allow for the possibility of one even if none is actually observed, it would be necessary to expand the set beyond 60—perhaps to 240. To emphasize that random forces are involved, the variable L is called a *random variable*.

A graph of the results might be as in Figure 9–1. Notice that the variable L is plotted along the x-axis, while the frequency of the occurrence of each possible value of L is plotted along the y-axis and is labeled $f(L)$. [It is convenient, and in fact is common prac-

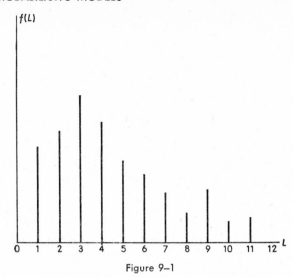

Figure 9–1

tice, to distinguish by some notational convention between ordinary variables and random variables. Some probabilists denote a random variable by placing a tilde, $\sim$, over the symbol for the variable, $\tilde{L}$, $\tilde{x}$, etc.; others use capital letters to denote random variables. However, no special notation will be used here for random variables.]

If more accuracy is required in the measurements, to seconds, tenths of seconds, or perhaps millionths of seconds, the measurements could, conceptually at least, be recorded to this accuracy. It turns out to be preferable in most cases to permit the random variable L to assume any value from $-\infty$ to $+\infty$; i.e., to be any real number. This convention permits one, since the set of all possible values for L can be represented by all the points on a line, to conceive of and to consider continuous measurements. In Figure 9–2 the irregularities of the discrete measurements of the experiment have been ignored.

Letting the variable L take on any value in the open interval $(-\infty, +\infty)$ does not mean that telephone messages of $+\infty$ or -316 minutes can be or are observed. In fact, the curve in Figure 9–2 indicates clearly that there were no calls over 25 minutes or of zero minutes.

Obviously, some liberties have been taken in describing the results in Figure 9–2: calls of every length between 0 and 25 minutes were not observed (this would be impossible!). The actual observations have been "smoothed" by drawing a continuous line to repre-

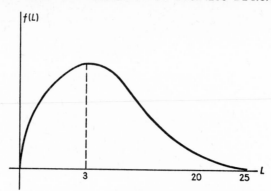

Figure 9–2

sent frequency. This is useful, not only when representing actual observations of L, but, more importantly, when indicating what is believed to be the range of possibilities for L.

The importance of Figure 9–2 is that it relates the ideas of probability and area. Suppose it is desired to ask about the frequency of calls of more than 20 minutes' duration. This is equivalent to asking about the probability that L is more than 20—i.e., $P(L > 20)$ if $P(\quad)$ denotes the "probability of . . . ." The question is crucial to understanding even the present brief discussion of probability: the argument is moving from *frequency of occurrence* ("*x*% of the incoming calls are more than 20 minutes long") to *probability* ("the probability that any given call is more than 20 minutes long is *x*") to *area* ["the area under the curve over the interval $(20, +\infty)$ is *x*"].

In other words, after generalizing from discrete information (Figure 9–1) to a curve (Figure 9–2) which represents the "true" state of affairs, it is agreed that the area under the curve and over any specified interval shall represent the probability that L will or does fall in that interval. That is, $P(L > 20)$ is the area under the curve beyond (to the right of) $L = 20$; the probability that a call will be between 0 and 3 minutes, $P(0 < L < 3)$, is the area between 0 and 3; etc.

But as seen in Chapter 8, the area under a continuous curve for any given interval, e.g., $(0, 3)$, is given by a definite integral,

$\int_0^3 f$. All that remains is to identify the function, f, which is to be

integrated. Such a function is called a *probability density function* (p.d.f.) and indicates the probability that the random variable will assume any specified value.

Note that under this definition the probability of the point $L = 3$ is zero; since the area over a point must necessarily be zero $\left(\int_{3}^{3} f = F \Big|_{3}^{3} = 0 \right)$. On the other hand, it is no longer necessary to worry about the end points of intervals since the area over the closed interval $[a, b]$ is the same as that over the open interval (a, b) if the function is continuous.

The issue of the origin of the p.d.f. can be ignored in order to proceed to a consideration of its characteristics. Clearly, it would be convenient for the probability that L will take on "some value" to be certain; i.e., $P(-\infty < x < +\infty) = 1$. Thus it is required that

$$\int_{-\infty}^{+\infty} f(x)dx = 1 \tag{1}$$

if f is to be a p.d.f. Similarly, "negative probabilities" are disallowed by requiring that

$$f(x) \geq 0 \text{ for all } x \tag{2}$$

The p.d.f. may assume any form, subject only to the conditions of this paragraph. There are, however, a number of common "shapes"; Figure 9–3 shows some of these.

An example of the language of probability theory as well as of the use of integrals follows. Suppose there is a filament in an electronic tube that has a use-life of t hours. Suppose further that the probability of t being any particular value is given by the p.d.f. $f(t) = \frac{1}{2}e^{-\frac{1}{2}t}$, shown in Figure 9–3(b). It can be verified easily that this function satisfies requirements (1) and (2); also $t \geq 0$ is understood since "negative life" is not defined. On the other hand, there is no conceptual upper limit even though one might be quite certain no filament would ever last a thousand years.

Let the symbol A designate the *event* that any given filament (chosen at random) will last, for example, more than 100 hours; the probability that event A will occur is written $P(A)$. Then

$$P(A) = \int_{100}^{\infty} f(t)dt = \int_{100}^{\infty} \frac{1}{2}e^{-t/2}\,dt = -e^{-t/2}\Big|_{100}^{\infty} = 0 + e^{-50} \tag{3}$$

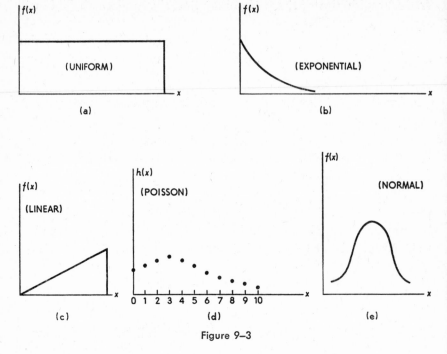

Figure 9–3

Similarly, defining B as the event that the filament will last more than 1000 hours,

$$P(B) = \int_{1000}^{\infty} f = \frac{1}{2} \int_{1000}^{\infty} e^{-t/2} = -e^{-t/2} \Big|_{1000}^{\infty} = 0 + e^{-500} \tag{4}$$

The probability that the filament will last at least 100 but not more than 1000 hours is given by

$$P(A) - P(B) = \int_{100}^{1000} f = -e^{-t/2} \Big|_{100}^{1000} = \frac{1}{e^{50}} - \frac{1}{e^{500}} \tag{5}$$

It is often necessary to ask about the average life of the filaments. In other words, what value should one expect t to assume, on the average?

This question involves the concept of the *expected value* of a random variable, the everyday counterpart of which is the arithmetic average or mean. The expected value of the variable t, denoted $E(t)$, is a number and is defined as

$$E(t) = \int_{-\infty}^{\infty} tf(t)dt \tag{6}$$

Each possible value of t is multiplied by the probability that it will occur; $E(t)$ is then the integral of this product over all possible values of t.

Consider a very simple p.d.f., the uniform function where all values of x are equally likely (Figure 9–4),

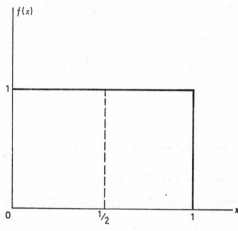

Figure 9–4

$$f(x) = 1 \text{ for } 0 \leq x \leq 1$$
$$= 0 \text{ elsewhere} \tag{7}$$

Clearly this function satisfies requirements (1) and (2). The expected value, $E(x)$, is, by (6),

$$\int_0^1 xf = \int_0^1 x = \left(\frac{x^2}{2}\bigg|_0^1\right) = (\tfrac{1}{2} - 0) = \tfrac{1}{2} \tag{8}$$

This, of course, is what one would expect the "average" to be for this function even if expected value had never been defined.

The following examples will illustrate further the use of the integral in analyzing the concepts of probability and expected value.

Example (i)

　If $f(x) = \tfrac{1}{4}$ for $-1 \leq x \leq 3$,
　　 $= 0$ elsewhere,
　find $E(x)$.

Solution:

　This function obviously is a p.d.f. and therefore

$$E(x) = \int_{-1}^3 xf = \int_{-1}^3 x \cdot \frac{1}{4} = \frac{x^2}{8}\bigg|_{-1}^3 = \tfrac{9}{8} - \tfrac{1}{8} = 1$$

Example (ii)

If $g(x) = 3x^2 - 2x + 1$ for $0 \leq x \leq 1$,
     $= 0$ otherwise,

verify that g is a p.d.f.; find $E(x)$.

Solution:

To verify that $g(x)$ is a p.d.f., it must first be shown that $g(x) \geq 0$ for $0 \leq x \leq 1$. The minimum value of $g(x)$ is obtained from $g'(x) = 6x - 2 = 0$: $x = \frac{1}{3}$ and $g(\frac{1}{3}) = \frac{2}{3}$. Since $g''(x) = 6$, it follows that the function has only a single extreme point and and hence is everywhere positive. Next it must be shown that

$$\int_0^1 g(x)dx = 1:$$

$$\int_0^1 g(x)dx = \int_0^1 (3x^2 - 2x + 1)dx = \left(3\frac{x^3}{3} - \frac{2x^2}{2} + x\right)\Big|_0^1$$

$$= [1 - 1 + 1] = 1$$

The expected value of the variable is $\frac{7}{12}$, found as follows:

$$\int_0^1 xg(x)dx = \int_0^1 x(3x^2 - 2x + 1) = \int_0^1 3x^3 - 2x^2 + x$$

$$= \left(\frac{3x^4}{4} - \frac{2x^3}{3} + \frac{x^2}{2}\right)\Big|_0^1 = \tfrac{3}{4} - \tfrac{2}{3} + \tfrac{1}{2} = \tfrac{7}{12}$$

Example (iii)

Find $E(x)$ if $h(x) = \gamma e^{-\gamma x}$ for $x \geq 0$,
     $= 0$ otherwise.

Solution: $h(x)$ is a p.d.f. if $\gamma > 0$, since then $h(x) \geq 0$ and

$$\int_0^\infty \gamma e^{-\gamma x}dx = -e^{-\gamma x}\ \Big|_0^\infty = 1$$

$$E(x) = \int_0^\infty x(\gamma e^{-\gamma x}) = \gamma \int_0^\infty xe^{-\gamma x}$$

$$= \frac{1}{\gamma}(-\gamma xe^{-\gamma x} - e^{-\gamma x})\ \Big|_0^\infty$$

$$= \frac{1}{\gamma}(-\gamma xe^{-\gamma x})\ \Big|_0^\infty - \frac{1}{\gamma}e^{-\gamma x}\ \Big|_0^\infty = \frac{1}{\gamma}(0 - 0 + 0 + 1) = \frac{1}{\gamma}$$

The antiderivative of $(xe^{-\gamma x})$ is taken from the list given in the Appendix. That it is indeed an antiderivative may be verified by differentiation.

The expected value of a random variable x, which has p.d.f. $=$ $f(x)$ in the interval (a, b), that is, where $\int_a^b f(x)dx = 1$, was defined as

$$E(x) = \int_a^b xf(x)dx \qquad (9)$$

A closely related characteristic of random variables is the *variance*, denoted by V and defined as

$$V(x) = \int_a^b [x - E(x)]^2 f(x)dx \qquad (10)$$

The deviation of each possible value of x from the expected value is squared and then multiplied by the probability of that value. The variance is then defined as the integral of this quantity over all possible values.

Although the variance for any p.d.f. can be computed using (10), it is usually easier to use a simpler form. Expanding the square in (10) gives

$$V(x) = \int_a^b [x^2 - 2xE(x) + (E(x))^2]f(x)dx \qquad (11)$$

Since $E(x)$, the expected value, is a definite quantity, not a function of x, this reduces to

$$= \int_a^b x^2 f(x)dx - 2E(x) \int_a^b xf(x)dx + [E(x)]^2 \int_a^b f(x)dx$$

$$= \int_a^b x^2 f(x)dx - 2E(x) E(x) + [E(x)]^2(1)$$

$$= \int_a^b x^2 f(x)dx - [E(x)]^2 \qquad (12)$$

The variance for the uniform distribution defined by (7) can now be computed:

$$\int_0^1 x^2 dx = \frac{x^3}{3} \Big|_0^1 = \frac{1}{3}$$

and, therefore,

$$V(x) = \tfrac{1}{3} - (\tfrac{1}{2})^2$$
$$= \tfrac{1}{12} \qquad (13)$$

Of the several p.d.f.'s shown in Figure 9–3, by far the most important in the practical application of probability theory is the one known as the *normal probability function:*

$$f(x) = \frac{1}{\sigma\sqrt{2\pi}} e^{-\frac{(x-\mu)^2}{2\sigma^2}} \qquad -\infty \leq x \leq \infty \quad (14)$$

Several normal p.d.f.'s are shown in Figure 9–5; each depends on a

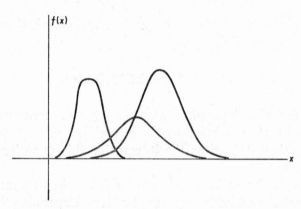

Figure 9–5

particular pair of values for the parameters, μ and σ^2. The first requirement that $f(x)$ be a p.d.f., that of nonnegativity, holds if $\sigma > 0$. The second requirement requires that the integral

$$\int_{-\infty}^{\infty} \frac{1}{\sigma\sqrt{2\pi}} e^{-\frac{(x-\mu)^2}{2\sigma^2}} \, dx \qquad (15)$$

be evaluated and found to be equal to 1. To perform this evaluation, let $t = (x - \mu)/\sigma$ so that (15) becomes

$$\int_{-\infty}^{\infty} \frac{1}{\sqrt{2\pi}} e^{-\frac{t^2}{2}} \, dt \qquad (16)$$

which is equal to one. Also

$$\int_{-\infty}^{\infty} x \frac{1}{\sigma\sqrt{2\pi}} e^{-\frac{(x-\mu)^2}{2\sigma^2}} \, dx = \mu \qquad (17)$$

and

$$\int_{-\infty}^{\infty} (x - \mu)^2 \frac{1}{\sigma\sqrt{2\pi}} e^{-\frac{(x-\mu)^2}{2\sigma^2}} \, dx = \sigma^2 \qquad (18)$$

which show that the expected value and variance of x are, respectively, the parameters μ and σ^2.

2. DISCRETE DISTRIBUTION FUNCTIONS

The previous section dealt with a random variable which could take on any value over an interval; this section will deal with random variables which can take on only certain discrete values.

Suppose one coin is tossed; will it come up heads or tails? The tossing of the coin is said to be a "trial," and the result is an "event." Let H be the event that the coin comes up heads, and T be the event that it comes up tails. The probability of the event H is denoted by $p(H)$ and, if the coin is "fair," is equal to $\frac{1}{2}$; similarly, the probability of the event T is denoted by $p(T)$ and is also equal to $\frac{1}{2}$.

Consider next a more complex trial, say, the tossing of two coins. Then there are four distinct mutually exclusive events that can occur; namely

$$HH, HT, TH, TT$$

where in each case the first symbol indicates whether coin No. 1 is heads or tails, and the second whether coin No. 2 is heads or tails; e.g., TH is the event that coin 1 is tails and coin 2 is heads. Clearly,

$$p(HH) + p(HT) + p(TH) + p(TT) = 1 \qquad (19)$$

since one of these events must occur. To compute the probability of the individual events requires the use of the following rule:

If the probability of event A is $p(A)$ and the probability of event B is $p(B)$ and the events are independent of each other, then the probability that both will happen is

$$p(AB) = p(A) \cdot p(B) \qquad (20)$$

From this and the fact that $p(H) = p(T)$, it follows that

$$p(HH) = p(HT) = p(TH) = p(TT) = (\tfrac{1}{2})(\tfrac{1}{2}) = (\tfrac{1}{4})$$

Suppose that one is interested in the number of heads that occur when two coins are tossed. Let this number be denoted by y; then the possible values of y are 0, 1, and 2. Clearly,

$$p(y = 0) = \tfrac{1}{4}$$

and

$$p(y = 2) = \tfrac{1}{4}$$

The case $y = 1$ can arise in two ways, HT and TH, and its probability is obtained by the following rule:

If the probability of an event A is $p(A)$ and the probability of an event B is $p(B)$, and the events are mutually exclusive, then the probability that one or the other will happen is

$$p(A + B) = p(A) + p(B)$$

From this rule it follows that

$$p(y = 1) = \tfrac{1}{4} + \tfrac{1}{4} = \tfrac{1}{2}$$

The variable y is a random variable as defined earlier and has the p.d.f.

$$p(0) = \tfrac{1}{4}$$
$$p(1) = \tfrac{1}{2}$$
$$p(2) = \tfrac{1}{4}$$

The expected value of y, the "average" number of heads obtained in a toss of two coins, is obtained by multiplying each possible value of y by the probability of that value, and then summing over all possible values:

$$E(y) = 0 \cdot \tfrac{1}{4} + 1 \cdot \tfrac{1}{2} + 2 \cdot \tfrac{1}{4} \qquad (21)$$
$$= 1$$

The variance, as defined analogously to the way it was defined for the continuous case in (10), is $V(y) = \Sigma[y - E(y)]^2 p(y)$ where the summation is over all values of y. In this case

$$V(y) = (0 - 1)^2 \cdot \tfrac{1}{4} + (1 - 1)^2 \cdot \tfrac{1}{2} + (2 - 1)^2 \cdot \tfrac{1}{4} \qquad (22)$$
$$= \tfrac{1}{2}$$

Example (i)

A remotely located transmitter, which requires a special fuse, is being operated. This fuse has a shelf life of one month; i.e., if it is not used in a month, it must be discarded. At the beginning of each month fuses can be purchased for $1.20 per fuse plus a delivery charge of $25, which does not depend on the number of fuses ordered. If a fuse is required and not on hand, it must be obtained for a cost of $20 per fuse including delivery.

The number of fuses required per month, y, is given by the following probability function:

y	p.d.f.
0	.2
1	.3
2	.3
3	.1
4	.1
	1.0

The problem is to determine how many fuses should be ordered if the expected cost is to be minimized.

Let x be the number of fuses to be ordered. One could consider ordering 0, 1, 2, 3, or 4 fuses; there being no point in ordering more than four. Suppose two fuses are ordered. Then the expected total cost is the cost of the two fuses, plus the delivery cost, plus the cost of getting one extra fuse if three are required, plus the cost of getting two extra fuses if four are required, or

$$
\begin{aligned}
E(TC \text{ if } x = 2) &= (2.40 + 25.00) + (20.00)(.1) + (40.00)(.1) \\
&= 2.40 + 25.00 + 2.00 + 4.00 \\
&= 33.40
\end{aligned}
\tag{23}
$$

Similarly,

$$
\begin{aligned}
E(TC \text{ if } x = 0) &= 32.00 \\
E(TC \text{ if } x = 1) &= 42.20 \\
E(TC \text{ if } x = 3) &= 30.60 \\
E(TC \text{ if } x = 4) &= 29.80
\end{aligned}
$$

and therefore the number of fuses that should be ordered each month is four. The computations show the *expected* cost of each possible action, taking due account of all contingencies. Thus, the optimal action is the ordering of four fuses. Note how the optimal action depends crucially on the several costs and on the shape of the p.d.f.

3. AN APPLICATION OF PROBABILITY THEORY

As a more significant example of the application of the theory of probability to making decisions in business, consider a situation where an order must be placed at the beginning of a period for a perishable item (flowers, meat, etc.), the demand for which varies randomly from one order period to the next. Assuming that there is a negligible loss of goodwill for being out of stock when an order is received, what is the optimum order quantity that should be ordered for each sales period?

Let

c = cost per unit for each unit ordered,
p = selling price for each unit sold,
x = number of units sold in any one period,
i = inventory or number of units ordered in any period,
π = profit in any period.

Clearly, π for any period will depend on the relative magnitudes of i and x. If more units are ordered than are sold, $i > x$, then

$$
\pi_1 = px - ci
\tag{24}
$$

If all units ordered are sold, $i \leqq x$, then

$$\pi_2 = pi - ci = (p - c)i \qquad (25)$$

The problem facing the decision maker is that of choosing the optimum value of i, say i^*, in order to maximize π. However, since π is a function of x, and x is a random variable, it is necessary to maximize not π but the *expected or average value of* π, $E(\pi)$.

Profit will be either π_1 or π_2 in the absolute sense, since π_1 and π_2 represent mutually exclusive conditions; that is, either inventory is greater than sales, in which case profit will be π_1 or inventory is not greater than sales, in which case profit will be π_2. However, when evaluating a future condition—sales unknown—expected profit is computed as the sum of the expectations of π_1 and π_2:

$$E(\pi) = E(\pi_1) + E(\pi_2) \qquad (26)$$

The two kinds of profit, π_1 and π_2, each occupy *part* of the total range of the p.d.f. of sales, as seen in Figure 9–6.

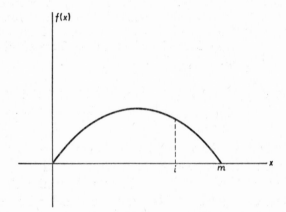

Figure 9–6

$E(\pi_1)$ over the entire p.d.f. is the expectation of π_1 from 0 to i since π_1 is zero otherwise. Thus

$$E(\pi_1) = \int_0^i \pi_1(x)f(x)dx \qquad (27)$$

a value which is the "average" value of π_1 over the entire interval $(0, m)$. Similarly,

$$E(\pi_2) = \int_i^m \pi_2 f(x) \qquad (28)$$

is the average of π_2 over the total range $(0, m)$.

These two integrals are summed for the total expected profit:

$$E(\pi) = E(\pi_1) + E(\pi_2)$$

$$= \int_0^i \pi_1(x)f(x)dx + \int_i^m \pi_2(x)f(x)dx \qquad (29)$$

Substituting (24) and (25) for π_1 and π_2 gives

$$E(\pi) = \int_0^i (px - ci)f(x)dx + \int_i^m i(p - c)f(x)dx \qquad (30)$$

$$= p\int_0^i xf(x)dx - ci\int_0^i f(x)dx + pi\int_i^m f(x)dx - ci\int_i^m f(x)dx$$

But

$$\int_0^m f(x)dx = 1 \qquad (31)$$

by definition and since

$$\int_0^i f + \int_i^m f = \int_0^m f \qquad (32)$$

equation (30) reduces to

$$E(\pi) = p\int_0^i xf(x)dx + pi\int_i^m f(x)dx - ci \qquad (33)$$

This expression cannot be evaluated further until $f(x)$ is specified. Three special cases are considered.

Case A. Uniform p.d.f. (Figure 9–7).

$$f(x) = \frac{1}{m} \quad 0 \leq x \leq m \qquad (34)$$

Then, from (33)

$$E(\pi) = p\int_0^i \frac{x}{m}dx + pi\int_i^m \frac{1}{m}dx - ci$$

$$= \frac{p}{m}\frac{x^2}{2}\Big|_0^i + \frac{pi}{m}x\Big|_i^m - ci$$

$$= \frac{p}{2m}i^2 + pi - \frac{pi^2}{m} - ci$$

$$= i(p - c) - \frac{pi^2}{2m} \qquad (35)$$

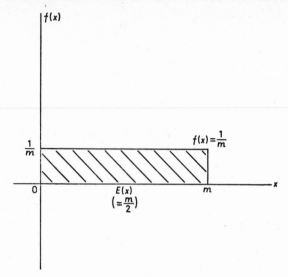

Figure 9–7

The optimum value, i^*, is the one for which

$$\frac{dE(\pi)}{di} = (p - c) - \frac{pi}{m} = 0$$

or

$$i^* = \frac{(p - c)m}{p} \tag{36}$$

The value results in a maximum since

$$\frac{d^2E(\pi)}{di^2} = -\frac{p}{m} \tag{37}$$

which is always negative since p and m are both positive.

Case B. Linear p.d.f. (*Figure 9–8*).

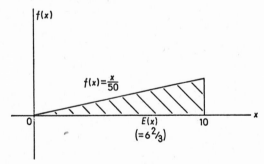

Figure 9–8

$$f(x) = \frac{x}{50} \qquad 0 \le x \le 10$$

Substituting in (33) gives

$$E(\pi) = p \int_0^i \frac{x^2}{50}dx + pi \int_i^m \frac{x}{50}dx - ci$$

$$= \frac{p}{50}\frac{x^3}{3}\Big|_0^i + pi\frac{x^2}{100}\Big|_i^m - ci$$

$$= \frac{pi^3}{150} + \frac{pi}{100}[m^2 - i^2] - ci$$

$$= -\frac{pi^3}{300} + \frac{pim^2}{100} - ci \quad \text{and using } m = 10,$$

$$= -\frac{pi^3}{300} + i(p - c) \tag{38}$$

Then, optimizing (38)

$$\frac{dE(\pi)}{di} = -\frac{3pi^2}{300} + (p - c) = 0$$

and

$$i^* = \sqrt{\frac{100(p - c)}{p}} \tag{39}$$

This extremum is a maximum since

$$\frac{d^2E(\pi)}{di^2} = -\frac{2pi}{100}$$

which is always negative.

Case C. Exponential p.d.f. (Figure 9–9).

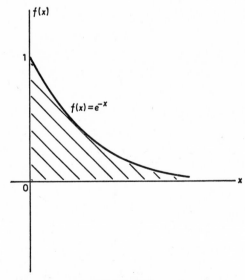

Figure 9–9

$$f(x) = e^{-x} \qquad x \geq 0 \tag{40}$$

Substituting in (33)

$$E(\pi) = p \int_0^i xe^{-x}dx + pi \int_i^\infty e^{-x}dx - ci$$

$$= p[-xe^{-x} - e^{-x}]\Big|_0^i - pie^{-x}\Big|_i^\infty - ci$$

$$= p[-ie^{-i} - e^{-i} + 1] + pie^{-i} - ci$$

$$= -pe^{-i} + p - ci \tag{41}$$

Then,

$$\frac{dE(\pi)}{di} = pe^{-i} - c = 0$$

or

$$e^{-i} = \frac{c}{p} \qquad \text{hence } i^* = \ln\frac{p}{c} \tag{42}$$

a maximum since

$$\frac{d^2E(\pi)}{di^2} = -pe^{-i} < 0$$

Case D. Unspecified p.d.f. It is possible to differentiate (33) without specifying any particular p.d.f. Of course, no "final" result can be obtained until the p.d.f. is known. The result obtainable, however, has an interesting interpretation. The differentiation to be performed requires slightly more advanced techniques than were developed in Chapter 8; the reader should nonetheless be able to

follow the mathematics if he recalls that $D_x \int_a^x g(t)dt = g(x)$ when

a is a constant (see Section 12, Chapter 8).

Expression (33) gives $E(\pi)$ in terms of some constants (p, i, c, m), the unspecified p.d.f. $f(x)$, and the decision variable x. $E(\pi)$ can be maximized in (33) in the usual way:

$$E(\pi) = p \int_0^i xf(x)dx + pi \int_i^m f(x)dx - ci \tag{[(33)]}$$

$$\frac{dE(\pi)}{di} = ipf(i) + p \int_i^m f(x)dx - ipf(i) - c = 0 \tag{43}$$

$$ipf(i) - ipf(i) + p \int_i^m f(x)dx - c = 0$$

The first two terms cancel, and thus,

$$\int_i^m f(x)dx = \frac{c}{p} \quad \text{or}$$

$$1 - \int_0^i f(x)dx = \frac{c}{p} \quad \text{since} \quad \int_0^i + \int_i^m = 1$$

$$\int_0^i f(x)dx = 1 - \frac{c}{p} = \frac{p - c}{p} \tag{44}$$

The integral $\int_0^i f(x)\,dx$ represents the proportion of the demand distribution that is covered by the inventory; if it is $= .25$, then on the average the inventory will be large enough to cover sales for one out of four days; if it is $=.75$, then the inventory will be enough to cover the demand for three days out of four. The ratio $\frac{p - c}{p}$ increases as the profit $(p - c)$ increases; it is 0 if profit is zero $(p = c)$, and tends to 1 as profit tends to p (c tends to zero). Therefore, the rule (44) has a reasonable interpretation: the proportion of the demand that should be covered to optimize expected profit is equal to the proportion of profit to selling price. The specific results of (36), (39), and (42) can be obtained directly from (44) by substitution of the relevant probability functions.

EXERCISES, SECTION 1

1. *a*) If $f(x) = \dfrac{9x}{2}$ for $0 \le x \le a$,

    $= 0$ otherwise,

    and if $\int_0^a f(x)dx = 1$, find a.

    b) Is the above function an acceptable p.d.f.? Explain.

    c) Compute the probability that x will be greater than $a/2$.

2. *a*) If $f(x) = 2x - 1 \quad$ for $0 \le x \le a$,

    $= 0 \qquad$ otherwise;

    and if $\int_0^a f(x)dx = 1$, find a.

    b) Is this an acceptable p.d.f.? Explain.

    c) Compute the probability that x will be greater than $a/4$ but less than $3a/4$.

3. Show that the value of the integral of e^{-x} is equal to 1, for $x \geq 0$. Compute the probability that $x > a$.

4. If $f(v) = \frac{1}{5}$ for $0 \leq v \leq 5$,
   $= 0$ otherwise,
   show that $f(v)$ is a valid p.d.f. What type of p.d.f. does it represent?

5. If $f(x) = \dfrac{3x}{2} + \dfrac{3x^2}{4}$ for $0 \leq x \leq 1$,

   $= 0$ otherwise,
   show that $f(x)$ is a p.d.f.

6. A quality control study has indicated that the number of defective items which will probably be found in any given lot of completed units (100 units per lot) is given by

$$p(x) = \frac{1}{4}e^{-\frac{1}{4}x}, \, 0 \leq x \leq 100$$

   where x is the number of defective items.
   a) Is $p(x)$ a valid p.d.f. for $0 \leq x \leq 100$? If not, is it reasonable to assume that it could be used anyway? Why?
   b) If $p(x)$ is in fact used as a p.d.f., what is the probability that more than ten units will be defective?
   c) What is the probability that exactly two units will be defective?

7. Determine whether the function

$$5x^4 - 3x^2 + 1, \qquad 0 \leq x \leq 1$$

   is a p.d.f.,
   a) By showing that the value of the integral is unity.
   b) By demonstrating that the value of the function is positive throughout the interval. (Suggestion: Locate the maxima and minima within the interval.)

8. Sketch the p.d.f.'s in Exercises 1, 2, 3, 4, 5, and 7 above. Compute the mean and variance of each.

9. Sketch the following p.d.f.'s and compute their means and variances:
   a) $f(x) = \dfrac{1}{b}, 0 \leq x \leq b$,

   $= 0$ otherwise.
   b) $f(x) = \dfrac{2x}{a^2}, 0 \leq x \leq a$,

   $= 0$ otherwise.
   c) $f(x) = 3ax^2 - 2ax + 1, 0 \leq x \leq 1$,
   $= 0$ otherwise.

10. In economic theory, a utility function represents an attempt to express the "value" of something in terms of its worth in the eyes of some entrepreneur, consumer, etc., this "value" not necessarily being the same as the money value of the commodity. For example, an individual stranded in the desert without water would place high value on water—much more than its cost per cubic foot at city rates.
    Utility functions may have many forms, of course; one which

may be used belongs to the family of learning curves, and is represented by

$$y(r) = 1 - e^{-ar}$$

where

r = net revenue from investment,
a = a constant measuring the investor's aversion to risk,
y = utility.

Graphically interpreted, this function shows that as net revenue from an investment rises, the utility to the investor also increases, but at a decreasing rate. The constant a, if large, indicates a very conservative investor since it suggests that the investor is satisfied quickly, with investments of low yield. Similarly, a small value for a indicates that the investor is somewhat less conservative. If it is assumed that net revenue, r, is normally distributed, the expected utility is

$$E(y) = \frac{1}{\sigma\sqrt{2\pi}} \int_{-\infty}^{\infty} (1 - e^{-ar})e^{-(r-\mu)^2/2\sigma^2}dr$$

Problem:

Show that expected utility is maximized if the expression

$$\mu - \frac{a\sigma^2}{2}$$

is maximized. (Hint: Solve by completing the square in the integral.)

EXERCISES, SECTION 2

11. Indicate which of the following situations should be represented by a discrete p.d.f., and which by a continuous p.d.f.
    a) The yield from a chemical reaction.
    b) Marginal cost of production, per unit.
    c) Distribution of height of 100 men.
    d) The number of automobiles waiting for service at a gas station.

12. Often a continuous p.d.f. will be used in a situation where a discrete p.d.f. seems more appropriate; e.g., in showing the distribution of IQ's of the population of the United States. Why would this be appropriate, from a mathematical point of view, and why would it be done?

13. In drawing a card at random from a deck of 52 playing cards, what is the probability that the card will be a King? What is the probability that four cards, drawn in succession without being put back into the deck after drawing, will all be Kings?

14. Consider a perfectly balanced die, of the usual type, having a number on each face from one to six. What is the expected value of the number which comes up when the die is thrown, assuming that there is an equal probability of each number coming up?

15. Let an event be the throwing of two dice. Compute the p.d.f. for the random variable which is the sum of the numbers appearing on the two dice.

16. A speculator must buy 100,000 units of a certain commodity by to-morrow in order to cover obligations incurred previously. The price of the commodity today is 10 cents per unit. Price for this item nor-mally changes in 1-cent increments, and the speculator knows from past experience that the probable price tomorrow may be described by the following p.d.f.

Price in Cents	Probability
8	.1
9	.2
10	.2
11	.3
12	.2

Find the expected price tomorrow. Should the speculator buy now or wait until tomorrow?

17. A firm has found the following distribution of industrial accident frequency in its plant:

No. of Weeks	No. of Accidents during Week
25	0
18	1
6	2
2	3
1	4

What is the expected number of accidents per week? What is the variance of the estimate? What is the probability that two or more accidents will occur?

EXERCISES, SECTION 3

18. A wholesaler has an arrangement to supply fresh-caught salmon to each of 20 retail markets daily. He sells the fish for 40 cents per pound. Since he has no cold-storage facilities (he just meets the boats at the dock and buys salmon for immediate delivery), he cannot re-tain any of his inventory at the end of the day; that is, he buys the fish in the morning and either sells them or throws them away at the end of the day (assume no salvage value for fertilizer, etc.). The fish cost him 30 cents per pound.

Each retailer either buys 100 pounds of fish, as agreed, or else buys nothing at all. There is no penalty or loss of goodwill attached to the wholesaler's being unable to supply the demands of his cus-tomers.

If x represents the number of retailers who buy fish on a given day, and $f(x)$ is the p.d.f. of x, how many pounds of fish should the wholesaler buy if $f(x) = x/200$? Solve the problem using the model discussed in Section 3.

19. Observe that Exercise 18 can be solved using a continuous p.d.f. How-ever, the function is actually a continuous approximation of what must, in real life, be a discrete situation. Formulate a discrete model and solve.

CHAPTER 10

THE MATHEMATICS OF FINANCE AND ACCOUNTING

Pᴿᴏʙʟᴇᴍꜱ involving the investment of capital will normally also involve time streams of costs and benefits deriving from the initial decision to invest. When management is considering whether to build a plant, bid on a long-term contract, etc., it will compare the initial and subsequent costs that may be incurred with the expected stream of income over the period of the investment.

Costs paid and benefits received in different periods are usually placed on a common basis by using the concept of interest. If a borrower pays interest at the rate of 6% per year, he will repay a dollar debt at the end of a year with $1.06. More generally, if the interest rate is i per year, a borrower must repay a dollar at the end of a year by $(1 + i)$ dollars. If the amount borrowed is A dollars, it must be repaid with $A(1 + i)$ dollars at the end of a year.

1. TYPES OF INTEREST

The simplest form of interest, *simple interest,* is the way in which interest on bonds is usually paid. It means merely that interest is earned only on the original amount borrowed, and not on interest which may be accrued subsequently.

For example, if a $100 bond paid 5% simple interest annually, the lender would receive $5.00 each year. As another example, consider the situation in which a bank pays simple interest at the rate i on a certain class of deposit. If a depositor deposits an amount A and makes no withdrawals for n years, the total amount on deposit at the end of n years is

$$V = \text{principal} + \text{total interest earned}$$
$$= A + I$$

The total interest earned is given by

$$I = Ani$$

so that

$$V = A + Ani$$
$$= A(1 + ni) \tag{1}$$

In this example it is implied that n is a positive integer, but the formula also holds for the case where n is a fraction.

A common use of simple interest is in connection with short-term promissory notes and some types of short-term loans. In such cases, the earning period is likely to be 30, 60, or 90 days. Interest calculations are usually simplified by assuming 360 days in a year, instead of the actual 365 or 366 days. Also, the period may be expressed in months in which case it is assumed that each month contains 30 days instead of the actual 28 to 31.

Example (i)

A loan of $1,000 is made at an annual simple interest rate of 10% and repaid in 90 days. The amount of interest which must be paid is

$$I = Ani$$
$$= (1000)\left(\frac{90}{360}\right)(.10)$$
$$= \$25$$

Example (ii)

An amount of $750 is invested in a ten-year trust fund which pays 4% annual simple interest. At the end of the ten years the total amount is equal to

$$V = A + Ani$$
$$= 750 + (750)(10)(.04)$$
$$= 750 + 300$$
$$= \$1050$$

Frequently the interest earned each year, during the term of a loan or investment, is added to the principal and therefore earns interest itself. This is called *compound interest*. Since this type of interest is more widely used in business than is simple interest, the unmodified term "interest," when used, is usually taken to signify compound interest.

If an amount A is deposited in a bank which pays compound interest at a rate i per year, the amount on deposit after one year is

$A + Ai = A(1 + i)$, at the end of two years it is $A(1 + i)(1 + i)$ or $A(1 + i)^2$, and at the end of n years it is

$$V = A(1 + i)^n \qquad (2)$$

The amount on deposit is said to increase "geometrically." Tables have been prepared to aid in the computation of compound interest. One such table appears as Appendix Table I.

Example (iii)

> An amount of $100 is deposited in a bank which pays 6% interest, compounded annually. The amount on deposit at the end of 0, 1, 2, . . . 50th . . . years is
>
> 100, 106, 112.36, 119.10, 126.25, 133.82, . . . 1,842.02 . . .
>
> Had the bank paid simple interest, the series would have been
>
> 100, 106, 112, 118, 124, 130, . . . 400 . . .

Interest is usually stated as an annual rate, say 6% per year, or 3% per year, etc. However, the interest is often computed and added to the principal semiannually or quarterly rather than annually.

If interest is compounded more than once per year, the stated annual rate must be divided by the number of times the interest is compounded. Suppose a bank pays interest at the annual rate i, compounded semiannually. Then at the end of six months, the amount on deposit will be

$$V = A\left(1 + \frac{i}{2}\right)$$

This amount will earn interest during the next six months at the rate of i per year, and therefore the amount on deposit at the end of a year is

$$V = \left[A\left(1 + \frac{i}{2}\right)\right]\left(1 + \frac{i}{2}\right)$$
$$= A\left(1 + \frac{i}{2}\right)^2$$

In general, if the interest is compounded m times per year, the amount on deposit at the end of one year will be

$$V = A\left(1 + \frac{i}{m}\right)^m \qquad (3)$$

and the amount at the end of n years will be

$$V = A\left(1 + \frac{i}{m}\right)^{mn} \qquad (4)$$

Appendix Table I can be used to evaluate formula (3). The interest rate for the table is i/m, and the number of periods is m.

Example (iv)

Suppose the bank in Example *(iii)* pays 6% interest, compounded semiannually. The amount on deposit at the end of the first six-month period is 100(1.03), and at the end of the second six-month period is 100(1.03)². The amounts for 0, 1, 2, . . . periods is:

100, 103, 106.09, 109.27, 112.55, 115.93, 119.41,
122.99, 126.68, 130.48, 134.39, . . .

These values are obtained from Appendix Table I for an interest rate of 3%. After five years the amount is $134.39; when the interest was compounded annually, the amount was $133.82; with simple interest, it was $130. If interest had been compounded quarterly, the amount would have been $134.69.

It is useful to make a distinction between the *nominal* rate of interest, which is the stated annual rate, and the *effective* rate when interest is compounded more than once per year.

The *effective rate of interest* is that rate which, when compounded once a year, gives the same amount of interest as a nominal rate compounded m times per year. Let j be the effective rate and i be the nominal rate. The relationship between i and j is given by

$$(1 + j) = \left(1 + \frac{i}{m}\right)^m \tag{5}$$

The right-hand side, from (3), is the amount that A grows to in one year if an annual rate i is compounded m times per year.

Example (v)

Suppose a borrower obtains $1000 to be repaid at the end of one year at an annual rate of 12%, but interest is compounded monthly. The borrower may think that he will have to repay $1000 plus 12% of $1000, or $1120, at the end of the year. How much will he actually have to pay?

Solution:

If compounded monthly, 12% interest means that A will pay 1% per month; the amount outstanding at the end of each month is, therefore, successively,

1000, 1010, 1020, 1030, 1041, 1051, 1062,
1072, 1083, 1094, 1105, 1116, 1127

The value 1127 appears under an interest rate of 1% for 12 periods in Appendix Table I. Therefore, he must pay $1127 rather than \$1120. The effective rate is therefore 127/1000, or 12.7% rather than 12%.

The previous example has shown that a nominal annual rate of 12% actually yields 12.7% as an effective rate when compounded monthly. It is desirable to know what happens if the compounding period is shortened. A comparison of effective rates for various nominal rates and compounding periods is given in the following table:

EFFECTIVE RATE WHEN COMPOUNDED

Nominal Rate of Interest	Annually	Half Yearly	Quarterly	Bimonthly	Monthly	Continuously
.02	.0200	.020100	.020151	.020167	.020184	.020201
.03	.0300	.030225	.030339	.030378	.030416	.030455
.04	.0400	.040400	.040604	.040673	.040742	.040811
.05	.0500	.050625	.050945	.051053	.051162	.051271
.10	.1000	.102500	.103813	.104260	.104713	.105171
.20	.2000	.210000	.215506	.217426	.219391	.221403
.30	.3000	.322500	.335469	.340096	.344889	.349859
.40	.4000	.440000	.464100	.472897	.482126	.491825
.50	.5000	.562500	.601807	.616489	.632094	.648721

In the example above, formula (3) was actually evaluated for $i = .12$ and $m = 12$. If interest were compounded daily the equation would be

$$1 + j = \left(1 + \frac{.12}{360}\right)^{360}$$

and in the limit, if interest were *compounded continuously*

$$1 + j = \lim_{m \to \infty} \left(1 + \frac{i}{m}\right)^m \tag{6}$$

It will be recalled from Chapter 6 that the right-hand side of (6) is the definition of e^i, and therefore if a nominal interest i is compounded continuously, \$1.00 will grow to e^i at the end of one year. Continuous compounding is so important in theoretical financial studies that the interest rate for continuous compounding is given a special name and a special symbol. It is termed the *force of interest* and denoted by δ. An amount A invested for n years with continuous compounding will grow to V where

$$V = Ae^{\delta n}$$

e.g.,   if $A = 1$, $\delta = 0.5$, and $n = 1$, then $V = 1.648721$ (7)

Continuous compounding is used most frequently where money flows uniformly during a period rather than being paid in a lump sum at, say, the end of a period. Suppose two alternatives are to be compared; one involves a uniform flow of money, and the other a discrete payment. The effective interest rates should be the same. What value of δ will lead to the same growth as the nominal annual rate? The required value of δ must satisfy the relation

$$A(1 + i)^m = Ae^{\delta n} \tag{8}$$

i.e., $$1 + i = e^{\delta} \text{ or } \delta = \ln(1 + i) \tag{9}$$

e.g., $$\text{if } i = 0.50, \ \delta = \ln(1 + i) = 0.40547.$$

To verify this, note that $e^{0.40547} = 1.5$.

Continuous compounding is not generally used in actual loan transactions. However, it is of considerable use in evaluating investment decisions, since it makes possible the use of a continuous function and therefore permits the use of calculus. Also, it permits the assumption of a continuous flow of funds throughout a period at a uniform rate, rather than an intermittent flow of discrete quantities.

Example (vi)

In Example (v), a loan of $1000 was obtained at 12% annual interest. Suppose that interest was compounded continuously. What would be the total amount of the repayment?

Solution:

$$\begin{aligned} V &= A(e^i) \\ &= 1000(e^{.12}) \\ &= (1000)(1.127) \\ &= \$1127 \end{aligned}$$

In this example, since approximations to the nearest dollar are being used, the result is the same as that for monthly compounding. Actually, the interest charge for continuous compounding is slightly higher, as would be revealed if larger dollar amounts or more precise figures were used. However, it should be noted that continuous compounding yields results which are very little different from compounding at short intervals and low interest rates. and in fact the result is not much different from that which would be obtained simply by compounding interest annually, i.e., $1120.

2. UNIFORM PERIODIC PAYMENTS

The problem discussed in the previous section was that of determining the value at the end of n years of an amount A deposited at interest rate i per year at either simple or compound interest. It was assumed that no additions were made to the principal except from interest. Frequently, however, a depositor will make additional deposits. In this section the case where deposits of an amount A are made at the end of each period is considered. An annual interest rate of i and annual compounding are assumed.

At the end of the first year the amount will be zero until the depositor adds an amount A. At the end of the second year the total amount will be

$$V = A(1 + i)$$

To this the depositor adds an amount A, and therefore at the end of the third year the total amount will be

$$\begin{aligned} V &= [A(1 + i) + A](1 + i) \\ &= A(1 + i)(1 + i) + A(1 + i) \\ &= A(1 + i)^2 + A(1 + i) \end{aligned}$$

Proceeding in the same way, at the end of n years, assuming an amount A has just been added, the total amount will be

$$V = A(1 + i)^{n-1} + \cdots + A(1 + i) + A$$

The first term is the value of $\$A$ on deposit for $n - 1$ years, the second term is the value of $\$A$ on deposit for $n - 2$ years, etc., and the last term is the value of $\$A$ which has just been deposited. Rewriting gives

$$V = A[1 + (1 + i) + (1 + i)^2 + \cdots + (1 + i)^{n-1}] \qquad (10)$$

This is a "geometric series" which can be summed by the following methods:

Multiply both sides of (10) by $(1 + i)$:

$$(1 + i)V = A[(1 + i) + (1 + i)^2 + \cdots + (1 + i)^n]$$

Subtracting the series in (10) from this one,

$$(1 + i)V - V = A[(1 + i)^n - 1]$$

or

$$V = A\left[\frac{(1 + i)^n - 1}{i}\right] \qquad (11)$$

Values of $\left[\dfrac{(1 + i)^n - 1}{i}\right]$ are given in Appendix Table III for various values of n and i.

Example

A "sinking fund" is a fund created to pay for some obligation which is to arise at a later date. Frequently such a fund is created by depositing equal amounts at equal intervals over time. Consider the case of a company which proposes to construct a plant which will cost $300,000, and which wishes to set up a sinking fund to assure the availability of that sum after ten years. It will invest a certain amount of money annually, at 6% interest, such that the value of the fund will be $300,000 at the end of the ten years. How much must it invest each year?

Solution:

If the firm invests an amount A at the end of one year, the amount will be worth A at the end of one year, $A(1 + i)$ after two years, etc., and $A(1 + i)^9$ after ten years. Similarly, if another payment A is invested after two years, this will be worth $A(1 + i)^8$ at the end of the ten-year period. Therefore, at the end of ten periods, the sum of the values of the payments will be

$$V = A + A(1 + i)^2 + A(1 + i)^3 + \cdots + A(1 + i)^9$$

The sum of this progression is given by (11). Substituting

$$V = 300,000$$
$$i = .06$$

and

$$n = 10$$

in (11) gives

$$300,000 = \frac{A(1.06^{10} - 1)}{.06}$$

Reference to Appendix Table I for values of $(1 + i)^k$ shows that $1.06^{10} = 1.7908$ so that

$$300,000 = \frac{A(.7908)}{.06}$$

Then $13.1808A = 300,000$
and $A = 22,760$

The firm must invest $22,760 annually in order to have $300,000 at the end of ten years.

This result could also have been obtained by using Appendix Table III which gives

$$\frac{(1.06)^{10} - 1}{.06} = 13.1808$$

3. PRESENT VALUE

In the previous sections the concern has been with determining the amount to which a deposit will grow in n years under various types of interest. In many business problems it is necessary to solve this problem in reverse: What is the value now of certain payments which will become available in the future?

A thousand dollars now is worth more than a thousand dollars to be received a year from now. The thousand dollars if received now can be invested and can bring in a profit in the form of interest; if it can be invested at 6%, it will bring in $60 during the next year. Alternatively, if the thousand dollars is not received until a year from now, the utilization of its earning power during that period will not be available. A thousand dollars to be received a year from now will have a "present value" of approximately $943.40 if the interest rate is 6%, since that amount could earn about $56.60 if invested now; i.e., $943.40, at the present time, will be worth $1000 at the end of a year.

If $1000 is to be received two years from now, and interest is 6% compounded annually, the present value of the $1000 is equal to an amount which if invested now at 6% compounded annually would yield $1000 in two years' time. This amount is approximately $890. In other words, if x is the present value of $1000 due a year from now, then

$$1.06x = 1000$$

and

$$x = \$943.40$$

Similarly, the present value of $1000 due two years from now is

$$(1.06)(1.06)x = 1000$$

and

$$x = \$890$$

Thus the "present value" of future receipts can be expressed in this case as

$\dfrac{1000}{1.06}$ if the 1000 is to be received a year from now

$\dfrac{1000}{(1.06)^2}$ if the 1000 is to be received two years from now

$\dfrac{1000}{(1.06)^3}$ if the 1000 is to be received three years from now

In general, an amount A to be received n years from now, is worth

$$\frac{A}{(1 + i)^n}$$

now if money can be invested at an interest i per year. To simplify the formula, let $1/(1 + i) = v$, and PV be the *present value of the amount A* so that

$$PV = Av^n \tag{12}$$

Values of $v^n = (1 + i)^{-n}$ are given in Appendix Table II for various values of n and i.

Analogous reasoning in the case where interest is compounded continuously leads to the formula

$$PV = Ae^{-\delta n}$$

since

$$\frac{1}{e^{\delta}} = e^{-\delta}$$

Example

What is the present value of $100 payable after ten years if $i = .05$ compounded annually? Substituting $A = 100$, $v = \frac{1}{1.05}$, and $n = 10$ in (12) gives

$$PV = \frac{100}{(1.05)^{10}}$$

so that

$$
\begin{aligned}
\log PV &= \log 100 - 10 \log 1.05 \\
&= 2 - (10)(.0212) \\
&= 2 - .212 \\
&= 1.788
\end{aligned}
$$

Therefore,

$$PV = \$61.39 \text{ (approximately)}$$

The entry in Appendix Table II for $n = 10$, $i = .05$ gives $v^n = .6139$ and, thus

$$PV = Av^n = 100(.6139) = 61.39$$

as before. Clearly use of the table simplifies the computations substantially.

Consider now the problem of computing the present value of a payment of amount A to be made at the end of each of the next n years. The present value of the first payment is Av because it will be received one year from now; the present value of the second payment is Av^2 because it will be received two years from now; and finally the last payment is worth Av^n because it will be received n

periods from now. The present value of all the payments is the geometric series

$$PV = Av + Av^2 + \cdots + Av^n$$
$$= Av[1 + v + v^2 + \cdots + v^{n-1}] \qquad (13)$$

Multiplication of (13) yields:

$$v[PV] = Av[v + v^2 + v^3 + \cdots + v^n]$$
$$v[PV] - PV = Av[v^n - 1]$$
$$PV = \frac{Av}{v-1}[v^n - 1]$$
$$= A\left[\frac{1 - v^n}{i}\right] \qquad (14)$$

Numerical values of $\dfrac{1 - v^n}{i} = \dfrac{1 - (1 + i)^{-n}}{i}$ are given in Appendix Table IV for various values of n and i.

Formula (11) was developed in Section 2 for the value of the series of payments at the end of n periods. The present value of the right-hand side of (11) must therefore be equal to the right-hand side of (14). This can easily be verified by noting that

$$A\left[\frac{(1 + i)^n - 1}{i}\right]v^n = A\left[\frac{1 - v^n}{i}\right] \qquad (15)$$

Example

A series of equal payments, at equal intervals, is frequently called an annuity in life insurance terminology. Suppose that an individual has purchased an annuity under which he will receive his first payment of $1000 in exactly one year and thereafter he will receive $1000 per year for 19 years. If he dies, the payment goes to his estate. Interest is 5%. What is the present value of the annuity?

Solution:

From (14)

$$PV = 1000\frac{[1 - (1.05)^{-20}]}{.05}$$

The value of $(1/1.05)^{20}$ can be obtained by using logarithms and the value is approximately

$$PV = \$12,460$$

The answer can be obtained from Appendix Table IV which shows the present value of an annuity for $n = 20$ and $i = .05$ as the value 12,462.20.

4. CASES

The four cases which follow illustrate the use of the present-value concept in business problems. The first two deal with the decision to undertake an investment. The decision criterion used is that an investment is to be undertaken only if it has a positive present value. The third case develops the formula for the interest rate "implied" by the price of a growth stock. The fourth case gives an example of the use of optimization methods in problems involving future costs.

Case No. 9. Decision on Whether to Bid on a Contract

A company wishes to bid on a contract that will yield net returns of $5000 annually for six years. It must spend $20,000 immediately on retooling if it secures the contract. The tooling will have no salvage value at the end of the six years. Alternative investments are available to the company which would yield 10% compounded annually. Should the company try to obtain the contract?

The present value of the costs involved is readily obtainable; $20,000 is to be spent immediately; hence, present value of costs is naturally $20,000. Present value of returns using Appendix Table IV is

$$5000[4.3553] = 21,725$$

Since the present value of returns from the project is greater than the present value of costs, the company should accept the contract.

Now suppose that the company had the same opportunity as described above, but that alternative investments were available which would yield a 20% return; i.e., $i = .20$ instead of .10. Present value of costs is still the same, $20,000, but the PV of the returns is now

$$5000[3.3255] = 16,585$$

Therefore, the company should not bid on the contract since the present value of the return is less than present value of costs.

Case No. 10. Decision to Purchase a Machine

Suppose a firm is considering buying a certain machine which has a cost of C dollars. Use of the machine will result in savings of R dollars per year for n years. After n years the machine will have a salvage value of L dollars. Interest rate (return possible from alternative investments) is i. Assume that the purchase price is paid in full immediately and that the savings are all obtained at the end of each year. Should the machine be purchased?

Present value of the savings of R dollars per year, for n years, is

$$R\left(\frac{1 - v^n}{i}\right)$$

Present value of the salvage, L, is

$$Lv^n$$

The present value of buying the machine is equal to the sum of these two quantities less the cost of the machine

$$PV = R\left[\frac{1 - v^n}{i}\right] + Lv^n - C$$

The machine should be purchased if PV is positive.

Sometimes the question arises in a different form: what level of annual savings would make the investment worthwhile; i.e., make the present value greater than zero? The present value will be equal to zero if

$$PV = 0 \quad \text{or if}$$
$$R\left[\frac{1 - v^n}{i}\right] + Lv^n - C = 0$$

To solve for the value of R, which makes $PV = 0$, write

$$R\left[\frac{1 - v^n}{i}\right] = C - Lv^n$$
$$R[1 - v^n] = Ci - Liv^n$$
$$R[1 - v^n] = Ci - Li + Li - Liv^n$$
$$= (C - L)i + Li(1 - v^n)$$
$$R = (C - L)\left[\frac{i}{1 - v^n}\right] + Li$$
$$= (C - L)\left[\frac{i(1 + i)^n}{(1 + i)^n - 1}\right] + Li$$

From this formula a minimum value of R can be computed. If the anticipated savings are greater than this value, the present value will be greater than zero and the machine should be purchased.

Assume that the cost of the machine, C, is \$10,000. After ten years it will have a salvage value of \$1000 and the interest rate is 5%. How much should annual savings amount to if the machine is to "pay for itself"?

Solution:

$$R = (10,000 - 1000) \frac{[.05(1.05)^{10}]}{1.05^{10} - 1} + (1000)(.05)$$

$$= \frac{(9000)(.05)(1.6289)}{1.6289 - 1} + 50$$

$$= \$1166 + 50$$

$$= \$1216$$

The machine, therefore, must offer an annual cost saving of \$1216 in order to "break even."

Case No. 11.   Value of a Growth Stock[1]

Suppose a firm

a) Retains a fraction, b, of its income.
b) Earns a fraction, r, on the book value of its stock.
c) Increases the book value of its stock by the amount of income retained.

Assume that the income and dividends are expressed as a rate in dollars per unit of time; e.g.,

$Y(t)$ = rate of income per share at time t,
$D(t)$ = rate of dividend payout, per share at time t.

Let

$B(0)$ = book value per share at time $t = 0$,
$P(0)$ = price per share at time $t = 0$.

If b and r are assumed to be constant for all future t, what is the force of discount, k, which will make the present value of all future dividend payments equal to present price of a share? Assume continuous functions and use instantaneous rates.

The firm earns a fraction r on book value but retains only a fraction b of that amount; therefore the "force of growth" is rb and the income per share, at time t, is given by

$$Y(t) = Y(0)e^{brt}$$

The dividend at time $t = D(t)$

$$= (1 - b)Y(t)$$

$$= (1 - b)Y(0)e^{brt}$$

$$= D(0)e^{brt}$$

[1] Adapted with permission from M. J. Gordon and Eli Shapiro "Capital Equipment Analysis: The Required Rate of Profit," *Management Science*, Vol. 3, No. 1 (October, 1956), pp. 102–10. For a different and more extensive treatment, see Case No. 20.

The present value of all future dividend payments is

$$\int_0^\infty D(t)e^{-kt}dt = \int_0^\infty D(0)e^{brt}e^{-kt}dt = D(0)\int_0^\infty e^{-t(k-br)}dt = -\left.\frac{D(0)}{k-br}e^{-t(k-br)}\right|_0^\infty$$

$$= \frac{D(0)}{k-br}$$

Therefore, the desired value of k is the solution of

$$P(0) = \frac{D(0)}{k-br}$$

which is

$$k = \frac{D(0)}{P(0)} + br$$

or, in words, the force of discount is equal to the present dividend yield plus the product of the fraction of earnings retained and the rate of earnings on book value.

It is of interest to determine the conditions under which the force of discount is equal to the income yield; i.e., the income per share divided by the price per share. From $D(t) = (1-b)Y(t)$ it is possible to obtain

$$b = \frac{Y(t) - D(t)}{Y(t)}$$

From the definition of r, $r = Y(t)/B(t)$ (both b and r are assumed constant functions of time). From the above,

$$k = \frac{D(0)}{P(0)} + br$$

$$= \frac{D(0)}{P(0)} + \left(\frac{Y-D}{Y}\right)\frac{Y}{B}$$

$$= \frac{D(0)}{P(0)} + \frac{Y-D}{B}$$

By definition the income yield

$$= \frac{Y}{P(0)}$$

$$= \frac{Y+D-D}{P(0)}$$

$$= \frac{D(0)}{P(0)} + \frac{Y-D}{P}$$

Therefore, k and the income yield can be equal only if $Y-D$ is zero or if $B = P$.

Case No. 12.   A Water Works Problem

The forecast for the water requirement for a certain city is

$$w = a + bt$$

where w is the requirement in millions of gallons per day and t is time measured from the present. The water itself can be obtained in unlimited quantities, but it must be purified by a plant designed especially for this purpose. The plants can be built only in multiples of one basic module. One module can purify one million gallons per day. The cost to build a plant is

$$c = \alpha + \beta n$$

where n is the number of modules and α and β are constants.

Assuming the forecast is correct, the cost function will not change, and water shortages will not be permitted, how often should plants be built and what size should they be? If a large plant is built, its capacity will go unused for a long period until the requirement increases enough; on the other hand, if small plants are built, the cost will be incurred frequently.

The present problem is to determine the optimum size and time between construction of plants. Assume a discount rate i is used, that the time to construct plants may be ignored, and that the capacity of the plants already constructed is equal to the requirement at the present time.

Let τ denote the period between construction of plants. From the assumptions it follows that τ will be a constant. The increase in demand during the period will be $b\tau$, and therefore the cost of building a plant which just equals the requirement a time τ from now is

$$c(\tau) = \alpha + \beta b\tau$$

This cost will be incurred now, a time τ from now, a time 2τ from now, etc. The present value of all these costs is

$$PV(\tau) = (\alpha + \beta b\tau)[1 + e^{-i\tau} + e^{-2i\tau} + \cdots]$$
$$= \frac{\alpha + \beta b\tau}{1 - e^{-i\tau}}$$

since

$$(1 - x)^{-1} = 1 + x + x^2 + x^3 + \cdots \qquad \text{where} \quad 0 < x < 1$$

The optimum value of τ is the one which minimizes $PV(\tau)$; it is found in the usual manner:

$$\frac{dPV(\tau)}{d\tau} = \frac{b\beta[1 - e^{-i\tau}] - [i(b\beta\tau + \alpha)e^{-i\tau}]}{[1 - e^{-i\tau}]^2} = 0$$

if

$$\beta b(1 - e^{-i\tau}) = i(\beta b\tau + \alpha)e^{-i\tau}$$
$$\beta b - \beta b e^{-i\tau} = \beta b\tau i e^{-i\tau} + \alpha i e^{-i\tau}$$
$$\beta b e^{i\tau} = \beta b + \beta b i\tau + \alpha i$$
$$e^{i\tau} = 1 + i\tau + \frac{\alpha i}{\beta b}$$
$$e^{i\tau} - 1 - i\tau = \frac{\alpha i}{\beta b}$$

In this formula the unknown appears only on the left-hand side, and a numerical value can be obtained for any set of numerical values for i, α, b, and β.

EXERCISES, SECTION 1

In Exercises 1–4, find the total interest earned if
a) Simple interest is earned.
b) Interest is compounded annually.
c) Interest is compounded semiannually.
d) Interest is compounded continuously.
1. $100 is invested at 4% annual interest.
2. $500 is invested at 6% annual interest.
3. $1000 is invested at 2% annual interest.
4. $10,000 is invested at 10% annual interest.
5. A man owns $500 worth of preferred stock; he receives a 3% dividend annually, based on the face value of the stock. What is his income from the stock over a ten-year period?
6. If an individual borrowed $470 from a bank, and after a year paid back $500, what is the effective interest rate charged?
7. Find the interest on $1000, invested at 6%, compounded semiannually, for $3\frac{1}{2}$ years.
8. Find the interest on $3000, compounded continuously, for five years, if the annual interest rate is 10%.
9. A sum of $10,000 is borrowed at a nominal interest rate of 10%, and interest is compounded continuously. What is the effective interest rate?

EXERCISES, SECTION 2

10. Suppose that $100 is deposited annually in an account earning 4% interest, compounded annually. What is the total amount on deposit after five years, assuming that the $100 is deposited at the end of each year?

11. If $500 is deposited at the end of each year in an account earning 5%, compounded annually, find the total amount on deposit after ten years.

12. A firm wishes to create a sinking fund which will yield $100,000 after five years. How much should it invest annually if interest is 6%?

13. A firm plans to invest $20,000 annually for eight years and expects the sinking fund thus created to be worth $200,000 at the end of the eight-year period. If interest is compounded annually, and investment is made at the end of each year, what interest rate (to the nearest per cent) does the firm anticipate earning?

EXERCISES, SECTION 3

Using the tables in the Appendix, find the present value of the amounts referred to in Exercises 14–17.

14. $1000 to be received ten years from now, if interest is 5%, compounded annually.

15. $500 to be received seven years from now, if interest is 10%, compounded annually.

16. $11,000 to be received four years from now, if interest is 6%, compounded semiannually.

17. $5000 to be received three years from now, if interest is 10%, compounded semiannually.

18. Find the present value of an annuity consisting of annual payments of $500, if the first payment is to be received in exactly one year and subsequent payments of $500 will be made each year as long as the recipient lives, which may theoretically be an indefinitely long period. Interest is 5%.

EXERCISES, SECTION 4

19. A company is considering a project which will require a cost outlay of $10,000 per year for five years, with no salvage value remaining at the end of the project. Costs are incurred at the beginning of each year. The project will yield returns estimated at zero for the first year, $10,000 for the second year, $20,000 for the third year, $20,000 for the fourth year, and $10,000 for the fifth year. There are no returns after the fifth year. Assume that returns are realized at the end of each year. Alternative investments are available which will yield a return of 10%. Should the company undertake the project?

20. The Nausicaä Company is considering two projects, of which it can select only one because of capacity limitations. Project A involves an initial investment of $2500 and will yield a net return of $1000 per year for three years. There is no salvage associated with the initial investment. Project B also involves an initial investment of $2500. There is a net return of $2800 during the first year, and nothing thereafter. Again, there is no salvage. Interest is 5%. Which project should be selected? (Assume that in both cases investment must be made immediately; returns are realized at the end of each year.)

21. Agamemnon Enterprises, Inc., manufactures and distributes molded plastic dishes, wastebaskets, trays, and similar items. The firm has developed a new type of dish drainer which allows for the racking of dishes on the sides of the drainer, thus increasing its capacity. While unique, the drainer is not patentable, and the firm realizes that it will soon be copied by competitors. The drainer will last indefinitely, so potential customers will normally buy only once. In view of these factors, the firm has made the following "product life" projections:

Times Period	Production Costs	Promotion	Sales Volume
Jan.–June, 1963	$5000	. . . .	. . . . . .
July–Dec., 1963	5000	$10,000	$10,000
Jan.–June, 1964	5000	7,500	35,000
July–Dec., 1964	5000	5,000	20,000
Jan.–June, 1965	. . . . . .	. . . .	5,000

Agamemnon Enterprises is relatively small, and its activities are flexible; hence, in a situation such as this one where prices and profit margins tend to fall off with the entry of competitors, the firm pursues a policy of retiring from the market after a product has "peaked"; it then turns its attention to new innovations.

Problem: If the firm expects a return of 10%, compounded semi-annually, should it undertake the production and distribution of the dish drainer?

CHAPTER 11

APPLICATIONS TO
BUSINESS DECISIONS

THIS CHAPTER consists of descriptions of business situations in which analysis requiring mathematics is employed. All are based more or less closely on actual, published accounts. Nearly all of the seven descriptions, called "cases," require some problem-solving activity on the part of the reader. The first three cases are short and relatively easy. The last case is quite long, and mastery of it requires a substantial amount of effort. The selections were made on the basis of variety of mathematics, subject matter, and difficulty.

Case No. 13. *Planning an Optimization Study*

A certain department head in a metal-working firm is concerned about whether or not he is pursuing an optimal policy in stocking rough castings. The castings are used in the manufacture of a standard item, and thus are in fairly constant demand. They require considerable floor space for storage.

The present policy for determining when to reorder a new supply, and how many to order, is quite simple. The foreman looks into the storage area on his way back from his coffee break each day; if the supply appears low, he orders more. Under this arrangement it has been determined that monthly reorder costs are $500 on the average. This includes fixed costs of $5.00 per order placed with the supplier, plus shipping and handling costs amounting to 40 cents per casting. Storage costs for the castings are not actually known; however, it is believed that a reasonable estimate could be obtained by considering the purchase price of each casting ($20) and the floor space occupied by a casting in storage (3 square feet). Cost of storage space is $3.00 per square foot per year; alternative uses of any unused floor space are probably available. Interest costs are also unknown, but company officials expect at least a 15% return on any investment.

The foreman says he keeps a reserve supply of about 200 castings on hand at all times; this is about a week's supply, as demand for the castings is, on the average, 1000 units per month. Demand is approximately uniform, as the castings are a standard item; however, some random fluctuations are manifested, and the foreman feels strongly that at least 100 castings should be on hand at all times; he keeps 200 to be "safe." The actual average number of items on hand at any given time is also unknown, but the foreman guesses that it would be around 400.

A representative from a consulting firm, engaged by the company for other purposes, has suggested to the manager that substantial reductions in cost could be effected by adopting a systematic inventory policy with regard to this item. To achieve these reductions, he proposes a study of demand for the item with the objective of determining whether the traditional economic lot size formula, or some modification of it, could be used. He thinks that this is probably the case, and will conduct a thorough study for a fee of $1000.

Questions

1. From the data already available in the foregoing, estimate the ordering and carrying costs associated with the item, and utilize an economic lot size formula to determine optimal ordering frequency, size of orders, and inventory.

2. Suppose that the analysis was conducted, as suggested, for the $1000 fee, and results were substantially the same as those obtained above in Question 1. Suppose further that the situation is such that the item will probably be used for the next three years only, after which demand will cease due to technological change. Determine the present value of the analysis. Should it have been accepted?

3. What other factors might be considered in setting up the analysis? How valid do you think the data are which were used in Questions 1 and 2? Do you think it likely that a trained analyst could have achieved significantly better results?

Case No. 14.   Span of Control[1]

The term "span of control" is widely used in classical management theory to refer to the number of people supervised by one

---

[1] Suggested by on article by J. L. Meig, "Some Fundamental Principles of a General Theory of Management," *Journal of Industrial Economics,* October, 1955, pp. 16–32.

leader or manager. Much attention has been given to the question of how many people can be effectively supervised by any one individual, and it has often been held that the ideal number, i.e., span of control, is five or six. The present discussion will develop a model for consideration of the span-of-control question in a context of an entire organization.

Suppose an organization has a work force of X men and an organizational structure such that there are n levels in the hierarchy above the first or bottom working level. If a span of control equal to r is desired, how many leaders are needed to staff the n levels?

Let Y represent the number of leaders. Since there are X men in the work force, X/r leaders are required at the lowest level of the supervisory structure. These X/r leaders will in turn report to X/r^2 (X/r divided by r) leaders and so on to the highest level of the organization, where X/r^n leaders will be required. Thus Y, the total number of leaders required for all levels, is the sum of the series:

$$\frac{X}{r} + \frac{X}{r^2} + \cdots + \frac{X}{r^n} \tag{1}$$

This is a geometric series whose sum can be obtained from the formula

$$Y = \frac{X(r^n - 1)}{r^n(r - 1)} \tag{2}$$

Presumably the top organizational level will have one leader—the company president—and therefore

$$\frac{X}{r^n} = 1 \tag{3}$$

Then

$$r = \sqrt[n]{X}$$

or

$$n = \frac{\log X}{\log r} \tag{4}$$

Since X is a known constant, n, the number of levels in the organizational structure, is inversely proportional to the log of r, the span of control. That is, as the span of control is increased, the number of organizational levels can be decreased, certainly a reasonable conclusion.

Questions

1. Using the formula for the summation of a geometric series

$$S = \frac{a(1 - q^n)}{1 - q}$$

where the sequence is $a, aq, aq^2, \ldots aq^{n-1}$ and $q < 1$

develop the expression shown in equation (2) above.

2. Show that the expression in equation (2) may be reduced to

$$Y = \frac{X - 1}{r - 1}$$

3. If $X = 1000$ and r is to be 10, how many organizational levels will be required above the working level?

4. Develop a formula for the salary of the chief executive as a function of the number of leaders in the organization if each executive receives b times the salary of one of his immediate subordinates. Is this assumption realistic?

Case No. 15.   Organization Size and Efficiency[2]

. . . a purely administrative organization becomes self-sufficient as soon as its staff numbers one thousand. From then onwards it generates sufficient internal correspondence to keep itself busy without any incoming mail or external contact of any kind . . . (Parkinson's Law).

Consider the situation of an organization whose primary functions are paper studies—such as a large applied research firm, for instance. Given certain assumptions, the efficiency of the organization as related to the amount of internally generated paper work can be evaluated.

The following notation will be used:

n = number of professional employees;
m = number of reports turned out per year;
t_w = average net time in days to complete a report (including investigation, analysis, writing, etc., but not counting time spent reading other reports);
t_r = average time in days to read a report;
k = fraction of all reports received by the average professional employee—reports which he is expected to read.

Assuming that everyone reads the km reports he receives in a year, and assuming further that there are 240 working days in a year, the net time the average employee has to do creative work on his own is equal to $(240 - kmt_r)$ days. Thus the number of reports

[2] Adapted with permission from F. P. Adler, "Relationships between Organization Size and Efficiency," *Management Science*, Vol. 7 (October, 1960), pp. 80–84.

that he himself can turn out is equal to $(240 - kmt_r)/t_w$, and consequently the total number of reports turned out by the organization, a measure of its productivity, since reports constitute its only product, is

$$m = \frac{n(240 - kmt_r)}{t_w} \tag{1}$$

The expression in (1) can be solved explicitly for m:

$$m = \frac{240n}{t_w + kt_r n} \tag{2}$$

Observe that as n grows very large (the number of professional employees becomes very large), m approaches a constant value of $240/kt_r$.

Define M, a measure of the efficiency of the organization, to be the ratio of m, the actual number of reports turned out, to m_0, the number of reports which could be turned out if all 240 days were used for report writing, with no time off for reading other reports. Since m_0 is equal to $240n/t_w$,

$$M = \frac{m}{m_0}$$

$$= \frac{1}{1 + \dfrac{knt_r}{t_w}} \tag{3}$$

The ratio M represents the fraction of total working time spent productively, i.e., in writing reports; $(1 - M)$ represents the fraction of total time spent reading reports generated by others.

Three conclusions emerge from the analysis:

1. There is an upper limit on the number of reports which can be produced, regardless of the number of people hired; this limit is $240/kt_r$, as shown above. In this limiting case, the firm has a vast number of professional employees, but all spend nearly full time reading each other's reports.

2. If no one reads any reports, they just don't look at their mail, but throw it away unopened; the number of employees required to produce this upper limiting number of reports would be

$$n = \frac{t_w}{kt_r} \tag{4}$$

   since n workers would turn out $240n/t_w$ reports per year under these circumstances, and if $240n/t_w = 240/kt_r$, then $n = t_w/kt_r$.

3. As n becomes very large, the efficiency ratio M, being inversely proportional to n, tends toward zero.

At this point, it is possible to question the validity of the model on the grounds that reading of other people's reports is presumed to bring about greater efficiency, and thus increase over-all productivity, even though requiring a substantial proportion of the available time. It can be shown, however, that the conclusions are valid even after a correction factor is introduced.

Suppose that t_w, the writing time required for a report, is in fact decreased as a result of the knowledge a worker gains by reading km reports a year. For small values of km, this decrease would presumably be very nearly linear, but for a large km, the linear relationship could not hold since t_w would become negative—an impossible situation. A logical relationship would be a negative exponential expression:

$$t_w = [f + (1 - f)e^{-ckm}]t_{w_0} \qquad (5)$$

where t_{w_0} is the writing time that would be required if no reading would be done, and f is a fraction chosen so that ft_{w_0} represents the irreducible minimum time for preparation; that is, $(1 - f)t_{w_0}$ represents the maximum reduction in preparation time which can be achieved through preparatory reading. This implies a "saturation point" beyond which further reading will not speed up report writing. The constant c represents the effectiveness of reading.

The basic model of (2) may be rewritten, incorporating the refinement of (5) so that

$$m = \frac{240n}{kt_r n + [f + (1 - f)e^{-ckm}]t_{w_0}} \qquad (6)$$

Notice that for large values of n this expression will reduce to $m = 240/kt_r$, as before.

Using (6), the new expression for the effectiveness ratio M, becomes

$$M = \frac{1}{1 + \dfrac{knt_r}{[f + (1 - f)e^{-ckm}]t_{w_0}}} \qquad (7)$$

This expression will give higher values for M than the previous one, but for large values of n the difference becomes small. Thus, the conclusions already stated are still valid.

Of more interest, however, is the effect on efficiency for smaller values of n. Consider an example:

Suppose no one reads a report; output is equal to $240n/t_{w_0}$. If n is 100 and t_{w_0} is 30 days, a total of 800 reports will be turned out in a year. But now introduce some reasonable parameter values reflecting the value of preparatory reading. Let

$$t_r = \frac{1}{16} \text{ days}$$

$$f = \frac{1}{2}$$

$$k = \frac{1}{10}$$

$$c = \frac{1}{100}$$

Then, using equation (6)

$$m = \frac{(240)(100)}{(\frac{1}{10})(\frac{1}{16})(100) + [\frac{1}{2} + (\frac{1}{2})e^{-(1/100)(1/10)m}](30)}$$

$$= \frac{24,000}{15\frac{5}{8} + \frac{30}{2} \cdot e^{-m/1000}}$$

This expression may be solved by interpolation and use of a table of negative exponentials; even without solving it, however, it is clear that the value of m will be substantially greater than 800; in fact, the value is over 1200, far above the limiting capacity under conditions of "no reading."

Now, however, use the same parameters but assume that n is, say, 5000 employees. Then

$$m = \frac{1,200,000}{46\frac{1}{4} + 15e^{-m/1000}}$$

$$= \text{approximately } 26,000$$

Comparing this with the value of m if no reading was done—40,000 —one can conclude that at this size level the organization has become unwieldy and inefficient. Furthermore, as n approaches infinity, the importance of the exponential term becomes negligible and the value of m approaches $240/kt_r$, or 38,400 reports.

Questions

1. Using the parameters stated in the example, find M when $n = 100$; find M when $n = 5000$. Comment on the results.

2. What is the most important factor, or factors, left out of this model? How could they be incorporated into the model?

3. Comment on the degree to which this model approximates real-life situations.

Case No. 16. *A Simplified Version of the Holt-Modigliani-Muth Model*[3]

Suppose that the demand for a product is known exactly for the next n production periods. Suppose further that a decision as to how

---

[3] C. C. Holt, F. Modigliani, J. F. Muth, H. A. Simon, *et al., Planning Production Inventories, and Work Force* (New York: Prentice-Hall, Inc., 1960).

much to produce must be made at the beginning of each production period, each week, perhaps.

Production requirements can be met by (1) varying the level of production while holding the size of the work force constant by working undertime or overtime, (2) varying the size of the work force by hiring or firing, or (3) changing the amount of the product in the inventory.

Certain costs are associated with each of these "control variables"; overtime or slack time will involve labor costs, hiring and firing men will also involve certain processing costs, and storage of inventory will entail the usual storage and handling costs. The objective is to minimize the sum of these costs, not only for a single time period but for a sequence of time periods. However, in order to keep this illustration simple, a single period will be considered even though the "optimum" solution for a single period will not be the optimum for that period if subsequent periods are considered.

The following notation will be used:

R_t = demand requirement for the product during period t
w_t = number of workers employed at the beginning of period t; assume no change during the period so that w_t is also the number of workers at the end of period t
I_t = net inventory at the beginning of period t
p_t = number of units produced during period t
C_1 = payroll costs
C_2 = hiring and firing costs
C_3 = costs associated with over- and under-production
C_4 = inventory costs
a_i = the several parameters.

Assuming that production *during* a period may be used to satisfy demands made during the same period, the production requirement R_t may be met by $I_t + p_t$ so that

$$I_{t+1} = I_t + p_t - R_t \tag{1}$$

This says that the inventory at the beginning of the next period, $t + 1$, will be the residual amount left over after the requirements of this period have been met.

Consider now the specification of the various costs associated with the problem. In the Holt-Modigliani-Muth Inventory Model, it is assumed that each cost term can be expressed as a linear or quadratic function of the "decision variables," i.e., of the number of workers and the production level. In practice, the relationships may become fairly complicated, but the assumptions are reasonable and the model may, in many cases, give a fairly good approximation of actual relationships.

Payroll costs, C_1, are assumed to be directly proportional to the number of workers; i.e.,

$$C_{1t} = a_1 w_t \qquad (2)$$

This states that the "payroll costs" for period t are equal to a_1, the cost in dollars for one worker, multiplied by the number of workers employed during period t.

Hiring and firing costs, C_2, are assumed to be a quadratic function of the change in the number of workers from last period to this:

$$C_{2t} = a_2(w_t - w_{t-1})^2 \qquad (3)$$

This may be interpreted as stating that the hiring and firing costs during period t are equal to a_2—a constant greater than zero—times the square of the change in number of workers employed. Note the logic of this expression: extensive changes in the composition of the work force will force proportionately higher costs, as compared with normal, small changes.

Costs associated with over- or under-production, C_3, are assumed to be a quadratic function of p_t and w_t, such that

$$C_{3t} = a_3(p_t - a_4 w_t)^2 + a_5 p_t - a_6 w_t \qquad (4)$$

where a_4 is the number of units produced by one worker per period, and a_3, a_5, and a_6 are positive constants.

Inventory costs, C_4, are assumed to be a quadratic function of the difference between actual inventory and some desired inventory level, a_8. When inventory is greater than this level, inventory holding costs are incurred; when less, shortage costs are incurred. This relationship is

$$C_{4t} = a_7(I_{t+1} - a_8)^2 \qquad (5)$$

where a_7 is a positive constant.

The objective function is

$$C(w_t, p_t) = C_{1t} + C_{2t} + C_{3t} + C_{4t} \qquad (6)$$

and it is to be minimized subject to the constraint that

$$I_{t+1} = I_t + p_t - R_t \qquad (1) = (7)$$

Substituting the cost definitions of (2) — (5) into (6) gives an expanded objective function,

$$C(w_t, p_t) = a_1 w_t + a_2(w_t - w_{t-1})^2 + a_3(p_t - a_4 w_t)^2 + \\ a_5 p_t - a_6 w_t + a_7(I_{t+1} - a_8)^2 \qquad (8)$$

The only variables involved in (8) are p_t and w_t; I_{t+1} is not a free variable since it depends on p_t. Note also that w_{t-1} is not a variable since it represents the number of workers employed in the previous period and hence is not subject to manipulation; it is a known constant in period t.

An analytical solution to the model can be obtained by application of the theory of extrema for functions of two variables subject to a side condition, i.e., by substitution or by the method of Lagrange's multipliers. Finding that solution and verifying that it does result in a minimum cost is left as an exercise for the reader.

Questions

1. Find expressions for w_t and p_t which will minimize $C(w_t, p_t)$ subject to the restraint given in (1).
2. Determine the optimum values of the p_t and w_t for the following values of the parameters:

$$a_1 = 340 \qquad\qquad a_5 = 51.2$$
$$a_2 = 64.3 \qquad\qquad a_6 = 281$$
$$a_3 = .2 \qquad\qquad a_7 = .0825$$
$$a_4 = 5.67 \qquad\qquad a_8 = 320$$

3. Formulate a model for optimizing cost over *two* periods. How would the solution differ from the one-period model?

Case No. 17. Organizational Structure and Pricing Policy[4]

Markets for goods can be classified as oligopolistic or perfectly competitive; an oligopolistic market being one which is controlled by a relatively few firms and in which market prices are not determined entirely by considerations of demand and cost. The firms operating within the market have considerable control over the prices which are to be charged so that a characteristic of oligopolies is the relative infrequency of price changes. In competitive markets, by contrast, there are many firms, none of which controls the market; price changes are frequent and are rigidly linked to changes in demand and cost.

Consider a special case—a duopoly—a market in which there are only two firms operating. In particular, consider the effect which the organizational structure of these firms might have on their pricing policies, and thus on their relative success in the face of changes in the demand for their product.

Assume that no collusion is involved in price setting, that the firms sell an identical product, and that they are charging the same price. A decision by either firm to change its price is based on expectations concerning future sales, costs, and its competitor's be-

---

[4] Adapted with permission from R. M. Cyert and J. G. March, "Organizational Structure and Pricing Behavior in an Oligopolistic Market," *American Economic Review*, Vol. 45 (March, 1955), pp. 129–39.

havior. Market behavior models for the two firms may now be developed. Suppose that the market demand function is

$$p = 25 - \frac{x + y}{3} \tag{1}$$

where

$p = $ price
$x = $ output of firm A
$y = $ output of firm B

Assume that demand has persisted long enough for both firms to perceive it accurately. Assume further that both firms' pricing structures are such that neither firm expects a reaction on the part of the other in response to a change in output; that is

$$\frac{dx}{dy} = \frac{dy}{dx} = 0 \tag{2}$$

Since each firm is seeking to maximize its own net earnings, a market solution is obtained by setting each duopolist's marginal profits equal to zero and solving the resulting equations to determine current outputs and price. First, the revenue function for firm A is the price from (1) times A's output:

$$px = 25x - x\frac{(x + y)}{3}$$

from which net profit is:

$$px - C_1 = 25x - x\frac{x + y}{3} - C_1 \tag{3}$$

where C_1 is cost. The optimum output for A, x^*, is obtained by maximizing (3) with respect to x; that is,

$$\frac{d(px - C_1)}{dx} = 25 - \frac{2x}{3} - \frac{x}{3}\frac{dy}{dx} - \frac{y}{3}\frac{dx}{dx} - \frac{dC_1}{dx} = 25 - \frac{2x}{3} - \frac{y}{3} - \frac{dC_1}{dx} = 0$$

requires that

$$x^* = \frac{75}{2} - \frac{y}{2} - \frac{3C_1}{2} \tag{4}$$

where C'_1 is marginal cost. Similarly, y^* for firm B can be determined as

$$y^* = \frac{75}{2} - \frac{x}{2} - \frac{3C_2'}{2} \tag{5}$$

where C'_2 is marginal cost. Solving (4) and (5) simultaneously will give the equilibrium market price, providing one exists and is unique. In this case a unique solution exists and is, letting $C'_1 = C'_2 = 3$,

$$x = 22, \qquad y = 22, \qquad p = 10.33 \qquad (6)$$

Let firm A's pricing structure now have the following characteristics:

a) Price is determined by a committee of equals.
b) Communication chains between the decision makers and the primary sources of information are long.
c) The decision-making unit is decentralized and is subject to restrictions from high authority with respect to the criteria for making price changes.

Let firm B's pricing structure have these characteristics:

a) Price is determined by an individual.
b) Communication chains between the decision maker and the primary source of information are short.
c) The decision maker also establishes the criteria for price decisions.

Two hypotheses about this duopoly situation are suggested by the theory of organizations:

1. As the length of the communication chain is increased, factors are introduced that tend to inhibit change, i.e., slow down the firm's reaction to external change.
2. The character of the communication chain introduces a bias into the information transmitted to the decision-making unit. For example, if firm A channels its pricing data through a cost relay point, while firm B channels its pricing data through a demand relay point, firm A's communication chain will exhibit a bias toward meeting costs, while firm B will be more responsive to demand changes.

Now consider what will happen if the market demand increases so that

$$p = 30 - \frac{x + y}{3} \qquad (7)$$

Firm A will be slow to realize that a change has occurred. It will tend to underestimate demand when its perception does change, and it will tend to give a positive value to dy/dx; that is, it thinks that firm B will change its output as firm A changes its production. Firm B, on the other hand, will respond quickly to changes in market demand, will tend to overestimate demand (since its pricing data comes through sales channels, which are traditionally optimistic), and will continue to give a value of zero to dx/dy.

Suppose that firm A's information system has shown no demand change, but it learns that firm B is increasing production; then firm A's expectations are

$$p = 25 - \frac{x + y}{3} \qquad \text{(1)-(8)}$$

as before and

$$\frac{dy}{dx} = 1$$

Firm B's estimates of key information might be

$$p = 100 - x - y \qquad \text{(9)}$$

which overestimates demand, and

$$\frac{dx}{dy} = 0 \qquad \text{(10)}$$

Under these conditions, the market equilibrium will be at

$$x = 7, \qquad y = 45, \qquad p = 12.67 \qquad \text{(11)}$$

Through a quicker response (even though erroneously overestimating demand) firm B has come to dominate the market.

Both firms are perceiving demand incorrectly. If after a period of time they come to perceive demand as shown in (7) rather than as in (8) or (9), and assuming they again hold the views represented by (2), the market will find its new equilibrium at

$$x = 27, \qquad y = 27, \qquad p = 12 \qquad \text{(12)}$$

Questions

1. Verify the solutions in (6) and (11), making certain in each instance that the extrema are indeed maxima.
2. Can these two firms increase their net earnings by collusion?
3. What would the answer to Question 2 be if the demand function was given by

$$p = 125 - 3(x + y)^2, \qquad x, y \geq 0$$

Case No. 18.   Interaction in Groups[5]

In recent years extensive attention has been given to a systematic, quantitative consideration of the factors involved in the

_____
[5] The model presented here is adapted from H. A. Simon's *Models of Man* (New York: John Wiley & Sons, Inc., 1957), pp. 99 ff.

functioning of small work groups, an area of study that obviously has considerable significance in the business field. By attempting to define and quantify the variables which enhance the success of such small groups, these studies may result in the development of rules which may improve the performance of working units within an organization.

Consider a project team composed of, say, six men working in collaboration on one or more research projects for an engineering firm. There may be opportunity or need for some amount of personal contact—discussions, information sharing, etc. A numerical value, on some sort of scale, can be assigned to the level of intensity of interaction among group members; this intensity function will depend on time and can be designated $I(t)$. The degree to which members get along with each other can be regarded as an important factor in the functioning of the group; it will be called $F(t)$. Activity generated within the group is denoted by a function $A(t)$, also a function of time. Finally, the assignments and orders imposed on the group by its external environment, i.e., the work it *must* do, are defined by a function $E(t)$.

Stated more concisely, the four time-dependent variables are:

$I(t)$ = intensity of interaction among group members,
$F(t)$ = level of friendliness among members,
$A(t)$ = amount of activity carried on by members within the group,
$E(t)$ = amount of activity imposed on the group by its external environment.

The relationships among these variables can be made more specific by the following (reasonable) assumptions:

$I(t)$ depends on, and increases with, $F(t)$ and $A(t)$. That is, the amount of interaction (contact) is affected by the degree of friendliness and by the amount of required activity, which will naturally force interaction. Furthermore, the amount of interaction will respond almost immediately to changes in F and A. A linear relationship is postulated for $I(t)$:

$$I(t) = a_1 F(t) + a_2 A(t) \tag{1}$$

The level of friendliness will increase if the level of interaction is higher than that which would be appropriate to the existing level of friendliness. In other words, if a group which is not especially friendly is forced to interact a great deal, friendliness will grow due to increased contact. On the other hand, if interaction is slight, friendliness will tend to decline due to lack of contact. This effect (both ways) would take time before being felt, however.

$$\frac{dF(t)}{dt} = b_1[I(t) - b_2F(t)] \tag{2}$$

The amount of activity carried on within a group, $A(t)$, will tend to increase if $F(t)$ is higher than the level appropriate to the existing level of activity, and will also increase if the amount of activity imposed externally, $E(t)$, is higher than the existing level of activity. Again, however, time will be required for these effects to be consummated.

$$\frac{dA(t)}{dt} = c_1[F(t) - c_3A(t)] + c_2[E(t) - A(t)] \tag{3}$$

The lower-case letters a_1, a_2, b_1, b_2, c_1, c_2, and c_3 are all constants of proportionality. From the assumptions, it follows that all parameters are positive.

Now, what can be done with this system of equations? They can be solved explicitly for the three unknown functions, I, F, and A; E is an "exogenous variable"—one which originates outside the system and thus is not a function of the other three variables. Such a solution would permit the determination of what would happen to the system if, starting from some initial state where values of I, F, and A and a function $E(t)$ are given, changes were introduced. Numerical results would be possible only if numerical values for the various parameters were available.

Another interesting possibility, however, one that does not depend on numerical information, is that of determining the conditions under which the system is at equilibrium, i.e., when the values of the variables are not changing. The mathematics of obtaining such a solution are not difficult. At the equilibrium position, dF/dt and dA/dt must be zero, otherwise $F(t)$ and $A(t)$ would vary with time. By definition, at the equilibrium position, $F(t)$ and $A(t)$ do not change with respect to time. Thus, equations (2) and (3) can be set equal to zero, and the set of three simultaneous equations (1), (2), and (3) solved for I^*, F^*, and A^*, where the asterisk denotes an equilibrium value.

Substituting $I(t)$ from (1) into (2) and solving for $F(t)$ gives

$$F^* = \frac{a_2A}{b_2 - a_1} \tag{4}$$

Substituting this value of F into equation (3) and solving for A^* gives:

$$A^* = \left[\frac{c_2(b_2 - a_1)}{c_2(b_2 - a_1) + c_1[c_3(b_2 - a_1) - a_2]}\right] E(t) \qquad (5)$$

Substitution of this value of A^* into (4) gives:

$$F^* = \left[\frac{c_2 a_2}{(c_1 c_3 + c_2)(b_2 - a_1) - c_1 a_2}\right] E(t) \qquad (6)$$

The value for I is then

$$I^* = a_1 F^* + a_2 A^* \qquad (7)$$

The expressions for A^*, I^*, and F^* are all in terms of constants except for the inclusion of $E(t)$. Clearly, then, equilibrium may be disturbed by changes in $E(t)$, the outside pressure to perform tasks. For an equilibrium, it must be assumed that $E(t)$ is also a constant. It can be concluded that an increase in the activities required of the group will tend to increase not only action within the group but also interaction and friendliness. As E decreases toward zero, A, I, and F tend toward zero, i.e., the group begins to disintegrate.

Since A is activity and E is expected or required activity, it should be of interest to see under what conditions A will exceed E; this can be regarded as a condition of *positive morale*—a group producing more than is demanded of it. From equation (5) it can be seen that A will exceed E if $c_3(b_2 - a_1) - a_2$ is less than zero. This means that a_2 should be large in relation to $c_3(b_2 - a_1)$ for high positive morale. But a large a_2 according to (1) implies that the group tasks are highly interrelated, forcing a large amount of inter-action. Now consider the other half of the inequality—$c_3(b_2 - a_1)$. First, from equation (3) it follows that $1/c_3$ must measure the amount of activity that is generated by friendliness, in the absence of outside pressure. Thus a small c_3 suggests a substantial amount of internally generated, or spontaneous activity, and $1/c_3$ might be called a "coefficient or spontaneity." If this coefficient is high, spontaneous activity will be high.

Also conductive to high morale is the situation where $(b_2 - a_1)$ is small. This implies that there should be a strong feedback from friendliness to more interaction to more friendliness; that is, that friendliness among group members creates more contact among members, which in turn increases friendliness. It can be shown, however, using more advanced mathematical techniques, that if $(b_2 - a_1)$ approaches zero the system tends to become unstable.

Questions

1. Derive the expressions for A^*, F^*, and I^*, from equations (1), (2), and (3). Show all pertinent steps in the derivation.
2. Comment on the difficulty of obtaining estimates of the parameters; which of the parameters associated with high morale is most readily controllable by management?
3. Antagonisms within a group are normally regarded as detrimental to productivity and morale. Comment, from the standpoint of the requirements shown above for "high morale."

Case No. 19.   Equipment Investment Analysis

An important area of managerial decision making is that of the determination of the replacement period for equipment subject to deterioration or obsolescence. As such equipment ages, its efficiency declines and the cost of maintaining it rises—that is, it becomes increasingly costly to produce a given output. On the other hand, due to the cost of the new equipment, there is a substantial benefit to be realized from delaying replacement. The replacement problem thus consists of balancing off these two considerations and deciding when to replace present equipment.

There is no general solution to the replacement problem, although there is a multitude of models and techniques for special cases. One of these is presented here.

Suppose a given piece of equipment generates a flow of earnings or revenue over its lifetime according to some function $E(t)$, where t is time measured in some convenient unit from the time the equipment is installed, i.e., from $t = 0$. Similarly, let there be two functions, $S(t)$ showing the salvage value of the equipment at time t, and $R(t)$ showing the costs of repair and maintenance at time t. Usually S is a decreasing function and R an increasing function of time. Let N be the initial cost of the new equipment.

Let $V(L)$ be the value of the investment in the equipment which will be sold at the end of L years for an amount $S(L)$. This value $V(L)$ is equal to the amount received from the machine less costs and expenses. The amount received is the salvage value (S) plus the earnings (E) over the L years; the costs and expenses are the initial cost (N) and the amount spent for repair and maintenance (R). These definitions may be summarized as follows:

$$V(L) \;=\; E \;+\; S \;-\; (N \;+\; R) \tag{1}$$

$$\begin{array}{l} \text{Value} \\ \text{after } L \\ \text{years} \end{array} = \text{Earnings} + \dfrac{\text{Salvage}}{\text{value}} - \left(\dfrac{\text{Initial}}{\text{cost}} + \dfrac{\text{Repair}}{\text{costs}}\right)$$

In this formulation the functions E, S, R, and, of course, V depend on L, the age of the equipment, exactly the information not yet available. Furthermore, the relevant information about E and R is the *sum* of earnings and repair costs over the life of the equipment, not just the earnings or repair costs in one given year, e.g., $E(15)$, $R(15)$. The remedy is to sum the functions E and R over the life of the equipment, from $t = 0$ to $t = L$ where L is the as-yet-undetermined life. For continuous functions this summing is the equivalent of integrating, so the total earnings and the total repair costs are given by

$$\int_0^L E(t)dt \quad \text{and} \quad \int_0^L R(t)dt$$

It is not appropriate to integrate the function S since there is only one value, $S(L)$, which is of interest.

Since the equipment may not be replaced for a considerable period of time, it is necessary to consider the time aspect of the problem. The earnings of the equipment are spread over time in some fashion, as are repair costs. If the management is indifferent to earning or spending a dollar now as against earning or spending it in the future, the time aspect would be irrelevant. In fact, however, the value of a dollar earned now is very much greater than that of one earned in the future, just as a future cost is less burdensome in some sense than is a present one of the same dollar amount. It is necessary, therefore, for the earnings of the equipment to be *discounted* by a factor which depends on t and on some number, i, which reflects the value of money to the firm. This latter number is often termed the firm's *internal rate of return*, i.e., the rate of interest which the management feels it can or should earn on capital investments.

Discounting in the continuous case can be accomplished by multiplying or weighting the three time functions, E, R, and S, by the discount factor, e^{-it}, before integrating. The mathematical statement of (1) now becomes

$$V(L) \;=\; \int_0^L E(t)e^{-it}dt + S(L)e^{-iL} - \left[N + \int_0^L R(t)e^{-it}dt \right] \tag{2}$$

where

$V(L)$ = the present or discounted value of the equipment if sold at time L,

$$\int_0^L E(t)e^{-it}dt = \text{the present value of the earnings stream,}$$

$S(L)e^{-iL}$ = the present value of the salvage value,

N = the equipment's initial cost,

$$\int_0^L R(t)e^{-it}dt = \text{the present value of the stream of repair costs,}$$

L = the life of the equipment,

i = the interest rate which is equal to the firm's internal rate of return.

The objective is to find that value of L which will maximize the function V. This is done according to the theory of extrema for functions of one variable:

Step 1. Differentiate V with respect to L.

$$\frac{dV}{dL} = E(L)e^{-iL} - iS(L)e^{-iL} + S'(L)e^{-iL} - 0 - R(L)e^{-iL} \qquad (3)$$

Observe that differentiation of the integral expressions in (2) is accomplished merely by substituting the value of the limits in the integrand since $E(0)$ and $R(0)$ are constants.

Step 2. Set $V' = 0$ and simplify.

$$E(L)e^{-iL} = iS(L)e^{-iL} - S'(L)e^{-iL} + R(L)e^{-iL}$$
$$E(L) = iS(L) - S'(L) + R(L) \qquad (4)$$

Step 3. Solve (4) for the optimum value of L.

Step 3 cannot be performed until the forms of the three functions are specified. Therefore, suppose that

$$\begin{aligned} N &= \$5000 \\ E(t) &= 3000 - 30t \\ R(t) &= 1000 + 140t \\ S(t) &= 5000e^{-t/4} \\ S'(t) &= -\frac{5000}{4}e^{-t/4} \\ i &= 10\% \end{aligned} \qquad (5)$$

Substituting these hypothetical but reasonable functions and parameters into (4) yields

$$(3000 - 30L) - (1000 + 140L) = (.10)(5000e^{-L/4}) + \left(\frac{5000}{4}e^{-L/4}\right)$$

$$-170L = -2000 + 1750e^{-L/4}$$

$$L = \frac{2000 - 1750e^{-L/4}}{170} \tag{6}$$

The result in (6) cannot be solved algebraically for L since L appears in an exponential expression on the right-hand side of the equation. However, a table of exponentials can be used to find values of the exponential expression for various values of L, and by trial-and-error method it is possible to find a value of L which will satisfy the equation. Frequently this can be most easily done by selecting values of L which are obviously too high and too low, and then interpolating other values. Using this procedure, it was found that (6) implies

$$L^* = 10.88$$
$$\doteq 11 \tag{7}$$

Substituting $L = 11$ and the information of (5) in (2) yields an approximation of the present value of the optimum replacement cycle:

$$V^* = \int_0^{11} (3000 - 30t)e^{-t/10} + (5000e^{-11/4})(e^{-11/10}) - 5000 -$$

$$\int_0^{11} (1000 + 140t)e^{-t/10}$$

$$= \int_0^{11} 2000e^{-t/10} - \int_0^{11} 170te^{-t/10} + 5000e^{-3.85} - 5000$$

$$= 2000(-10e^{-t/10})\Big|_0^{11} - 170(-10t - 100)e^{-t/10}\Big|_0^{11} + 5000e^{-3.85} - 5000$$

$$= -20,000e^{-11/10} + 20,000 - 170[(-110 - 100)e^{-11/10} -$$
$$(0 - 100)e^0] + 5000e^{-3.85} - 5000$$

$$= 15,700e^{-11/10} + 5000e^{-3.85} - 2,000$$

$$= \frac{15,700}{3.0042} + \frac{5000}{46.993} - 2000$$

$$= \$3300$$

Thus the model generates two valuable conclusions for the situation postulated. First, the optimal period of time for keeping this equipment in operation is about 11 years. Second, if the optimal action is taken the present value of the action is about $3300; that is, the opportunity to undertake this equipment investment is currently worth $3300 to the firm.

Questions

1. What would be the effect on L^* and hence on V^* of: (a) an increase in N; (b) a change in E, R, or S; (c) an increase in the company's internal rate of return.
2. Solve the problem for the case where $N = \$30,000$, $S(t) = A_1 + A_2 t$, $E(t) = A_3/A_4 + A_5 t$, and $R(t) = A_6 t^2$.
3. Formulate and solve the problem assuming that earnings and repair costs accrue at the end of each year.

Case No. 20.   A Theory of Capital[6]

Outline of the Basic Theory. The fundamental proposition of capital theory is that the value of an asset is the future payments it provides discounted at the appropriate rate. In this initial statement of the theory, the stream of future dividends the share is expected to provide is taken as the future payments investors consider in arriving at the value of a share in a corporation. Further, it is assumed that the corporation engages in no outside financing, in which case, it is shown, the dividend expectation is determined by the corporation's current income, its investment or retention rate (the two are the same with no outside financing), and its rate of return on investment. The product of the return and retention rates turns out to be the expected rate of growth in the dividend.

The result is a model that predicts the value of a share on the basis of four variables—current income, retention or investment rate, rate of return on investment, and the rate of profit investors require on the share. The decision variable a corporation may use to influence the price of its stock is its retention rate, and given the values of the other three variables, the price of a share for any retention rate may be determined.

Current income and the rate of return on investment (which may be a function of the investment rate) can be estimated by a corporation from internally available data. However, the rate of profit that investors require is not obtainable from data of the corporation. Alternative hypotheses with respect to the required rate of profit are explored, and the hypothesis that the variable is an increasing function of the expected rate of growth in the dividend is found to be attractive for a number of reasons. For one, the stock

[6] Abridged with permission from Myron J. Gordon, *The Investment, Financing, and Valuation of the Corporation* (Homewood, Ill.: Richard D. Irwin, Inc., 1962), pp. 3–4, 43–50. Several footnotes and references in the original have been omitted. The equations have also been renumbered. For a slightly different development of the model see Case No. 11.

price model is made empirically operational in that share price is made a function of observable variables, and the parameters of the function which determines the required rate of profit may be estimated from sample data. Given the parameters and the values of the variables for a corporation, the model may be used to find the optimum investment (retention) rate for the corporation.

The model developed . . . has one provocative implication. It implies that the retention rate per se (i.e., apart from the profitability of the investment undertaken) influences share price. The validity of this proposition is the subject of [later analysis which] begins on the question whether an investor buys a share's future earnings or its future dividends. The analysis reveals that between the two, the dividend must be what the investor buys. All that the earnings advocates may logically maintain is that the distribution of earnings between dividends and retention is irrelevant to the price of a share. However, for this to be true it is necessary that the rate at which the dividend expectation is discounted be independent of the expected rate of growth in the dividend.

Examination of the question reveals, however, that the required rate of profit may rise, fall, or remain unchanged as the rate of growth in the dividend expectation rises. What the required rate of profit does depends on how rapidly the uncertainty of a dividend increases with its time in the future and on investor aversion to risk. The conclusion reached therefore is that the relation between the required rate of profit on a share and the expected rate of growth in the dividend is a question of fact. The question cannot be resolved by deductive argument, from which it follows that there is no a priori basis for rejecting the model developed . . . . On the contrary, the analysis suggests that we should be most surprised to find the value of a share independent of a corporation's dividend rate.

The Model. . . . under neoclassical theory the objective of the firm is to maximize its value, the value is a function of its future income, and the future income is a function of its investment. The task of the theory is to provide information on the nature of these two functions. If the behavior postulate is correct, the information benefits both the investment decisions of firms and the study of capital formation and its relation to other economic variables in a capitalistic economy. . . . however, the usefulness of the theory is severely restricted by the assumption that the future is certain and by the related assumption that funds are freely available at a given rate of interest.

The purpose of this [model] is to construct an analogous theory of the valuation and investment of a corporation with the existence of uncertainty as to the future and aversion to risk on the part of investors recognized. The statement of the theory . . . will be under certain restrictive assumptions with respect to financing policy and the variation in risk among firms. The succeeding [analysis] will be devoted to the task of withdrawing these assumptions. Throughout the development of the theory a prime consideration will be its representation in models that have empirical content. That is, it will be possible to observe the variables, estimate the parameters, test the behavior statements, and implement the decision rules contained in the theory.

The first problem encountered in constructing the theory is deciding what is the future income provided by a share of stock in a publicly owned corporation. The three alternatives that readily come to mind are: (1) the future earnings per share; (2) the future dividends per share; and (3) the future dividends for a finite number of periods plus the price at the end of that time. Each of these alternatives appears to have some intuitive merit. However, in the absence of differential tax treatment of capital gains the third, it would seem, reduces to the second, since the price at any future date may be expected to depend on the subsequent income. The major issue is between dividends and earnings. The theory to be developed . . . assumes that the future dividends are what the investor buys in a share . . . .

The symbols to be used frequently . . . are defined below.

P_t = Price of a corporation's share of stock at end of period t.
D_t = Dividend per share paid by the corporation during t.
Y_t = Income per share earned by the corporation during t.
r = Return on investment the corporation is expected to earn in every future period.
b = Fraction of income the corporation is expected to retain in every future period.
k = Return on investment that stockholders require on the corporation's stock.
d = Dividend yield based on current dividend, $d = D_0/P_0$.

Under certain assumptions k may also be looked on as a corporation's cost of capital. When the time subscript refers to a period in the future, the value of a variable is the mean or expected value of a probability distribution the investor is assumed to estimate subjectively. . . .

Assume a corporation for which the following is true. (1) It engages in no outside equity financing. (2) It has a quick ratio of one[7] and no long-term debt; i.e., it does not use debt financing. (3) It *will* earn a return of r on investment in every future period. (4) It *will* retain the fraction b of its income in every future period.

For this corporation the dividend in any future period is certain, and it will simply be

$$D_t = (1 - b)Y_t \tag{1}$$

If the income per share during $t = 0$ was Y_0, the income in the next period will be

$$Y_1 = Y_0 + rbY_0 = Y_0(1 + rb) \tag{2}$$

In words, the fraction b of Y_0 has been retained and invested during $t = 0$. Income in $t = 1$ therefore will be Y_0 plus rbY_0, the amount provided by a return of r on bY_0. From the mathematics of compound interest it follows that

$$\begin{aligned} Y_t &= Y_0(1 + rb)^t \\ &= Y_0 e^{rbt} \end{aligned} \tag{3}$$

if growth takes place continuously. The product rb is the rate at which earnings will grow, and from Eq. (1) it is also the rate at which the dividend will grow.

The stream of receipts a stockholder in this corporation will receive on a share is the dividend. Hence, if k is the rate of return required on the dividend, D_t, $t = 1 \to \infty$, the value of the share at the end of $t = 0$ is

$$P_0 = \int_0^\infty D_t e^{-kt} dt \tag{4}$$

From Eqs. (1) and (3) we can rewrite Eq. (4) as follows:

$$\begin{aligned} P_0 &= \int_0^\infty (1 - b)Y_0 e^{rbt} e^{-kt} dt \\ &= (1 - b)Y_0 \int_0^\infty e^{-t(k-rb)} dt \end{aligned} \tag{5}$$

The condition for carrying out the integration is that $k > rb$. Since this is the condition for the price of the share to be finite, we may presume it is satisfied.

---

[7] The quick ratio is the ratio of cash, government bonds, and accounts receivable to current liabilities.

Carrying out the integration we find that

$$P_0 = \frac{(1 - b)Y_0}{k - rb} \tag{6}$$

Eq. (6) is a stock valuation model. It states that the price of a share is its current dividend divided by the amount that the rate of profit investors require on a share exceeds the rate of growth in the dividend. Eq. (6) is also an investment model on the assumption that the objective of the firm is to maximize its share price. By assumption, retention is the only source of funds to finance investment, and the value of b given Y_0, r, and k that maximizes P_0 is the optimum annual rate of investment.

The Optimum Investment and Retention Rate. To review the argument leading up to Eq. (6), we began with the plausible assumption that the value of a share is its expected future dividends discounted at the rate of profit required on the expectation. We then showed that under the assumptions (1) the corporation engages in no outside financing and (2) it is expected to earn r on investment and retain the fraction b of its income, the entire dividend expectation may be represented by $Y_0(1 - b)$, its current value, and rb, its rate of growth. We saw further that the value of a share is equal to

$$P_0 = \frac{(1 - b)Y_0}{k - rb} \tag{6}$$

It would seem possible to estimate the values of Y_0, r, and b from the history of a corporation, . . . However, how one finds k, the rate of profit investors require on the share, is not immediately evident. This question will be taken up [later].

Given k as well as the other variables, Eq. (6) may be used not only to find the value of a share but also to find the investment (equal retention) rate that maximizes the value. Assuming that r and k as well as Y_0 are independent of b, we take the derivative of P_0 with respect to b and obtain

$$\frac{\partial P_0}{\partial b} = \frac{Y_0}{(k - rb)^2}(r - k) \tag{7}$$

The first conclusion to note . . . is that price is independent of the retention rate when $r = k$. If $r > k$, price increases with the investment rate, and if $r < k$, price falls as the retention rate increases.

No one would find any disagreement between these conclusions and the neoclassical theory on the subject as stated for instance by

Modigliani and Miller[8] . . . A point worth noting is that the question they considered was whether or not a particular investment has a rate of profit above k. Their argument was that share price will rise, fall, or remain unchanged, depending on whether the investment's rate of profit is above, below, or equal to k. Considering only a single investment, they could only state what the change in price would be. To predict the current level of a share's price, the profitability of all future investments must be considered, since future dividends depend on future investments. Every stock price model contains—by design or default—a prediction of future investment and its profitability.

A moment's reflection on the conclusion just reached with respect to the variation in share price with b, reveals that a corporation should retain all of its income or liquidate, depending on whether $r \gtrless k$. There is of course an easy way out of this implausible conclusion. It may be argued that the assumption, r is independent of b, conflicts with highly plausible economic laws, and that we should consider r a function of b. Specifically, r is the average rate of return on net investment in a period when the investment is the fraction b of income in the period. The terms $\partial r / \partial b$ and r' will refer respectively to the change in the average return with b and the return on the incremental investment. Under the assumption that investment opportunities are perfectly divisible, r' falls continuously, and r, which is an average of the r' up to b, falls less rapidly. $\partial r / \partial b$ is, of course, always negative since r is falling. The relation among r, $\partial r / \partial b$ and r' is illustrated in Figure 11–1 (page 232). (The curves r' and r asymptotically approach a limit on the assumption that a corporation at the worst can buy securities in other corporations to earn some positive rate of return.)

Keeping the assumption that k is independent of b, the variation in price with retention rate with r, a function of b, is

$$\frac{dP}{db} = \frac{Y}{(k - rb)^2} \left[-k + rb - (1 - b) \left(-r - b \frac{\partial r}{\partial b} \right) \right]$$

$$= \frac{Y}{(k - rb)^2} \left[r - k + b(1 - b) \frac{\partial r}{\partial b} \right] \tag{8}$$

There is some finite b at which P is maximized in this model. If $r > k$ when $b = 0$, dP/db is positive at $b = 0$. However, as b rises, r falls and the absolute value of $b\,(1 - b)\,\partial r / \partial b$, which is negative,

---

[8] "The Cost of Capital. Corporation Finance and the Theory of Investment," *American Economic Review*, Vol. 48 (June, 1958), pp. 261–97.

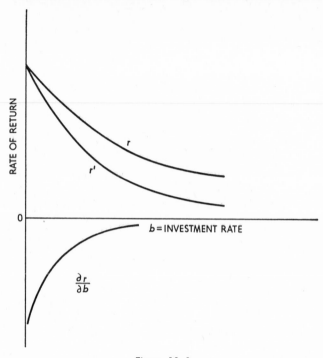

Figure 11–1
Average, Change in Average, and Marginal Return on Investment

rises. Hence, there is some finite b at which $dP/db = 0$ and P is maximized. If $r < k$ at $b = 0$, P is maximized by a negative net but possibly positive gross investment.

All this is very good if k is known and independent of b. The function r is of b may presumably be obtained by a corporation from internally available data. However, not only do we have the problem of observing k, but it may possibly vary with b, in which case the function must also be established.

CHAPTER 12

LINEAR SYSTEMS AND MATRICES

Implicit in many situations examined earlier has been the problem of solving an equation—for instance, $3x + 1 - 10 = 0$. "Solving" has meant finding the equation's roots, the values of x which make the statement "$f(x) = 0$" a true one.

This problem has been referred to previously, particularly in Chapter 4, where it was found that an equation may have a unique solution, no solution at all, many solutions, or, in particular, infinitely many solutions. Even if a solution exists, it is sometimes difficult to identify.

Similar considerations are involved, as has been seen before, in the analysis of systems of equations such as

$$r - 2s = 0$$
$$r + s - 1 = 0$$

Solutions in these instances, when solutions existed, have been obtained without difficulty by elementary algebraic operations. However, when a substantial number of variables and equations are involved, the problem of finding a solution ceases to be "easy."

In addition, the problem will often be further complicated by the fact that there may be more variables than equations, or, more equations than variables. And finally, making analysis even more difficult, the equations may be replaced by inequalities such as these:

$$x - 2y \geq 0$$
$$x + y - 1 < 0$$

The present chapter will focus on methods, matrix methods, which can be used to solve systems of equations in situations where ordinary elementary algebra without a systematic procedure is too burdensome. The following chapter will consider problems involving systems of inequalities; there the theory and techniques of linear programming will be described.

1. MATRICES

A matrix is a rectangular array of numbers or elements and is represented by writing down the elements and enclosing them in brackets; for example,

$$\begin{bmatrix} 5 & 4 & 6 \\ 3 & 2 & 7 \end{bmatrix}$$

is a matrix. For convenience, matrices may be represented by a single symbol, which by convention is usually a capital letter. The matrix given above might be called the matrix A, and this definition would be written as

$$A = \begin{bmatrix} 5 & 4 & 6 \\ 3 & 2 & 7 \end{bmatrix}$$

The array of elements of a matrix must be rectangular; for example,

$$\begin{bmatrix} 5 & 4 & 6 \\ & 2 & 7 \end{bmatrix}$$

is not a matrix because one element is missing. Other examples of matrices are:

$$B = \begin{bmatrix} 25 & 50 & 75 \\ 15 & 25 & 35 \\ 0 & 1 & 1 \end{bmatrix}; \quad X = \begin{bmatrix} x_1 \\ x_2 \\ x_3 \end{bmatrix}; \quad Y = [y_1 \ y_2];$$

and

$$C = \begin{bmatrix} 1750 \\ 850 \\ 25 \end{bmatrix}$$

These examples illustrate the fact that matrices may have one or more rows of elements and one or more columns of elements; the matrix B has 3 rows and 3 columns; X has 3 rows and 1 column; Y has 1 row and 2 columns; and C has 3 rows and 1 column. A matrix which has the same number of rows as columns is a *square matrix*; B is a square matrix.

Addition and subtraction of matrices, defined as one might expect, are easily performed: two matrices, A and B, may be added (or subtracted) one to (from) the other provided only that they have the same number of rows and columns. The resulting sum (or difference) will be a matrix, call it C, with the same number of rows and columns as the given matrices. If

$$A = \begin{bmatrix} 1 & 3 \\ 0 & 4 \end{bmatrix} \quad \text{and} \quad B = \begin{bmatrix} 0 & 2 \\ 3 & 3 \end{bmatrix}$$

and if $C = A + B$, then, since the elements of C are simply the sums of the correspondingly positioned elements of A and B,

$$C = \begin{bmatrix} 1+0 & 3+2 \\ 0+3 & 4+3 \end{bmatrix}$$

$$= \begin{vmatrix} 1 & 5 \\ 3 & 7 \end{vmatrix} \tag{1}$$

Also

$$\begin{aligned} &\text{if } A + B = C, &\text{then} &\quad B + A = C &\text{and} \\ &\text{if } C - B = A, &\text{then} &\quad C - A = B \end{aligned}$$

It should be emphasized that matrix addition (or subtraction) requires only that the matrices which are to be added (or subtracted) have the same numbers of rows and columns (although they need not be square).

Matrix multiplication is more complex, interesting, and important. First, a matrix A can be multiplied by a matrix B if and only if B *has the same number of rows as A has columns.* Suppose A has q rows and p columns whereas B has s rows and r columns. Then the product AB is defined if and only if $p = s$. Note that nothing is said about q and r in this case: they need not be equal.

Finding the elements of the product matrix, call it C, involves finding a number of sums of products. For example, suppose

$$A = \begin{bmatrix} a & b & c \\ d & e & f \end{bmatrix} \quad \text{and} \quad B = \begin{bmatrix} g & j \\ h & k \\ i & m \end{bmatrix}$$

Then if $C = AB$,

$$C = \begin{bmatrix} a & b & c \\ d & e & f \end{bmatrix} \cdot \begin{bmatrix} g & j \\ h & k \\ i & m \end{bmatrix} = \begin{bmatrix} (ag + bh + ci) & (aj + bk + cm) \\ (dg + eh + fi) & (dj + ek + fm) \end{bmatrix} \tag{2}$$

$$\;\;\;\;\;(2 \times 3) \;\;\;\;\;\; (3 \times 2) \;\;\;\;\;\;\;\;\;\;\;\;\;\;\;\;\;\; (2 \times 2)$$

$$= \begin{bmatrix} t & v \\ u & w \end{bmatrix}$$

where $t = (ag + bh + ci)$, $u = (dg + eh + fi)$, $v = (aj + bk + cm)$, and $w = (dj + ek + fm)$.

Notice that A is a "2 by 3" matrix, meaning only that it has 2 rows and 3 columns, whereas B is a 3×2. Thus, they meet the condition for multiplication. Note also that the product C is 2×2. In general, if a $p \times r$ matrix B is premultiplied ("pre-" referring to the order, whether AB or BA) by a $q \times p$ matrix A, the product AB is a $q \times r$ matrix. Of course, if A and B are square matrices of order $r \ (= q = p)$, then an $r \times r$ matrix is being multiplied by one which is $r \times r$ and the product matrix C will be $r \times r$.

The order of multiplication is important, for even if AB is defined, BA may not be. Thus, if A is 2×3 and B is 3×4, the 2×4 matrix AB exists but BA does not. If the matrices are square and of the same order, both AB and BA are defined but they are not, in general, equal; that is, in general,

$$AB \neq BA$$

Consider the matrices

$$A = \begin{bmatrix} 1 & 3 \\ 0 & 4 \end{bmatrix} \quad \text{and} \quad B = \begin{bmatrix} 0 & 2 \\ 3 & 3 \end{bmatrix}$$

Then,

$$AB = \begin{bmatrix} (1 \cdot 0 + 3 \cdot 3) & (1 \cdot 2 + 3 \cdot 3) \\ (0 \cdot 0 + 4 \cdot 3) & (0 \cdot 2 + 4 \cdot 3) \end{bmatrix} = \begin{bmatrix} 9 & 11 \\ 12 & 12 \end{bmatrix}$$

and

$$BA = \begin{bmatrix} (0 \cdot 1 + 2 \cdot 0) & (0 \cdot 3 + 2 \cdot 4) \\ (3 \cdot 1 + 3 \cdot 0) & (3 \cdot 3 + 3 \cdot 4) \end{bmatrix} = \begin{bmatrix} 0 & 8 \\ 3 & 21 \end{bmatrix}$$

Hence, the order of multiplication—whether A is premultiplied (BA) or postmultiplied (AB) by B—is of great importance.

2. MATRIX SOLUTIONS OF LINEAR SYSTEMS

Suppose a problem generates a system of three equations,

$$\begin{aligned} 25x + 50y + 75z &= 1750 \\ 15x + 25y + 35z &= 850 \\ y + z &= 25 \end{aligned} \tag{3}$$

which must be solved simultaneously for values of x, y, and z. This is, essentially, a simple problem: elementary methods will do.

Solution of (3) by Method of Elimination:

Given:

i) $25x + 50y + 75z - 1750 = 0$
ii) $15x + 25y + 35z - 850 = 0$
iii) $\qquad\quad y + z - 25 = 0$

From (iii):

iv) $y = 25 - z$

Substitute (iv) into (i) and (ii):

$5x + 10(25 - z) + 15z - 350 = 0$
$5x + 5z - 100 = 0$ (divide by 5)

v) $x + z = 20$

$3x + 5(25 - z) + 7z - 170 = 0$

vi) $3x + 2z = 45$

From (v):

vii) $x = 20 - z$

Substitute (vii) into (vi):

$$3(20 - z) + 2z = 45$$
$$- z = 45 - 60$$
$$\underline{z = 15}$$

viii)

Substitute into (vii) and (iii):

ix) $x = 20 - 15$
$\underline{x = 5}$

x) $y + 15 - 25 = 0$
$\underline{y = 10}$

Thus (3) has a solution, and it is unique: 5, 10, 15.

Consider now a solution using *matrices.* Just as algebraic symbols have been used, e.g., x and $f(x)$, to express relationships, so matrices can be used to represent systems of equations such as (3).

Let the coefficients of x, y, and z in (3) be rewritten but without the unknowns:

$$\begin{matrix} 25 & 50 & 75 \\ 15 & 25 & 35 \\ & 1 & 1 \end{matrix}$$

This is not quite a matrix, for a matrix must be a rectangular array of elements. Thus, it is necessary to recognize explicitly that the coefficient of x in the third equation of the system is 0. The resulting array can then be defined as the matrix A:

$$A = \begin{bmatrix} 25 & 50 & 75 \\ 15 & 25 & 35 \\ 0 & 1 & 1 \end{bmatrix}$$

Now let the variables, the unknowns, be relabeled x_1, x_2, and x_3, respectively, and be represented by the matrix X where

$$X = \begin{bmatrix} x_1 \\ x_2 \\ x_3 \end{bmatrix}$$

Finally, let the right-hand side of (3) be represented by the matrix C where

$$C = \begin{bmatrix} 1750 \\ 850 \\ 25 \end{bmatrix}$$

The system of (3)

$$\begin{aligned} 25x_1 + 50x_2 + 75x_3 &= 1750 \\ 15x_1 + 25x_2 + 35x_3 &= 850 \\ x_2 + x_3 &= 25 \end{aligned}$$

may now be conveniently written in matrix notation as

$$AX = C \tag{4}$$

where A, X, and C are as defined above since

$$\begin{bmatrix} 25 & 50 & 75 \\ 15 & 25 & 35 \\ 0 & 1 & 1 \end{bmatrix} \begin{bmatrix} x_1 \\ x_2 \\ x_3 \end{bmatrix} = \begin{bmatrix} 25x_1 + 50x_2 + 75x_3 \\ 15x_1 + 25x_2 + 35x_3 \\ x_2 + x_3 \end{bmatrix}$$

Clearly, in a two-equation system little is gained notationally; equally clearly, much is gained if the system becomes even moderately large, say six or seven variables and equations. It should be noted that nothing new has been brought into the original problem; it has simply been described in a more economical way.

But matrices are more than a very useful notational convention. They also are a part of a technique for solving equation systems such as (3). Furthermore they are particularly useful in the analysis of systems where the number of unknowns and variables are not equal—certainly the usual condition for business and economic problems. Before matrix solutions can be explored, however, it is necessary to define two special matrices.

First, define the *identity matrix* which has the special characteristics that (i) it is square, (ii) its diagonal elements (those going from the top left-hand corner to the bottom right-hand corner) are all 1, and (iii) its nondiagonal elements are all 0. In other words, the identity matrix, always designated I and playing a role which is analogous to that played by 1 in elementary algebra, is defined as

$$I = \begin{bmatrix} 1 & 0 & \dots & 0 \\ 0 & 1 & \dots & 0 \\ & \dots\dots\dots\dots & \\ 0 & 0 & \dots & 1 \end{bmatrix} \tag{5}$$

where the number of rows and number of columns are equal. It is easy to verify that $IA = AI = A$, where A is any matrix and I has the necessary rows and columns.

Next, define the *inverse matrix*. This matrix is analogous to the reciprocal of a number; that is, it is defined only in relation to something else. Thus, if A is a given *square* matrix, its inverse is designated A^{-1} and is defined as that matrix which will, when properly multiplied by A, result in a product which is the identity matrix, I. Thus A^{-1} is the inverse matrix of A if and only if

$$A^{-1}A = I = AA^{-1} \tag{6}$$

The inverse will also be square and have the same number of rows and columns as do A and I. The inverse does *not* always exist, even if A is square; but when it does, it can be of great value in solving equation systems.

Now return, thus equipped, to the problems of solving the equation system

$$AX = C$$

for the matrix of unknowns, X. Consider first the analogous problem, using the familiar algebraic rules. Given

$$ax = c \tag{7}$$

where x is the unknown to be determined, one procedure would be to multiply both sides by $1/a$, that is, by a^{-1}. Thus

$$a^{-1}ax = a^{-1}c$$

Recognizing that

$$a^{-1}a = 1$$
$$x = a^{-1}c \tag{8}$$

and it is possible to assert, correctly, that an analytical solution to the original problem ("solve $ax = c$") has been obtained. Notice that the procedure depends on understanding what is meant by a^{-1} and by the product $a^{-1}a$.

The matrix solution to (4) depends on similar understandings. First, where A^{-1} is the inverse of A, premultiply both sides of the equation by A^{-1}:

$$A^{-1}AX = A^{-1}C$$

Next, recognize that

$$A^{-1}A = I$$

and that

$$IX = X$$

Thus,

$$IX = A^{-1}C$$
$$X = A^{-1}C \tag{9}$$

i.e., the product matrix $(A^{-1}C)$ is the desired solution just as $(a^{-1}c)$ was the solution in the elementary case.

For the system in (3)

$$A = \begin{bmatrix} 25 & 50 & 75 \\ 15 & 25 & 35 \\ 0 & 1 & 1 \end{bmatrix} \quad \text{and} \quad C = \begin{bmatrix} 1750 \\ 850 \\ 25 \end{bmatrix}$$

Since A is a 3×3 matrix, A^{-1}, if it exists at all, will also be 3×3. And pre-multiplication of C, a 3×1 matrix, by a 3×3 matrix is possible, the product being a 3×1 matrix. This state of affairs will always prevail with systems such as (3). Thus, the only question is that of finding A^{-1}.

The first step is to return to the definition of an inverse as that matrix A^{-1} whose product with A is the indentity matrix, I:

$$A^{-1}A = I$$

Substituting for A and I yields

$$A^{-1} \cdot \begin{bmatrix} 25 & 50 & 75 \\ 15 & 25 & 35 \\ 0 & 1 & 1 \end{bmatrix} = \begin{bmatrix} 1 & 0 & 0 \\ 0 & 1 & 0 \\ 0 & 0 & 1 \end{bmatrix}$$

Let the elements of A^{-1} be designated by the letters a, b, c, etc.

$$\begin{bmatrix} a & b & c \\ d & e & f \\ g & h & i \end{bmatrix}$$

Then, recalling the procedure for multiplication of matrices, the following can be written:

$$A^{-1}A = \begin{bmatrix} a25 + b15 + c0 & a50 + b25 + c1 & a75 + b35 + c1 \\ d25 + e15 + f0 & d50 + e25 + f1 & d75 + e35 + f1 \\ g25 + h15 + i0 & g50 + h25 + i1 & g75 + h35 + i1 \end{bmatrix}$$

Equating corresponding elements in $A^{-1}A$ and I gives

$$\left. \begin{aligned} (a25 + b15 + c0) &= 1 \\ (a50 + b25 + c1) &= 0 \\ (a75 + b35 + c1) &= 0 \end{aligned} \right\} \text{which can be solved for } a, b, c$$

$$\left. \begin{aligned} (d25 + e15 + f0) &= 0 \\ (d50 + e25 + f1) &= 1 \\ (d75 + e35 + f1) &= 0 \end{aligned} \right\} \text{which can be solved for } d, e, f \tag{10}$$

$$\left. \begin{aligned} (g25 + h15 + i0) &= 0 \\ (g50 + h25 + i1) &= 0 \\ (g75 + h35 + i1) &= 1 \end{aligned} \right\} \text{which can be solved for } g, h, i$$

Solving these nine equations in sets of three for the elements of A^{-1} gives

$$A^{-1} = \begin{bmatrix} -2\!/\!25 & 1\!/\!5 & -1 \\ -3\!/\!25 & 1\!/\!5 & 2 \\ 3\!/\!25 & -1\!/\!5 & -1 \end{bmatrix}$$

Finally, pre-multiplication of C yields

$$X = A^{-1}C$$

$$= \begin{bmatrix} -2\!/\!25 & 1\!/\!5 & -1 \\ -3\!/\!25 & 1\!/\!5 & 2 \\ 3\!/\!25 & -1\!/\!5 & -1 \end{bmatrix} \begin{bmatrix} 1750 \\ 850 \\ 25 \end{bmatrix}$$

$$= \begin{bmatrix} 5 \\ 10 \\ 15 \end{bmatrix}$$

as before.

At this point the reader deserves the assurance that no one ever uses matrix methods of solution for small systems since, clearly, aside from the notational convenience, it is at least as difficult to solve by elementary methods of elimination for the elements of the inverse matrix as it is to solve the original problem. This is not the whole picture, however, since there are many standard procedures for the inversion of matrices for large systems, procedures which rely on electronic computers rather than on tedious hand calculations. It is this development, the ability to invert large coefficient matrices, that has made linear analysis so important and powerful in the analysis of business and economic problems. It is also relevant to note that many problems involve finding the matrix X for various C matrices while the coefficient matrix A—and hence A^{-1}—stays fixed. Under such circumstances, the matrix method of solution becomes quite efficient.

3. SUBSCRIPT NOTATION

A matrix with m rows and n columns has mn elements and each one appears in some row and some column. It is often quite convenient to identify the elements by using the row and column in which they appear as subscripts. If A is a matrix with 2 rows and 3 columns, it can be written as

$$\begin{bmatrix} a_{11} & a_{12} & a_{13} \\ a_{21} & a_{22} & a_{23} \end{bmatrix} \tag{11}$$

Using this notation, the operations of addition, subtraction, and multiplication can be defined in general as follows, where the subscript indices i and j indicate, respectively, the row and column positions of the element:

if $C = A + B$, then $c_{ij} = a_{ij} + b_{ij}$

if $C = A - B$, then $c_{ij} = a_{ij} - b_{ij}$ (12)

if $C = AB$,   then $c_{ij} = \displaystyle\sum_{k=1}^{r} a_{ik}b_{kj}$ (where r is the number of rows of B and the number of columns of A)

if $C = A^{-1}$,   then $CA = I$ or $\displaystyle\sum_{k=1}^{r} c_{ik}a_{kj} = 1$ if $i = j$

$$= 0 \quad \text{if } i \neq j$$

4. EXISTENCE OF AN INVERSE

In the previous sections it has been stated that a system of equations may or may not have a unique solution and that a matrix may or may not have an inverse. It is desirable to obtain or develop a criterion to determine whether or not a system has a solution or whether a matrix has an inverse. The condition is most easily stated in terms of the *determinant*.

An intuitive feeling for the definition of the determinant can be obtained by considering the general case of two equations in two unknowns:

$$a_{11}x_1 + a_{12}x_2 = b_1 \tag{13}$$
$$a_{21}x_1 + a_{22}x_2 = b_2 \tag{14}$$

in which neither a_{11} nor a_{22} is zero. Since a_{11} is not zero,

$$x_1 = \frac{b_1 - a_{12}x_2}{a_{11}} \quad \text{from (13)} \tag{15}$$

And similarly, since a_{22} is not zero,

$$x_2 = \frac{b_2 - a_{21}x_1}{a_{22}} \quad \text{from (14)} \tag{16}$$

Substituting (16) into (15) gives

$$x_1 = \frac{b_1}{a_{11}} - \frac{a_{12}}{a_{11}}\left[\frac{b_2 - a_{21}x_1}{a_{22}}\right]$$

or

$$a_{11}a_{22}x_1 - a_{12}a_{21}x_1 = a_{22}b_1 - a_{12}b_2$$

and

$$x_1 = \frac{a_{22}b_1 - a_{12}b_2}{a_{11}a_{22} - a_{21}a_{12}} \tag{17}$$

Substituting (15) into (16) gives

$$x_2 = \frac{a_{11}b_2 - a_{21}b_1}{a_{11}a_{22} - a_{21}a_{12}} \tag{18}$$

The symbol

$$\begin{vmatrix} a_{11} & a_{12} \\ a_{21} & a_{22} \end{vmatrix} \tag{19}$$

is called a *determinant* of the system of equations, and its value is defined to be

$$a_{11}a_{22} - a_{12}a_{21} \tag{20}$$

Using this definition, the solutions to the system of equations can be written as the ratio of two determinants:

$$x_1 = \frac{\begin{vmatrix} b_1 & a_{12} \\ b_2 & a_{22} \end{vmatrix}}{\begin{vmatrix} a_{11} & a_{12} \\ a_{21} & a_{22} \end{vmatrix}} \tag{21}$$

$$x_2 = \frac{\begin{vmatrix} a_{11} & b_1 \\ a_{21} & b_2 \end{vmatrix}}{\begin{vmatrix} a_{11} & a_{12} \\ a_{21} & a_{22} \end{vmatrix}} \tag{22}$$

Expression (21) is merely another way of writing (17), and expression (22) is another way of writing (18). The solution to the set of equations

$$4x_1 + 2x_2 = 4800$$
$$2x_1 + 13x_2 = 4800$$

is

$$x_1 = \frac{\begin{vmatrix} 4800 & 2 \\ 4800 & 13 \end{vmatrix}}{\begin{vmatrix} 4 & 2 \\ 2 & 13 \end{vmatrix}} = \frac{13(4800) - 2(4800)}{13(4) - 2(2)} = \frac{11(4800)}{48} = 1100$$

$$x_2 = \frac{\begin{vmatrix} 4 & 4800 \\ 2 & 4800 \end{vmatrix}}{\begin{vmatrix} 4 & 2 \\ 2 & 13 \end{vmatrix}} = \frac{4(4800) - 2(4800)}{48} = 200$$

The expression of the solution to a system of n linear equations as a ratio of two determinants is known as Cramer's Rule. Equations (21) and (22) are the application of this rule to the case where $n = 2$.

It has been shown above that the inverse of the matrix

$$\begin{bmatrix} a_{11} & a_{12} \\ a_{21} & a_{22} \end{bmatrix}, \quad \text{namely} \quad \begin{bmatrix} c_{11} & c_{12} \\ c_{21} & c_{22} \end{bmatrix} \tag{23}$$

can be obtained by solving two sets of simultaneous linear equations:

$$a_{11}c_{11} + a_{12}c_{21} = 1$$
$$a_{21}c_{11} + a_{22}c_{21} = 0$$

$$a_{11}c_{12} + a_{12}c_{22} = 0$$
$$a_{21}c_{12} + a_{22}c_{22} = 1$$

Using (21) and (22), the inverse of A can be written as

$$\begin{bmatrix} c_{11} & c_{12} \\ c_{21} & c_{22} \end{bmatrix} \tag{24}$$

where

$$c_{11} = \frac{\begin{vmatrix} 1 & a_{12} \\ 0 & a_{22} \end{vmatrix}}{\begin{vmatrix} a_{11} & a_{12} \\ a_{21} & a_{22} \end{vmatrix}} \qquad c_{21} = \frac{\begin{vmatrix} a_{11} & 1 \\ a_{21} & 0 \end{vmatrix}}{\begin{vmatrix} a_{11} & a_{12} \\ a_{21} & a_{22} \end{vmatrix}} \tag{25}$$

$$c_{12} = \frac{\begin{vmatrix} 0 & a_{12} \\ 1 & a_{22} \end{vmatrix}}{\begin{vmatrix} a_{11} & a_{12} \\ a_{21} & a_{22} \end{vmatrix}} \qquad c_{22} = \frac{\begin{vmatrix} a_{11} & 0 \\ a_{21} & 1 \end{vmatrix}}{\begin{vmatrix} a_{11} & a_{12} \\ a_{21} & a_{22} \end{vmatrix}} \tag{26}$$

For example, if

$$A = \begin{bmatrix} 4 & 2 \\ 2 & 13 \end{bmatrix}$$

then

$$C = \begin{bmatrix} +\frac{13}{48} & -\frac{1}{24} \\ -\frac{1}{24} & \frac{1}{12} \end{bmatrix}$$

From these solutions it is clear that if the determinant $\begin{vmatrix} a_{11} & a_{12} \\ a_{21} & a_{22} \end{vmatrix}$ is zero, the inverse matrix will not exist since division by zero is not defined. On the other hand, if the determinant is not zero, the inverse matrix will exist and satisfy the necessary equations.

The same reasoning can be extended to cases of more variables; for example, consider the system of three equations in three unknowns:

$$a_{11}x_1 + a_{12}x_2 + a_{13}x_3 = b_1$$
$$a_{21}x_1 + a_{22}x_2 + a_{23}x_3 = b_2 \tag{27}$$
$$a_{31}x_1 + a_{32}x_2 + a_{33}x_3 = b_3$$

The solution to this set of equations may be written formally as:

$$x_1 = \frac{\begin{vmatrix} b_1 & a_{12} & a_{13} \\ b_2 & a_{22} & a_{23} \\ b_3 & a_{32} & a_{33} \end{vmatrix}}{\begin{vmatrix} a_{11} & a_{12} & a_{13} \\ a_{21} & a_{22} & a_{23} \\ a_{31} & a_{32} & a_{33} \end{vmatrix}}$$

$$x_2 = \frac{\begin{vmatrix} a_{11} & b_1 & a_{13} \\ a_{21} & b_2 & a_{23} \\ a_{31} & b_3 & a_{33} \end{vmatrix}}{\begin{vmatrix} a_{11} & a_{12} & a_{13} \\ a_{21} & a_{22} & a_{23} \\ a_{31} & a_{32} & a_{33} \end{vmatrix}} \tag{28}$$

$$x_2 = \frac{\begin{vmatrix} a_{11} & a_{12} & b_1 \\ a_{21} & a_{22} & b_2 \\ a_{31} & a_{32} & b_3 \end{vmatrix}}{\begin{vmatrix} a_{11} & a_{12} & a_{13} \\ a_{21} & a_{22} & a_{23} \\ a_{31} & a_{32} & a_{33} \end{vmatrix}}$$

where the determinant in the denominator is the determinant of the system, and the determinant in the numerator is obtained by replacing the elements in the ith column of the system matrix by the right-hand side of (27) while leaving the remaining elements unchanged.

The value of a third-order determinant may be found by using the following rule:

a) Write the determinant and then repeat the first two columns:

$$\begin{matrix} a_{11} & a_{12} & a_{13} & a_{11} & a_{12} \\ a_{21} & a_{22} & a_{23} & a_{21} & a_{22} \\ a_{31} & a_{32} & a_{33} & a_{31} & a_{32} \end{matrix}$$

b) Sum the three products of the three terms linked by solid lines, and subtract the sum of the three products of the three terms linked by broken lines; i.e., the value of the determinant, D, shown above is:

$$D = (a_{11}a_{22}a_{33} + a_{12}a_{23}a_{31} + a_{13}a_{21}a_{32}) - (a_{13}a_{22}a_{31} + a_{11}a_{23}a_{32} + a_{12}a_{21}a_{33}) \tag{29}$$

Reasoning as before, the system matrix will have a unique inverse if and only if its determinant is different from zero.

This same reasoning can be extended to cases of four, five, and a higher number of variables, although the computation of the determinant becomes more difficult and other rules are used to compute determinants with more coefficients. This generalization, which shall be shown without proof, is as follows:

a) The system of equations

$$AX = C$$

has a solution if and only if the determinant of A, written as $|A|$, is different from zero.
b) The matrix A has an inverse if and only if the determinant of A is different from zero.
c) From this it follows that the solution to the system of equations exists if and only if the matrix A has an inverse.

5. AN APPLICATION: LINEAR REGRESSION ANALYSIS

Most problems in this text involve some notion of a functional relationship. Generally the relationship is stated and the problem is to manipulate it in some way, e.g., optimize it. For instance, it might be stated that if $y =$ cost of production and $x =$ number of units produced, then $y = \$3x$. Before such a statement can be made, however, it is necessary to determine the stated relationship itself from data. In such a situation, the analyst would not merely guess at the relationship of y to x; if he did, his entire model might be based on a spurious relationship.

Sometimes the relationship may be almost exact, and thus easily found by trying a few different values of the independent variable and determining the corresponding values of the dependent variable. But in many cases the relationship will not be exact; that is, successive observations will yield results which do not *fit* each other exactly; then some sort of estimate must be made in order to approximate the unknown true relationship.

Suppose that it is believed that some functional relationship does exist between two variables, x and y, such that y depends on x. Suppose further that the relationship is believed to be such that it can be described by a linear function. Then, without knowledge of the exact nature of the relationship, the function can be expressed as

$$y = a + bx \qquad (30)$$

where a and b are unknown parameters.

If y is cost of production and x is number of units produced, as in the example suggested above, an estimate of the values of a and b

could be obtained by collecting pairs of observations (x, y) and plotting each pair as a point on a rectangular coordinate system as in Figure 12–1.

It is apparent that the points do not all fall along a single straight line. This may be due to the existence of other variables, not considered in the equation but which exert influence on the values assumed by y, or it may be due to random fluctuations—variations which would cause some deviations from a "perfect" relationship even if all possible variables were being considered in the equation.

Figure 12–1

(A deterministic philosopher might assert that there is no such thing as "chance," and if all pertinent variables were considered, there would be no random fluctuations. Since including all possible influences is manifestly impossible, the only practical alternative is to confine the model to those variables which are believed to be most important, and hope that the excluded variables cancel each other out randomly or are unimportant for other reasons.)

The question now is: How can the relationship between x and y be expressed in the form of an equation, $y = a + bx$, in such a way that the equation is the best possible estimate of the real relationship? There are various ways in which the parameters of such an equation might be estimated; the simplest is probably that of merely drawing a straight line through the graph in a manner which "looks" about right, and then determining the equation which describes the straight line. But such a method is subject to error which cannot be adequately measured, and thus it is ordinarily not appropriate for further analysis.

The most widely used method for approaching this kind of problem is known as the *method of least squares;* when a relationship between two variables is involved, the method of least squares is called *simple regression analysis.* Essentially the method consists of determining the equation of a line which, when drawn through

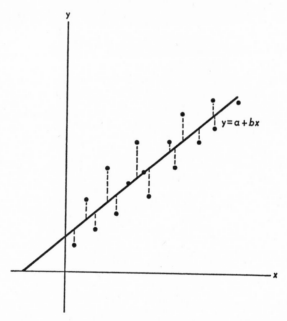

Figure 12–2

the chart in Figure 12–1, will minimize the sum of the squares of the vertical distances from each point (x, y) to the line. The vertical distances are shown by dashed lines in Figure 12–2.

To develop estimates of the parameters of the equation, it must first be recognized that the equation is not going to fit the points exactly; errors, or deviations, will appear, and the objective is to make these errors (or rather, the sum of the squares of the errors) as small as possible, i.e., to minimize them.

If the errors are represented by u, equation (30) may be rewritten as

$$y = a + bx + u \tag{31}$$

To minimize the sum of the squares of the n errors associated with the n observations, let

$$S = u_1{}^2 + u_2{}^2 + u_3{}^2 + \cdots + u_n{}^2 \qquad (32)$$

Substituting $u_i = y_i - a - bx_i$ from (31), (32) becomes

$$S = (y_1 - a - bx_1)^2 + (y_2 - a - bx_2)^2 + \cdots + (y_n - a - bx_n)^2 \quad (33)$$

Minimization requires the usual calculus operation of differentiating S with respect to a, performing a similar operation with respect to b, and solving the two resulting equations simultaneously for the optimal values of a and b:

$$\frac{\partial S}{\partial a} = -2(y_1 - a - bx_1) - 2(y_2 - a - bx_2) - \cdots -2(y_n - a - bx_n)$$
$$= -2\Sigma y_i + 2an + 2b\Sigma x_i = 0$$

or

$$\Sigma y = an + b\Sigma x \qquad (34)$$

$$\frac{\partial S}{\partial b} = -2x_1(y_1 - a - bx_1) - 2x_2(y_2 - a - bx_2) - \cdots -2x_n(y_n - a - bx_n)$$
$$= -2\Sigma x_i y_i + 2a\Sigma x_i + 2b\Sigma x_i{}^2 = 0$$

or

$$\Sigma xy = a\Sigma x + b\Sigma x^2 \qquad (35)$$

The usual operations of algebra will suffice to solve (34) and (35) simultaneously for a and b. Thus

$$\hat{b} = \frac{n\Sigma xy - \Sigma x\Sigma y}{n\Sigma x^2 - (\Sigma x)^2}$$
$$\hat{a} = \frac{\Sigma x^2\Sigma y - \Sigma x\Sigma xy}{n\Sigma x^2 - (\Sigma x)^2} \qquad (36)$$

with the "hat" on the a and b indicating that these are estimates of the true a and b.

Given a series of n observations, (x, y), the formulas in (36) may be applied directly to obtain the estimates. Sometimes, when hand calculation is being used, the x values are transformed to values which express the distance of x from the mean, or midpoint, of x, say

$$z_i = x - \bar{x} \qquad (37)$$

where

$$\bar{x} = \frac{1}{n}\Sigma x$$

Example

Suppose the following observations of x and y have been made:

x	y
8	4
9	6
6	3
3	0
11	9
10	6

Find the regression equation $y = a + bx$.

Solution:

It is convenient to represent the data in tabular form, as below:

x	y	xy	x^2
8	4	32	64
9	6	54	81
6	3	18	36
3	0	0	9
11	9	99	121
10	6	60	100
Sums: 47	28	263	411

It is apparent from the table that $\Sigma x = 47$; $\Sigma y = 28$; $\Sigma xy = 263$; $\Sigma x^2 = 411$. Noting also that $n = 6$, all the information required to solve for $\hat{a}$ and $\hat{b}$ is now available. Substituting into the formulas shows that

$$\hat{b} = \frac{6(263) - (47)(28)}{6(411) - (47)(47)} \doteq 1.02$$

$$\hat{a} = \frac{(411)(28) - (47)(263)}{6(411) - (47)(47)} \doteq -3.32 \tag{38}$$

Therefore the regression equation is

$$y = 1.02x - 3.32 \tag{39}$$

A convenient way to extend the foregoing analysis to cover the situation where y is a linear function of several or many x's is to use matrices. Suppose that y is a function of m variables, denoted by x_1, $x_2, \cdots x_m$. Then the equation $y = f(x_i)$, $i = 1, 2, \cdots , m$, may be written as

$$y = b_1x_1 + b_2x_2 + \cdots + b_mx_m + u \tag{40}$$

Observe that it is not necessary to deal specifically with the constant, a, as described in the previous section; a can be included in the above equation simply by letting one of the x's be equal to unity.

If a total of n observations has been obtained, the following matrix system is generated:

$$\begin{bmatrix} y_1 \\ y_2 \\ \cdot \\ \cdot \\ \cdot \\ y_n \end{bmatrix} = \begin{bmatrix} x_{11} & x_{12} & \cdots & x_{1m} \\ \cdot & & & \cdot \\ \cdot & & & \cdot \\ \cdot & & & \cdot \\ x_{n1} & x_{n2} & \cdots & x_{nm} \end{bmatrix} \cdot \begin{bmatrix} b_1 \\ b_2 \\ \cdot \\ \cdot \\ b_m \end{bmatrix} + \begin{bmatrix} u_1 \\ u_2 \\ \cdot \\ \cdot \\ \cdot \\ u_n \end{bmatrix} \qquad (41)$$

This may conveniently be rewritten as

$$Y = XB + U \qquad (42)$$

where Y is an $n \times 1$ matrix, X is $n \times m$, B is $m \times 1$, and U is $n \times 1$. Thus each term in the equation has the dimension $n \times 1$. The X's and Y's are the values which are *observed*. The goal is to express B in terms of these observed variables in such a way as to minimize the sum of the squares of the u's. Since $U = Y - BX$, and each individual

$$u_i = y_i - \sum_{k=1}^{m} x_{ik} b_k \qquad (43)$$

The objective is to minimize the sum of the squares of the u_i's.

To illustrate the method in general, consider the case where $m = 3$. Then

$$y_i = b_1 x_{i1} + b_2 x_{i2} + b_3 x_{i3} + u_i$$

or

$$u_i = y_i - (b_1 x_{i1} + b_2 x_{i2} + b_3 x_{i3})$$

and

$$S = \sum_{i=1}^{n} u_i^2 = \sum_{i=1}^{n} [y_i - (b_1 x_{i1} + b_2 x_{i2} + b_3 x_{i3})]^2$$

For each value of k, $\partial S / \partial b_k$ is equal to

$$-2 \sum_{i=1}^{n} x_{ik} [y_i - (b_1 x_{i1} + b_2 x_{i2} + b_3 x_{i3})] \qquad k = 1, 2, 3$$

To minimize S, $\partial S / \partial b_1$, $\partial S / \partial b_2$, and $\partial S / \partial b_3$ are set equal to zero. The resulting equations are

$$\sum_{i=1}^{n} (b_1 x_{ik} x_{i1} + b_2 x_{ik} x_{i2} + b_3 x_{ik} x_{i3}) = \sum_{i=1}^{n} x_{ik} y_i \qquad \text{for } k = 1, 2, 3$$

or

$$\begin{aligned} b_1 \Sigma x^2_{i1} + b_2 \Sigma x_{i2} x_{i1} + b_3 \Sigma x_{i1} x_{i3} &= \Sigma x_{i1} y_i \\ b_1 \Sigma x_{i2} x_{i1} + b_2 \Sigma x^2_{i2} + b_3 \Sigma x_{i2} x_{i3} &= \Sigma x_{i2} y_i \\ b_1 \Sigma x_{i3} x_{i1} + b_3 \Sigma x_{i3} x_{i2} + b_3 \Sigma x^2_{i3} &= \Sigma x_{i3} y_i \end{aligned} \qquad (44)$$

This is a system of three equations in three unknowns which can be written, from (4), in the form

$$AB = C$$

where

$$B = \begin{bmatrix} b_1 \\ b_2 \\ b_3 \end{bmatrix}$$

and A and C appear to involve X and Y. The actual expressions can be derived by noting that an element of C, say $\sum\limits_{i=1}^{n} x_{i2}y_i$, is the product of two matrices

$$[x_{12}\ x_{22}\ \cdot\ \cdot\ x_{n2}] \begin{bmatrix} y_1 \\ y_2 \\ \cdot \\ \cdot \\ \cdot \\ y_n \end{bmatrix}$$

and C therefore is the product of the matrices

$$\begin{bmatrix} x_{11}\ x_{21}\ \cdot\ \cdot\ x_{n1} \\ x_{12}\ x_{22}\ \cdot\ \cdot\ x_{n2} \\ x_{13}\ x_{23}\ \cdot\ \cdot\ x_{n3} \end{bmatrix} \begin{bmatrix} y_1 \\ y_2 \\ \cdot \\ \cdot \\ \cdot \\ y_n \end{bmatrix}$$

The second matrix is Y; the first differs from X only in that its rows are the columns of X. To change rows into columns, the matrix is transposed and this is denoted by a prime, e.g.,

$$\text{if } M = \begin{bmatrix} m_{11} & m_{12} \\ m_{21} & m_{22} \\ m_{31} & m_{32} \end{bmatrix} \quad \text{then } M' = \begin{bmatrix} m_{11} & m_{21} & m_{31} \\ m_{12} & m_{22} & m_{32} \end{bmatrix}$$

Therefore $C = X'Y$.

In the same way it can be verified that

$$A = X'X$$

and the system of equations which yield the least-square estimates are

$$X'XB = X'Y$$

Since $X'X$ is a square matrix, it may have an inverse. If the inverse exists, then

$$B = (X'X)^{-1}X'Y \tag{45}$$

The advantage of the development and equation (45) is that it is perfectly general; it applies to any value of n and any value of $m < n$ in (41).

Example

      Again consider the example stated previously for which the solution $y = 1.02x - 3.32$ was obtained. Suppose that this example is now defined as

$$y = b_1 x_1 + b_2 x_2 \qquad (46)$$

with the understanding that $x_1 = 1$. In matrix form

$$\begin{bmatrix} 4 \\ 6 \\ 3 \\ 0 \\ 9 \\ 6 \end{bmatrix} = \begin{bmatrix} 1 & 8 \\ 1 & 9 \\ 1 & 6 \\ 1 & 3 \\ 1 & 11 \\ 1 & 10 \end{bmatrix} \begin{bmatrix} b_1 \\ b_2 \end{bmatrix} + \begin{bmatrix} u_1 \\ u_2 \\ u_3 \\ u_4 \\ u_5 \\ u_6 \end{bmatrix} \qquad (47)$$

or

$$Y = XB + U$$

Then, as described in the foregoing,

$B = (X'X)^{-1}X'Y =$

$$\left\{ \begin{bmatrix} 1 & 1 & 1 & 1 & 1 & 1 \\ 8 & 9 & 6 & 3 & 11 & 10 \end{bmatrix} \cdot \begin{bmatrix} 1 & 8 \\ 1 & 9 \\ 1 & 6 \\ 1 & 3 \\ 1 & 11 \\ 1 & 10 \end{bmatrix} \right\}^{-1} \cdot \begin{bmatrix} 1 & 1 & 1 & 1 & 1 & 1 \\ 8 & 9 & 6 & 3 & 11 & 10 \end{bmatrix} \cdot \begin{bmatrix} 4 \\ 6 \\ 3 \\ 0 \\ 9 \\ 6 \end{bmatrix}$$

$$\begin{bmatrix} 6 & 47 \\ 47 & 411 \end{bmatrix}^{-1} \cdot \begin{bmatrix} 28 \\ 263 \end{bmatrix}$$

Following the usual procedure for inverting a matrix, it is seen that $(X'X)^{-1}$ is equal to

$$\begin{bmatrix} \dfrac{411}{257} & \dfrac{-47}{257} \\ \dfrac{-47}{257} & \dfrac{6}{257} \end{bmatrix} = \frac{1}{257} \cdot \begin{bmatrix} 411 & -47 \\ -47 & 6 \end{bmatrix} \qquad \text{since } cA = (ca_{ij}) \text{ where } c \text{ is a constant.}$$

Then

$$(X'X)^{-1}X'Y = \begin{bmatrix} -3.32 \\ 1.02 \end{bmatrix}$$

as before, and the equation is

$$y = -3.32x_1 + 1.02x_2$$

or   (48)

$$y = -3.32 + 1.02x_2$$

EXERCISES, SECTION 1

In Exercises 1–3, find the sum $A + B = C$, and the difference $A - B = D$. If the matrices cannot be added or subtracted, so indicate.

1.
$$A = \begin{bmatrix} 1 & 3 & 0 \\ 2 & 0 & 6 \\ 3 & 3 & 5 \end{bmatrix} \qquad B = \begin{bmatrix} 0 & 0 & 2 \\ 1 & 10 & 4 \\ 0 & 7 & 6 \end{bmatrix}$$

2.
$$A = \begin{bmatrix} 0 & 3 \\ 1 & 9 \\ 2 & 3 \end{bmatrix} \qquad B = \begin{bmatrix} 6 & 8 & 3 \\ 2 & 1 & 1 \end{bmatrix}$$

3.
$$A = \begin{bmatrix} 0 & 0 & 0 & 0 \\ 1 & 8 & 2 & 0 \\ 4 & 4 & 7 & 0 \end{bmatrix} \qquad B = \begin{bmatrix} 2 & 3 & 12 & 7 \\ 0 & 9 & 9 & 0 \\ 3 & 3 & 1 & 1 \end{bmatrix}$$

In Exercises 4–6, find the product $AB = C$ where multiplication is possible. If multiplication is not possible, so indicate. Then find the product $BA = D$, where possible.

4.
$$A = \begin{bmatrix} 2 & 1 \\ 0 & 3 \end{bmatrix} \qquad B = \begin{bmatrix} 6 & 4 \\ 5 & 0 \end{bmatrix}$$

5.
$$A = \begin{bmatrix} 6 & 0 & 3 \\ 0 & 2 & -1 \\ 4 & -2 & 0 \end{bmatrix} \qquad B = \begin{bmatrix} 0 & 2 \\ 1 & 1 \\ 3 & 0 \end{bmatrix}$$

6.
$$A = \begin{bmatrix} 2 & 0 & 1 \end{bmatrix} \qquad B = \begin{bmatrix} 3 \\ 2 \\ 7 \end{bmatrix}$$

7. Construct a simple example of a set of matrices A and B such that $AB = BA$.

8. Construct a simple example of a set of matrices A and B such that $AB = 0$, and $A \neq 0$, $B \neq 0$.

9. Show that $(AB)^{-1} = B^{-1}A^{-1}$ where

$$A = \begin{bmatrix} 4 & 1 \\ 2 & 1 \end{bmatrix} \qquad B = \begin{bmatrix} 2 & 1 \\ 2 & 3 \end{bmatrix}$$

EXERCISES, SECTION 2

10. Given the equations

$$2x + y = 6$$
$$x - y = \tfrac{3}{2}$$

express the system in matrix form and solve for x and y by inverting the matrix of coefficients.

11. Given the equations

$$2x + z = 2$$
$$2y + 2z = 4$$
$$x + y + z = 2$$

express the system in matrix form and solve for x, y, and z by inverting the matrix of coefficients. Show the inverse matrix explicitly as part of your answer.

EXERCISES, SECTION 4

In Exercises 12–14 determine whether the inverse of A exists (it is not necessary actually to compute the inverse):

12. $A = \begin{bmatrix} 2 & 0 \\ 0 & 3 \end{bmatrix}$

13. $A = \begin{bmatrix} 0 & 1 \\ 3 & 1 \end{bmatrix}$

14. $A = \begin{bmatrix} 1 & 1 & 1 \\ 0 & 2 & 3 \\ 1 & 0 & 6 \end{bmatrix}$

15. Obtain the solutions to Exercises 10 and 11, using determinants.

16. Given the system of equations

$$2x + 4y = 5$$
$$6x - y = 1$$

find x and y, using determinants. Show all computations.

17. Solve the system

$$25x + 50y + 75z = 1750$$
$$15x + 25y + 35z = 850$$
$$y + z = 25$$

using determinants.

EXERCISES, SECTION 5

18. Suppose that a is zero in (31) and the function is merely $y = bx$. Using the algebraic method first described, show that the estimate of b is $\dfrac{\Sigma xy}{\Sigma x^2}$.

19. Again supposing that a is zero and there exists a relationship $y = bx$, that is, only one x-variable, show that the matrix method yields the same estimate of b.

20. A firm has found that the price of a certain required raw material has been increasing over time; it desires to express the price-time relationship in the form of an equation

$$p = a + bt$$

where

$$p = \text{price}$$
$$t = \text{time, in years}$$

a and b are parameters.

Over a seven-year period, prices of the commodity have been as follows:

Year (t)	Price (p)
1	$ 2
2	1
3	3
4	5
5	7
6	7
7	10

a) Determine the regression equation, using either method discussed in this text.

b) As indicated in the discussion, computation can be simplified by letting the values of x be represented by $(x - \bar{x})$; i.e., by setting the midpoint or mean of x equal to zero, and expressing all values of x in terms of their difference or deviation from the mean. In the example above, find the mean of t and subtract it from all values of t. (Note that this results in $\Sigma t = 0$.) Perform the analysis again. How can the results be reconciled with the results of (a) above?

CHAPTER 13

LINEAR PROGRAMMING

Linear programming is a mathematical technique for determining the most desirable or most profitable course of action for a situation where a number of variables are involved, where many possible courses of action are available, and where the problem can be expressed in linear terms. Thus, linear programming is another optimizing technique, a technique, however, which is applicable to many types of decision problems for which the methods of Chapters 4 and 7 do not work.

1. THE LINEAR PROGRAMMING MODEL

It would not be necessary to resort to linear programming if the conditions of the decision situation could be expressed as, for example,

$$x + 2y = 100$$
$$3x + y = 100 \tag{1}$$

There is only one solution $(x = 20,\ y = 40)$, and this (necessarily optimal) solution can be determined easily by elementary methods. See Figure 13–1.

Suppose, however, that *many* acceptable, or feasible, solutions exist; e.g., suppose the system is

$$x + 2y \leq 100$$
$$3x + y \leq 100 \tag{2}$$
$$x \geq 0$$
$$y \geq 0$$

There are now many possible solutions which would satisfy the inequalities of (2). The graph of these inequalities, Figure 13–2, shows that any point (x, y) within the shaded area will satisfy the restrictions set forth in the problem. Linear programming provides a method for deciding which of the possible points is optimal.

257

First, consider a specific industrial problem which might lead to a situation such as (2). Suppose that the Proteus Company makes two products—X and Y. Each of these must be processed on a milling machine and on a turret lathe. The total amount of machine time available weekly on each machine is 100 hours, approximately a two-shift operation, six days a week.

Now suppose that product X requires *one* hour of machine time on the milling machine and *three* hours on the turret lathe; whereas product Y requires *two* hours on the milling machine and

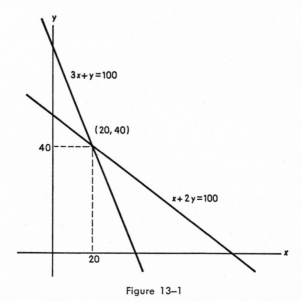

Figure 13–1

one hour on the turret lathe. To describe the quantities of X and Y which may be produced in a week, where x is the quantity of product X and y is the quantity of product Y, it is necessary and sufficient that

$$\begin{aligned}
x + 2y &\le 100 \\
3x + y &\le 100 \\
x &\ge 0 \\
y &\ge 0
\end{aligned} \qquad (3)$$

It can be seen that $x = 33\frac{1}{3}$ if only X is produced, or that $y = 50$ if only Y is produced. Both of these possibilities, however, would result in considerable idle machine time: $y = 0, x = 33\frac{1}{3}$ gives $66\frac{2}{3}$ hours of idle time on the milling machine; while $x = 0, y = 50$ gives 50 hours idle time on the turret lathe; and seldom would either be considered a practical alternative. A third alternative is to produce nothing at all; the machines would be idle all the time. Each of these three possibilities is *feasible* since the conditions of (3) would be satisfied. Negative values of x and y, on the other hand, are excluded from consideration by (3).

Is it possible to identify the optimal values for x and y? Clearly, not, since no decision criterion has been stated. Suppose therefore that the company wishes to maximize its net revenues (earnings) from the production and sale of these two products. It is still impossible to set a production program, i.e., choose x^* and y^*, the opti-

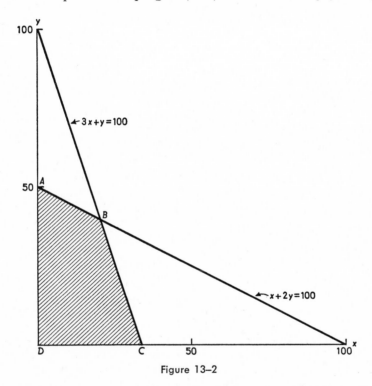

Figure 13–2

mum values. It is necessary to introduce economic information—as opposed to the engineering information embodied in (3)—in order to specify the company's objective in terms of x and y.

This can be accomplished by introducing the information that the company's earnings are $4.00 per unit on X and $3.00 per unit on Y. Letting $E(x, y)$ represent earnings, the earnings function is thus

$$E(x, y) = 4x + 3y \qquad (4)$$

The firm's management wants to maximize (4), subject to the restrictions on output which are imposed by machine time limitations as represented by the inequalities in (3). E is a function of x and y, and its graph is shown in Figure 13–3 along with the two equations implicit in the system of (3). For instance, if E is $900, then $4x + 3y = 900$; if $x = 210$, y must equal 20; if $x = 180$, y must equal 60, etc. Construction of the graph is facilitated by re-writing the earnings function $E = 4x + 3y$ explicitly in terms of y, as

$$y = \frac{E}{3} - \frac{4x}{3}$$

so that by choosing any value for E and x the corresponding value y can be determined. For any given value of E there exists a line having the y-intercept $E/3$ and a slope of $-4/3$. Several such lines are shown in Figure 13–3.

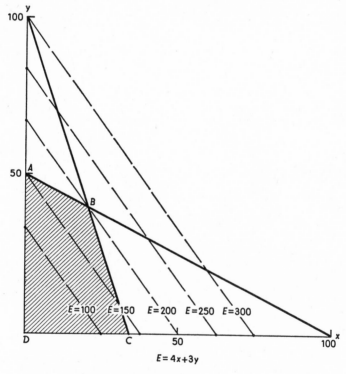

Figure 13–3

The decision problem is to find the highest value of E obtainable within the machine time restrictions stated in (3). This means that the line expressing E must contain at least one point which will satisfy the inequalities, $x + 2y \leq 100$, $3x + y \leq 100$, $x \geq 0$, and $y \geq 0$.

Clearly, the highest value of E, say E^*, is represented by the line which is tangent to the shaded area on the graph at the point $(x = 20, y = 40)$. At this point, B, the function $E = 4x + 3y$ has the value 200 and maximum earnings are \$200. The graph of the equation $E = 4x + 3y$ for all values of $E \geqq 200$ is entirely outside the shaded area.

By finding that E^* requires a production plan such that $x = 20$ and $y = 40$, a simple linear programming problem has been solved —one in which the solution was intuitively clear as soon as the profit function and the constraints were shown on the same graph (Figure 13–3). This simple problem, however, has illustrated certain aspects of the linear programming method which will be helpful in considering more complicated problems later on. These features are:

a) The set of all *feasible solutions* to the problem is represented graphically by a polygon—$ABCD$—the shaded area in Figure 13–2.

b) The *optimum solution* appears at a vertex, or corner, of the polygon. It does not matter what the coefficients are as long as the earnings function and the constraints are linear; the solution will always be at one of the corner points of the polygon. For instance, suppose there were no earnings at all on product Y, and the earnings function was $E = 4x$; the optimum solution would have been at vertex C. Or if the earnings function had been $E = 2x + 10y$, the vertex A would have been the optimum solution. Clearly the optimum vertex position depends only on the ratio of the two coefficients in (4).

c) A linear programming problem may not have any feasible solution. If the lines were such that no point in the positive quadrant (when $x, y > 0$) satisfied both inequalities, there would be no feasible solution.

d) If a linear programming problem has a feasible solution, then there also exists an optimum solution.

The graphical method for solving linear programming models is useful only for small problems, in fact, only for problems with two variables. For problems with more than two variables, more powerful techniques are necessary. One such technique is that of enumerating all the alternatives, computing E for each one, choosing the optimum, E^*, by inspection. This technique is useful for explanatory purposes. However, it quickly becomes less useful in practice as the problem grows in size and complexity.

The *enumeration technique* is applicable because of properties (a) and (b), for if a linear programming problem has any feasible solutions, the optimum solution is at one of the vertices and the number of vertices is limited. The technique consists of enumerating all the vertices, computing the earnings at each one and selecting as the optimum the vertex giving the highest earnings. For example for (3) and (4) the following table can be developed:

Vertex	x	y	E
A	0	50	150
B	20*	40*	200*
C	$33\frac{1}{3}$	0	$133\frac{1}{3}$
D	0	0	0

Simply by inspection of the last column, and remembering that the objective is to maximize E, it is seen that E^* implies $x^* = 20$ and $y^* = 40$, the same solution as before.

2. A THREE-PRODUCT PROBLEM

Now suppose that the Proteus Company has added a third product, Z, to its line. The earnings on each unit of Z are $5.00. Product Z requires two hours of machine time on the milling machine and three hours on the turret lathe.

The company's earnings function is now $E = 4x + 3y + 5z$, and the problem is to find x^*, y^*, and z^* which will result in E^*. In other words, how much of each of the three products should the company produce each week? The machine time restrictions governing the output of X, Y, and Z are expressed by

$$x + 2y + 2z \leq 100$$
$$3x + y + 3z \leq 100 \tag{5}$$
and also
$$x \geq 0$$
$$y \geq 0$$
$$z \geq 0$$

The equations implicit in (5) now represent planes instead of simply straight lines. It is necessary to imagine a three-dimensional graph of these planes. Considering the axes of this graph as perpendicular (technically, orthogonal) planes instead of as lines, the two additional planes described by the equations ($x + 2y + 2z = 100$ and $3x + y + 3z = 100$) will form a polyhedron whose sides are planes. (If this is difficult to visualize, take a look at a cardboard box. Seen from the top, it is a rectangle whose edges are four straight lines. Seen from any other angle, the sides are observed as planes.)

This polyhedron has corner points, or vertices, just as did the two-dimensional polygon. The previous result that the optimum solution of the problem will be found at one of these vertices applies here, and even though it is not easy to construct the graph, the values at each vertex can be computed. Then the vertex having the highest value in terms of earnings can be selected as the optimum point.

To evaluate the vertices by a process of enumeration, it is necessary first to identify the several planes which intersect to form the several vertices. The equations

$$x + 2y + 2z = 100 \qquad\qquad (6)$$
$$3x + y + 3z = 100$$

make up two sides of the polyhedron. The other three sides of the polyhedron are the yz-plane, the xz-plane, and the xy-plane. These planes are represented by the equations

$$x = 0$$
$$y = 0 \qquad\qquad (7)$$
$$z = 0$$

When any two of the five planes intersect, a straight line, rather than a point, is formed. When three planes intersect, i.e., when there is a common solution to any three of the five equations, the intersection may be a straight line or a single point. If it is a point, it may form a vertex of the feasible polyhedron. (Cf. the example of the cardboard box; when three sides of the box come together simultaneously, a corner of the box—a "point"—is formed.)

Given the set of five equations, x, y, and z must be evaluated at each vertex. That is, each combination of three equations is solved for the three unknowns as follows:

The Equations (Planes)
a) $x + 2y + 2z = 100$
b) $3x + y + 3z = 100$
c) $x = 0$
d) $y = 0$
e) $z = 0$

Vertex	x	y	z	$E =$ $4x + 3y + 5z$
a, b, c	0	25	25	200
a, b, d	$-33\frac{1}{3}$	0	$66\frac{2}{3}$	..
a, b, e	20	40	0	200
b, c, d	0	0	$33\frac{1}{3}$	$166\frac{2}{3}$
b, c, e	0	100	0	..
c, d, e	0	0	0	0
b, d, e	$33\frac{1}{3}$	0	0	$133\frac{1}{3}$
a, c, d	0	0	50	..
a, c, e	0	50	0	150
a, d, e	100	0	0	..

There are ten vertices. Only six of them, however, are within the set of feasible solutions, i.e., are vertices of the polyhedron of feasible solutions. Examine the vertex formed by the intersecting planes of equations a, b, and c. The values of x, y, and z are, respectively, 0, 25, and 25. Each of these is an allowable value; hence, the resulting value of $E = 200$ is feasible. Consider the next intersection, the one formed by equations a, b, and d. The respective values of x, y, and z are $-33\frac{1}{3}$, 0, and $66\frac{2}{3}$. Clearly, x cannot be $-33\frac{1}{3}$; hence, this intersection is outside the set of feasible solutions and the E-value implied by $(-33\frac{1}{3}, 0, 66\frac{2}{3})$ is irrelevant since it is not feasible.

Similarly, three other vertices must be excluded as being unobtainable: (b, c, e) because y cannot be greater than 100/2 by equation (a); (a, c, d) because z cannot be greater than 100/3 by equation (b); and (a, d, e) because x cannot be greater than 100/3 by equation (b).

Now that six potential optima have been isolated, it is a simple task to glance at the E-value implied by each in order to find the optimal course of action. The largest possible profit is $E^* = 200$, and it is obtainable with either of two production plans: $(0, 25, 25)$ or $(20, 40, 0)$. The fact that there are two optima is not particularly significant. It is significant, however, that each optimum involved produces only two of the three products. This point will be considered below.

The reader should not be concerned if the spatial aspects of the foregoing example are difficult to grasp. The use of analytic geometry in linear programming is limited, and visual or spatial concepts are of no use when more than three dimensions are involved anyway. It is only important to know that the vertices or edges of the geometric figures formed will always be the only points (or lines) which are potentially optimal points. In the particular example, the earnings plane happened to be parallel to an edge of the polyhedron rather than intersecting the polyhedron at a single point so that there was more than one optimum.

To summarize the argument to this point:

1. The first step was to realize that the feasible solutions were contained within or on a polyhedron created by the intersection of the planes implied in the several inequalities.
2. Next, the values of the vertices of this polyhedron were identified by solving each set of three equations in three unknowns; the values of x, y, and z thus obtained were substituted into the

profit function to find the value of each vertex—i.e., the value of the profit function at that vertex.

3. Those vertices which lay outside the feasible polyhedron were discarded. The feasible region does not include the solutions which have values of x, y, or z which are too high or too low in view of the machine-time restrictions or of the restriction that x, y, z are all nonnegative.

4. The vertex at which profit was highest was determined by inspection. In this case, there were two, indicating that the profit plane touched an edge rather than a corner of the polyhedron. (Strictly speaking, there were more than two optimal production schedules, although there were only two identified by the enumeration procedure. Why?)

The results suggest that the Proteus Company gained nothing by adding product Z. It can make no more profit now than it did with products X and Y only. On the other hand, it would be just as well off to drop product X and to produce only Y and Z.

In order to illustrate a case where the optimum is unique, suppose the company has found ways of improving the profitability of product Z so that the earnings function is now

$$E = 4x + 3y + 7z \qquad (8)$$

The results are somewhat different, as the enumeration procedure reveals:

Vertex	x	y	z	E
a, b, c	0	25	25	250
a, b, d	$-33\frac{1}{3}$	0	$66\frac{2}{3}$	. .
a, b, e	20	40	0	200
b, c, d	0	0	$33\frac{1}{3}$	$233\frac{1}{3}$
b, c, e	0	100	0	. .
c, d, e	0	0	0	0
b, d, e	$33\frac{1}{3}$	0	0	$133\frac{1}{3}$
a, c, d	0	0	50	. .
a, c, e	0	50	0	150
a, d, e	100	0	0	. .

The feasible region has not changed; the same four vertices must still be excluded. But now there is a unique optimum at the vertex defined by (a, b, c). Under these circumstances, it is clear that the company should now drop product X and manufacture 25 units per week of product Y and 25 units of product Z.

It may seem strange that the company can obtain more profit by producing two products than it can by producing all three, a result which is generally true. A careful statement of this important result is as follows:

Suppose there is limited time available on each of m machines which can produce n different products each of which requires time on each machine $(n \geqq m)$. Suppose further that earnings is a linear function of the number of units of each product produced. Then the optimum earnings can be obtained by producing only k products where $k \leqq m \leqq n$.

To show intuitively why this is true, consider the last example described. In mathematical terms the problem is:

$$\text{Maximize: } E = 4x + 3y + 7z \tag{9}$$
$$\text{Subject to: } x + 2y + 2z \leq 100 \tag{10}$$
$$3x + y + 3z \leq 100 \tag{11}$$

$x, y,$ and z nonnegative. The answer is, as already seen, $x = 0, y = 25, z = 25,$ which gives

$$E^* = 250$$

Now write the inequalities as equations in the form

$$2y + 2z = c_1 \tag{12}$$
$$y + 3z = c_2 \tag{13}$$

where $c_1 = 100 - x$ and $c_2 = 100 - 3x$. Then solve for y and z. Subtracting 2 times (13) from 3 times (12) and dividing by 4 gives

$$1 \cdot y + 0 \cdot z = \frac{3c_1 - 2c_2}{4}$$
$$= \tfrac{1}{4}[300 - 3x - 200 + 6x]$$
$$= 25 + \tfrac{3}{4}x$$

Similarly, subtracting (12) from 2 times (13) and dividing by 4 gives

$$0y + 1z = \frac{2c_2 - c_1}{4}$$
$$= \tfrac{1}{4}[200 - 6x - 100 + x]$$
$$= 25 - \tfrac{5}{4}x$$

or

$$y = 25 + \tfrac{3}{4}x \tag{14}$$
$$z = 25 - \tfrac{5}{4}x \tag{15}$$

This solution says that if there is to be no idle time, i.e., the equality sign holds in (10) and (11), then *a)* $y = 25$ and $z = 25$ if $x = 0$,

b) $y = 28$ and $z = 20$ if x has some positive value, say $x = 4$.

These results can, of course, be obtained from (10) and (11), but it is much easier to get them from (14) and (15). Furthermore, the set (14) and (15) can be substituted in (9) to give

$$E = 4x + 3[25 + \tfrac{3}{4}x] + 7[25 - \tfrac{5}{4}x]$$
$$= 250 - \tfrac{10}{4}x \tag{16}$$

This form of the earnings function says that $x = 0$ is the optimum production level for if $x > 0$, then $E < 250$, i.e., as x increases from 0, E declines: product X should not be produced.

The reason why only two products should be produced is now clear. From (14) and (15) it follows that since all the machine time is already being used to produce Y and Z, some X can be produced only by reducing the amount of time for Y and Z. In particular (14) and (15) say that if $x = 1$, i.e., one unit of X is produced, and the rest of the machine time is used for Y and Z, then $y = 25\tfrac{3}{4}$ and $z = 23\tfrac{3}{4}$. The net increase in earnings will be the earnings from one unit of x *less* the earnings that would have been received if the machine time was used to produce $\tfrac{3}{4}$ of a unit less of Y and $\tfrac{5}{4}$ units more of Z, namely,

$$4(1) - [3(-\tfrac{3}{4}) + 7(+\tfrac{5}{4})] = 4 + \tfrac{9}{4} - \tfrac{35}{4}$$
$$= - \tfrac{10}{4}$$

which is the coefficient that appears in (16). The same conclusion can be read directly from (16):

$$E = 250 - \tfrac{10}{4}x$$

Considering this as a function of one variable, the other two having been eliminated by the substitution of (14) and (15), it is clear by inspection that E^* implies $x = 0$.

The "new" form of the earnings function can be computed for each vertex of the polyhedron. The results for the example at hand are shown in the following table. It should be noted that there is at least one positive coefficient in each case. In the case where only one product is produced, one of the inequalities, (10) or (11), is redundant. The controlling inequality is shown in the table. The equations for X and Z only show that the solution must be $x = -100/3$, $y = 200/3$ if there is to be no idle time. This solution, of course, is not feasible.

Products	Equations from	Earnings Function
X	$x = \dfrac{100}{3} - \dfrac{y}{3} - z$ (11)	$E = 4x + 3y + 7z$ $E = \frac{400}{3} + 1\frac{2}{3}y + 3z$
Y	$y = 50 - \dfrac{x}{2} - z$ (10)	$E = 150 + 2\frac{1}{2}x + 4z$
Z	$z = \dfrac{100}{3} - x - \dfrac{y}{3}$ (11)	$E = \frac{700}{3} - 3x + \frac{2}{3}y$
X and Y	$x = 20 - \frac{4}{5}z$ (10) $y = 40 - \frac{3}{5}z$ (11)	$E = 200 + 2z$
X and Z	$x = -\frac{100}{3} + \frac{4}{3}y$ (10) $z = \frac{200}{3} - \frac{5}{3}y$ (11)	(not feasible since x cannot be negative)
Y and Z	$y = 25 + \frac{3}{4}x$ $z = 25 - \frac{5}{4}x$	$E = 250 - \frac{5}{2}x$

3. ADDITIONAL INFORMATION FROM LP SOLUTIONS

It has been shown in the preceding section that if there are two restricting inequalities, only two products are produced even though there were three possible products. The optimal number of products would have been the same even if there had been four, five, or a hundred possible products. The number of products which will be produced in a linear programming solution can never be larger than the number of constraints, regardless of how many products are technologically possible.

This fact can be used to elicit additional information from the linear programming model. First, define two fictitious products: U and W, and let u and w denote the quantities produced of each. Suppose each unit of U requires one hour of milling machine time and no time on the lathe, while each unit of W requires one hour of lathe time but no milling machine time. In fact, u and w are nothing more than the quantity of *idle* time on the milling machine and turret lathe, respectively. Since the time required to produce products *plus* the idle time on each machine must *equal* the total time available, the restricting inequalities of (5) become the equations of (17).

$$x + 2y + 2z + 1u + 0w = 100$$
$$3x + y + 3z + 0u + 1w = 100 \qquad (17)$$
$$x \geq 0, y \geq 0, z \geq 0, u \geq 0, w \geq 0$$

This is a set of two linear equations in five unknowns. From Chapter 12 it is known that two equations in two unknowns can have a unique solution, but that if the number of unknowns is greater than the number of equations, there can be an infinite number of solutions.

It is known that the optimum solution in the linear programming model of the preceding section calls for the production of at most two products, the other products not being produced. In terms of the equation this means that at most two of the variables will have nonzero values while the others will be zero. From the previous section, the optimum solution requires production of y and z so that the solution is known to require that $x = 0$, $u = 0$, $w = 0$. The optimum values of y and z can then be found by solving (18) which is derived directly from (17):

$$2y + 2z = 100$$
$$y + 3z = 100 \qquad (18)$$

Of course, $y^* = 25$, and $z^* = 25$, as before.

The earnings function of (9) becomes

$$E = 4x + 3y + 7z + 0u + 0w \qquad (19)$$

since U and W do not contribute to earnings. In this case $E^* = 3(25) + 7(25) = 250$. The solution indicates what should be produced and what the earnings will be.

Frequently the management also wants to know whether it should acquire more machine time or what the decrease in earnings will be if some X must be produced. These questions can be answered relatively easily by the method given above if x, u, and w are not set to zero but are carried along as variables.

The equations of (17) become

$$2y + 2z = 100 - x - 1u - 0w \qquad (20a)$$
$$y + 3z = 100 - 3x - 0u - 1w \qquad (20b)$$

and the solutions can be obtained as follows:

Subtracting 2 times (20b) from 3 times (20a) and dividing by 4

$$1 \cdot y + 0 \cdot z = 25 + \tfrac{3}{4}x - \tfrac{3}{4}u + \tfrac{1}{2}w \qquad (21)$$

Subtracting (20a) from 2 times (20b) and dividing by 4 gives

$$0 \cdot y + 1 \cdot z = 25 - \tfrac{5}{4}x + \tfrac{1}{4}u - \tfrac{1}{2}w \qquad (22)$$

The system of (21) and (22) has the same solutions as (18). Because (21) does not contain z and (22) does not contain y, the solutions obtained when $x = u = w = 0$ can be read off directly as $y = 25$ from (21) and $z = 25$ from (22). Furthermore, if, for example, $x = 4$, $u = 8$, and $w = 2$, the solution can also be obtained easily as

$$y = 25 + 3 - 6 + 1 = 23$$
$$z = 25 - 5 + 2 - 1 = 21 \qquad (23)$$

It should be noted that to obtain this solution from (17) would require the solution of a system of two equations in two unknowns. Equations (21) and (22) can be substituted in (19) to give

$$E = 4x + 3[25 + \tfrac{3}{4}x - \tfrac{3}{4}u + \tfrac{1}{2}w] + 7[25 - \tfrac{5}{4}x + \tfrac{1}{4}u - \tfrac{1}{2}w] + 0u + 0w$$
$$= 250 - 2\tfrac{1}{2}x - \tfrac{1}{2}u - 2w \qquad (24)$$

This formula for earnings reveals the following:

1. Since the coefficients of x, u, and w are negative, and since x, u, and w themselves must, by definition, be nonnegative it follows that the solution $x = u = w = 0$, $y = 25$, $z = 25$, which results in earnings of 250, is optimum.

2. The coefficient of x in (24), namely $-2\tfrac{1}{2}$, says that earnings will be reduced by $2\tfrac{1}{2}$ dollars if one unit of X is produced. This can easily be verified as follows: to produce one unit of X requires one hour of milling machine time and three hours of lathe time. Therefore the quantities of Y and Z that can be produced are given by the solution of the equation

$$2y + 2z = 99$$
$$y + 3z = 97$$

which is

$$y = 25\tfrac{3}{4}, \qquad z = 23\tfrac{3}{4} \qquad (25)$$

and

$$E = 4 + 3(25\tfrac{3}{4}) + 7(23\tfrac{3}{4}) = 247\tfrac{1}{2}$$

3. If an additional hour of milling machine time is available the earnings will be increased by $.50 and if an additional hour of lathe time is available, earnings will be increased by $2.00.

To show the third conclusion, suppose the new problem is written in the form,

$$\text{Maximize } E = 4x + 3y + 7z$$
$$\text{Subject to } \quad x + 2y + 2z \le 100 + F_1$$
$$3x + y + 3z \le 100 + F_2 \qquad (26)$$
$$x \ge 0, y \ge 0, z \ge 0$$

where F_1 is the change in the amount of milling machine time and F_2 the change in the amount of lathe time (the changes may be + or −). Adding the "slack variables" (i.e., the fictitious variables u and w) gives:

$$x + 2y + 2z + u = 100 + F_1$$
$$3x + y + 3z + w = 100 + F_2 \qquad (27)$$

Solving for y and z yields

$$y = 25 + \frac{3F_1}{4} - \frac{1F_2}{2} + \tfrac{3}{4}x - \tfrac{3}{4}u + \tfrac{1}{2}w$$
$$= 25 + \tfrac{3}{4}x - \tfrac{3}{4}(u - F_1) + \tfrac{1}{2}(w - F_2)$$
$$z = 25 + \frac{F_2}{2_2} - \frac{F_1}{4} - \tfrac{5}{4}x + \tfrac{1}{4}u - \tfrac{1}{2}w$$
$$= 25 - \tfrac{5}{4}x + \tfrac{1}{4}(u - F_1) - \tfrac{1}{2}(w - F_2)$$

(28)

These values are substituted into the earnings function:

$$E = 250 - 2\tfrac{1}{2}x - \tfrac{1}{2}(u - F_1) - 2(w - F_2)$$ (29)

In the case where an additional hour of milling machine time is available, i.e., $F_1 = 1$, $F_2 = 0$, the optimum solution, if $x = u = w = 0$, is

$$y = 25 + \tfrac{3}{4}$$
$$= 25\tfrac{3}{4}$$
$$z = 25 - \tfrac{1}{4}$$
$$= 24\tfrac{3}{4}$$

(30)

This solution is certainly feasible since

$$0 + 2(25\tfrac{3}{4}) + 2(24\tfrac{3}{4}) = 101 \le 100 + 1$$
$$0 + (25\tfrac{3}{4}) + 3(24\tfrac{3}{4}) = 100 \le 100$$

Then, by substituting into (29)

$$E = 250 + \tfrac{1}{2}$$
$$= 250\tfrac{1}{2}$$

(31)

It is possible, of course, that the products produced in the optimal program if 100 hours of milling machine time are available will not be produced by the optimal program if 101 hours of milling machine time are available. It is therefore essential to check that the solution obtained by this method is in fact feasible.

This technique of examining the change in earnings under unit changes of machine time is an important aspect of the application of linear programming. From a theoretical point of view it shows the relationship between linear programming and marginal analysis.

The technique also makes it possible to compute the solution of a slightly changed linear programming problem with much less effort than was required for solving the original problem.

An outline summary of the linear programming model follows.

SUMMARY OF THE LINEAR PROGRAMMING MODEL

A. *Description*

A problem can be placed in the linear programming format if it satisfies the following conditions:

1. There are n variables which must be nonnegative.
2. There are m linear inequalities restricting these variables.
3. The earnings function is a linear function of the n variables.

B. *Major Results*

The major results are:

1. There may or may not be any feasible solution. A feasible solution is one which satisfies the m linear inequalities and in which all the variables are nonnegative.
2. If there is a feasible solution, then there is also an optimum solution; an optimum solution is one which results in at least as high a value of the profit function as does any other feasible solution.
3. In the optimum solution no more than m of the variables will be different from zero and at least $n - m$ of the variables will be equal to zero.

C. *Computation*

The solution to a linear programming problem can be determined numerically by selecting a set of m variables out of the n, taking the other $n - m$, placing them on the right-hand side of the equation and then solving the m equations in m unknowns. The solutions are substituted into the earnings function, and the coefficients of the $n - m$ variables computed. If all of these coefficients are negative, an optimum solution has been obtained. If one or more of the coefficients is positive, then the solution is not optimum.

If n and m are relatively small, the solution can be obtained by trial-and-error enumeration of all sets of up to m variables until all coefficients are negative. If the number of variables is large, a more systematic procedure known as the Simplex Method is used. The Simplex Method may be applied "by hand" or on a computer.

D. *Other Information*

The information obtained in the solution of the linear programming model is as follows:

1. The solution is the set of values of the m variables which jointly maximize the earnings function.
2. The earnings which can be obtained by choosing alternative, nonoptimal solutions can be computed using the coefficients in the earnings function.
3. The value of additional resources can be computed using the coefficients in the earnings function.

4. APPLICATIONS OF LINEAR PROGRAMMING

Linear programming has been presented in this chapter in the context of a production scheduling decision—a determination of the optimum product mix—with selling prices and costs known and with a fixed but flexible productive capacity. The linear programming approach has proved to be very useful for a whole class of problems whose essential characteristic is the allocation of scarce resources among competing activities. The particular production scheduling decision considered here is but one example of this class. The LP model can also be applied to a wide range of other problems. Illustrations of most of these must be made in the context of the subject matter itself, not in a discussion of mathematics. However, two additional illustrations, somewhat simplified, are presented in this section.

Case No. 21.   The Laocoön Company[1]

The Laocoön Company has always used an outside carrier to make its deliveries. It is now investigating the possibility of buying trucks and making its own deliveries. Three types of trucks are available. If the company decides to do its own carrying, which should be purchased?

Laocoön has available 150 man-days which it can use for the trucking operation, and is ready to invest $400,000 in the purchase of trucks. The maximum number of trucks which it is feasible to purchase is 30 because of a limitation on loading facilities. The amount of trucking to be done exceeds 350,000 ton-miles, and any trucking not done by the firm itself can still be subcontracted to the outside carrier. The characteristics of the three types of trucks under consideration are in the following table:

Type	Ton-miles per Day	Man-days per Vehicle	Purchase Cost
A	6,300	3	8,000
B	10,800	6	13,000
C	11,340	6	15,000

The first requirement for a problem to be susceptible to an LP approach is that there must be a number of variables about which the decision maker must make a choice. In this case the decision is how many of each type of truck to buy. Thus, the decision variables are

x_1 = the number of type A trucks to be purchased,
x_2 = the number of type B trucks to be purchased,
x_3 = the number of type C trucks to be purchased.

The second requirement of the LP model is that the objective function be linear. While the present problem does not state so

---

[1] Suggested by an article by Johannes F. Sehwär, "Operations Research in the Field of Transportation Engineering," *The Civil Engineer in South Africa*, January, 1961, pp. 7–12.

explicitly, it is implicit that the objective is to maximize the number of ton-miles per day within the restrictions imposed by the number of man-days available, the available loading space, and the amount available for purchase. The objective then is to maximize T, the total ton-miles per day, which is, of course, the sum of the daily ton-miles for each type of truck multiplied by the number of trucks of each type:

$$T = 6300x_1 + 10,800x_2 + 11,340x_3 \tag{32}$$

The third requirement is that the constraints must be linear inequalities of the variables. The first restriction in the present case, that the total number of man-days must be less than or equal to 150, is indeed linear:

$$3x_1 + 6x_2 + 6x_3 \leq 150 \tag{33}$$

The second restriction, also linear, is that the purchase cost must not exceed \$400,000:

$$8000x_1 + 13,000x_2 + 15,000x_3 \leq 400,000 \tag{34}$$

And finally, since the number of loading spaces is limited, the total number of trucks purchased must be less than or equal to 30:

$$x_1 + x_2 + x_3 \leq 30 \tag{35}$$

These linear inequalities, together with the several implied non-negativity conditions complete the problem. Since all the requirements are satisfied, this problem can be solved by linear programming. A complete statement of the problem is as follows:

$$
\begin{aligned}
\text{Maximize } T = {}& 6300x_1 + 10,800x_2 + 11,340x_3 \\
\text{Subject to} \quad & 3x_1 + 6x_2 + 6x_3 \leq 150 \\
& 8000x_1 + 13,000x_2 + 15,000x_3 \leq 400,000 \qquad (36) \\
& x_1 + x_2 + x_3 \leq 30 \\
& x_1 \geq 0 , \ x_2 \geq 0 , \ x_3 \geq 0
\end{aligned}
$$

Since this problem has three variables and six inequalities, the number of possible vertices is not too large for the method of enumeration. However, in practice the number of variables would probably be larger so that a computer would be used to obtain a solution. Suppose, in order to avoid the detail of enumerating all the possibilities, it has been "guessed" that the optimum decision involves the purchase of type A and C trucks, and that it is desired to verify whether the guess is correct.

To do so, first define the slack variables:

x_4 = the number of man-days not used,
x_5 = the number of dollars of the total investment which will not be used,
x_6 = the number of loading spaces which will not be used.

Since positive values of these variables do not contribute to the total number of ton-miles, the objective function becomes

$$T = 6300x_1 + 10,800x_2 + 11,340x_3 + 0x_4 + 0x_5 + 0x_6 \qquad (37)$$

The inequalities become the equations:

$$
\begin{aligned}
3x_1 + \quad\; 6x_2 + \quad\;\; 6x_3 + x_4 &= 150 \\
8000x_1 + 13,000x_2 + \;15,000x_3 + x_5 &= 400,000 \\
x_1 + \qquad x_2 + \qquad\; x_3 + x_6 &= 30
\end{aligned}
\qquad (38)
$$

A further guess is made that the total purchase price will not require all the money available for investment. Thus, x_5 will be greater than zero. The system of equations of (38) is then rewritten as:

$$
\begin{aligned}
3x_1 + \quad\; 6x_3 + 0x_5 &= \quad\;\; 150 - \quad\;\; 6x_2 - \;x_4 - 0x_6 \\
8000x_1 + 15,000x_3 + \quad x_5 &= 400,000 - 13,000x_2 - 0x_4 - \; x_6 \\
x_1 + \qquad x_3 + 0x_5 &= \qquad 30 - \qquad\; x_2 - 0x_4 - \; x_6
\end{aligned}
\qquad (39)
$$

Solving (39) for $x_1, x_3,$ and x_5 gives

$$
\begin{aligned}
x_1 + 0x_3 + 0x_5 &= \quad\;\; 10 - \quad\;\; 0x_2 + \quad \tfrac{1}{3}x_4 - \quad\;\; 2x_6 \\
0x_1 + \; x_3 + 0x_5 &= \quad\;\; 20 - \qquad x_2 - \quad \tfrac{1}{3}x_4 + \qquad x_6 \\
0x_1 + 0x_3 + \; x_5 &= 20,000 + 2000x_2 + \tfrac{7000}{3}x_4 + 1000x_6
\end{aligned}
\qquad (40)
$$

Substituting into the objective function then yields

$$T = 289,800 - 540x_2 - 1680x_4 - 1260x_6 \qquad (41)$$

This form of the objective function shows that the guess was indeed correct and that the maximum number of ton-miles that can be obtained within the restrictions is 289,800. The coefficient 540 shows that the purchase of any type B trucks would reduce T by 540 for each truck purchased. Analogously the coefficient 1680 tells us that each additional man-day could result in an increase in T of 1680. Furthermore, if additional loading space becomes available so that additional trucks could be purchased, the ton-miles would be increased by 1260 per additional loading space. Additional funds for investment would not increase the ton-miles since the solution has $x_5 = 20,000$, which implies that the optimal buying decision requires only $380,000.

Case No. 22.   An Investment Problem

An investor wishes to diversify his portfolio and make due allowance for long-term growth potentialities, but at the same time maximize his current dividend income. He has considered the various securities in which he might invest, and has classified them into four types:

Type A: Relatively high element of risk, with commensurately high dividend returns and considerable growth potential.

Type B: Speculative stocks with considerable risk, high dividends, but less growth potential than type *A*.

Type C: Stocks with little risk, considerable growth potential, but relatively low dividend income at present.

Type D: Stocks with little risk, not much growth potential, and fairly high dividends.

Because of the element of risk, the investor wishes to restrict purchases of types *A* and *B* to not more than 30% of his total investment. To enhance prospects for long-term growth of his investments, he wishes to have at least 40% of his total outlay in types *A* and *C*. Within these restrictions, he wishes to maximize his current dividend income.

Total investment is \$100,000. Dividend returns on the four types of investment are

$$A: \quad 6\%$$
$$B: \quad 7\%$$
$$C: \quad 3\%$$
$$D: \quad 5\%$$

Problem: How should the total investment be allocated?

In linear programming notation, the problem may be stated as

$$\begin{aligned}
&\text{Maximize } 6A + 7B + 3C + 5D \\
&\text{Subject to } A + B \le 30 \\
&\qquad\qquad A + C \ge 40 \\
&\qquad\qquad A + B + C + D = 100
\end{aligned} \tag{42}$$

where A, B, C, and D now represent the *amount* of investment in each of the four types. Observe that 100 instead of 100,000 is being used for the total investment figure; it makes no difference in the allocation. The first two inequalities may be rewritten by introducing slack variables E and F so that the system becomes:

$$\begin{aligned}
A + B + E &= 30 \\
A + C - F &= 40 \\
A + B + C + D &= 100
\end{aligned} \tag{43}$$

Note that the sign of the slack variable F is negative; this is because of the direction of the inequality.

The optimal solution is not immediately obvious, but the alternatives are few. Suppose that the investor has considered these alternatives and has concluded that the best plan is to invest \$30,000 in A, \$10,000 in C, and \$60,000 in D. The linear programming format can be used to determine whether this is in fact the best solution.

The first step is to define A, C, and D—the variables included in the final solution—in terms of the variables not included. Following a procedure analogous to that in the preceding example, it is seen that

$$
\begin{aligned}
A &= 30 - B - E \\
C &= 10 + B + E + F \\
D &= 60 - B - F
\end{aligned}
\tag{44}
$$

Substituting the derived values of (44) into the objective function yields

$$
\begin{aligned}
R &= 6(30 - B - E) + 7B + 3(10 + B + E + F) + 5(60 - B - F) \\
&= 510 - B - 3E - 2F
\end{aligned}
\tag{45}
$$

This result shows that the solution is indeed optimal, since the coefficients of all the variables not included in the solution are negative. The coefficient of B in equation (45) tells us that he will lose \$10 income for every unit investment in B; that is, for every thousand dollars invested in B. Similarly, the coefficient of E indicates that if the maximum allowable investment in types A and B were 31 instead of 30, interest would be increased by \$30. And the coefficient of F shows that if minimum investment in A and C (constraint number two) were 39 instead of 40, interest would be increased by \$20.

Result (45) also shows that by following the procedure outlined, the investor will earn interest of \$5100.

EXERCISES, SECTION 1

1. Find the maximum value of $F(x, y) = 3x + 4y$, subject to the constraints:

$$
\begin{aligned}
2x + y &\le 6 \\
x + 3y &\le 8 \\
x &\ge 0 \\
y &\ge 0
\end{aligned}
$$

Develop the solution using the graphical method and verify the solution by the method of enumeration of vertices.

2. Maximize $G(x, y) = 3x + 2y$, if
$$x + y < 5$$
$$2x + 4y < 12$$
$$x > 0$$
$$y \geq 0$$
Show the solution graphically and by enumeration.

3. The Ilium Corporation manufactures electronic devices, final assembly of which is accomplished by a small group of trained workers operating simultaneously on the devices. Due to space limitations, the working group may not exceed ten in number. The firm's operating budget allows \$4500 per month as salary for the group.

   A certain amount of discrimination is evidenced by the fact that the firm pays men in the group \$500 per month, while women doing the same work receive \$400. However, previous experience has indicated that a man will produce about \$1000 in "value added" per month, while a woman worker adds only \$900. If the firm wishes to maximize the value added by the group, how many men and how many women should be included?

4. A manufacturer of lawn furniture makes three products: lawn chairs, benches, and tables. Processing of these products is done on a tube-bending machine and a drilling machine. A lawn table requires one hour of time on the tube-bending machine and two hours on the drill; profit per table is \$5.00. A lawn chair requires one hour on the tube bender and one hour on the drill; profit per chair is \$3.00. A bench requires one hour on the tube bender and no time on the drill; profit per bench is \$3.00 There are ten hours of time per day available on the tube bender and 12 hours on the drill.

   What should be the daily production of each of the three products? Assume that they are not sold in sets; i.e., sales of one product do not affect the sales of the others.

EXERCISES, SECTION 2

5. Find the maximum value of $5x + 6y + 7z$

$$\text{Subject to } x + y \leq 10$$
$$2x + 2z \leq 18$$
$$(x, y, z \text{ all } \geq 0)$$

6. Find the maximum value of $5x_1 + 6x_2 + x_3 + 2x_4$

$$\text{Subject to } x_1 + x_2 + x_3 + x_4 \leq 10$$
$$2x_1 + x_3 \leq 12$$
$$2x_2 + x_4 \leq 14$$
$$(x_1, x_2, x_3, x_4 \text{ all } \geq 0)$$

7. An office manager is considering which kind of filing cabinets he should purchase. The supplier has suggested three types, having the following characteristics:

Type	Cost per Unit	Square Feet of Floor Space Required	Usable Capacity, in Cubic Feet
A.............	$50	4	12
B.............	70	6	24
C.............	60	8	28

The budget department has allocated $2100 for the purchase of filing cabinets. Seventy-two square feet of floor space are available for placement of the new units; units may not be stacked on top of each other. The manager's objective is to get as many cubic feet of usable storage capacity as possible, within the limitations imposed by floor space and budgetary restrictions. What kind of cabinets should he buy, and how many?

8. A business consulting firm has been offered four contracts simultaneously. Company A and Company B, both electronics firms, have asked for assistance on similar types of problems. Company A, being large and prosperous, has offered $500 per day for an indefinite period for services of two highly qualified specialists on the consultant's staff. Company B wants one of these men and is willing to pay $100 per day. The two men asked for have a total of 12 man-days of free time available per month. Company C, an aeronautics firm, has asked for two other men having a different kind of training, and is willing to pay $600 per day for the services of the two men. Company D, also in aeronautics, will pay $200 per day for one of these men. These two men have a total of 14 man-days per month of free time.

To further complicate the situation, the consulting firm's president has indicated that the four men in question should not be committed for more than a grand total of ten man-days per month, since certain old established customers may make unexpected demands on their time.

Problem: Which contracts should be accepted, and how much time should be spent on each in order to maximize revenue?

EXERCISES, SECTION 3

9. In Exercise 3,
   a) What would be the value of increasing available work space so that one more worker could be hired?
   b) What would be the cost of hiring one additional woman worker, at the expense of losing a male worker?

10. In Exercise 4,
    a) What does the solution state about the value of additional time on the tube-bending machine?
    b) On the drilling machine?

11. In Exercise 7,
    a) What is the value of additional funds for purchase of cabinets?

b) What is the value of additional floor space, in terms of the added storage capacity it will allow?

12. In Exercise 8, what is the effect on revenue if C demands an additional day's work?

13. In previous chapters, the concepts of Lagrange multipliers and "marginals"—marginal cost, revenue, profit, etc.—have been discussed. In this chapter, the relationship between linear programming and marginal analysis was shown; it was demonstrated that the value of an additional hour of machine time—i.e., a relaxing of a given constraint—could be determined from the linear programming solution. Comment on the relationship of Lagrange multipliers, marginals, and the coefficients of the slack variables in a linear programming solution, and show that these are in fact three names for essentially the same thing.

CHAPTER 14

MANAGEMENT SCIENCE MODELS

THE PREVIOUS chapters have dealt with the development of mathematical relationships among variables and the development of mathematical operations such as differentiation and integration. These concepts and techniques have been applied to various problems which purported to deal with practical business problems; at least the names of the variables are familiar to businessmen: earnings, cost, production level, etc.

In this, the final chapter, it is appropriate to ask just how practical the application of mathematics to business problems really is. The chapter has been titled "Management Science Models" because the words "management science" are coming to be associated with the practical application of mathematics and quantitative techniques to business problems.

The application of mathematics to business problems can be termed successful if it aids the manager in his tasks of decision making, planning, and administering, or if it aids in the development of a body of knowledge and techniques which reduces formerly unsolvable problems to solvable ones.

The first section describes how management science is the culmination of a series of attempts to develop a systematic approach to decision making. The approach is illustrated by some examples drawn from cases presented earlier. The second section then discusses some of the objections that a practical manager might raise and ways in which the limitations of the models can be reduced. The last section contains part of a bibliographical essay on decision making that indicates the extent to which a body of knowledge has been developed.

1. THE MANAGEMENT SCIENCE APPROACH

Management science models have their origins in certain qualitative and para-quantitative decision-making methods which have long been used by managers. These methods are based primarily on intuition and experience. The decision maker by accumulating experience has acquired, perhaps subconsciously, the ability to make a "good" or "the best" decision.

A further improvement in decision making usually occurs when the decision maker explicitly formulates his alternatives and the qualitative effect of his proposed decision. For example, suppose a decision maker is concerned with the economic order quantity, a problem discussed in Chapter 5. He has presumably been using some order quantity in the past, say x_0, which he is considering increasing. He might prepare, or have in mind, a table such as the following:

Desirable Consequences	*Undesirable Consequences*
1. If the order quantity is increased, there will have to be fewer orders in any given time period, and hence the clerical cost of ordering will be decreased.	1. If the order quantity is increased, the average inventory will be increased, and hence more money will be tied up in carrying the inventory.
2. If the price should rise, the firm would have received a larger number of units at the old price.	2. Because of the larger inventory there is more danger that the item will become obsolete, and hence a loss will be suffered.

As a refinement of this approach, the decision maker can attach subjective weights to the several effects and then determine whether or not the order quantity should be increased. Since the method is still essentially qualitative, no information is given about the amount of change in the order quantity.

The procedure can be made more quantitative by specifying the objectives more explicitly and by assigning numerical weights to each according to its importance. This is an *index-number* approach. In the example, the decision maker might decide that he has two major objectives—to reduce clerical cost and to guard against obsolescence—and that the first objective is twice as important as the second. He might then determine that doubling the quantity ordered would reduce clerical costs by $100 and increase the potential cost of obsolescence by an amount equivalent to $50. The value of doubling the quantity ordered is then

$$100 - 50 = 50$$

Since this is positive, he would probably want to double the order quantity. The calculation would be carried out for other plausible changes in the quantity ordered and a decision made.

Many other examples of nearly quantitative techniques and rules of thumb are no doubt familiar to the reader who has had administrative experience. Management science models as they are known today are simply formal, logical extensions of the earlier, less systematic decision processes. The following is a description of the elements in the development of these more formal and more quantitative models.

Quantitative analysis of business problems has several important characteristics. First, the problem is encountered in a "real-world setting," in an "environment." After identifying it in qualitative or verbal terms, the problem must be translated into quantitative terms; that is, the problem must be abstracted from its environment. This step, probably a large part of the whole analytical process, means building a model which is an abstract representation of the situation being analyzed. This step of abstracting to a formal model is a very difficult one and requires a degree of skill which rests in large part on experience and judgment.

The model will not, and should not, be an exact equivalent of the situation as the analyst encounters it; the whole approach is based on the premise that the problem as encountered is too complex, too "environmentally rich," to be solved by direct attack. If this is not true, then, of course, no formal analytical apparatus is necessary.

The verbal descriptions of problems are actually verbal models of particular situations. The following is a typical political model:

> The right wing of the French electorate is sufficiently aroused by the inept handling of overseas affairs that if the Communist vote lines up with them, as is possible due to the Communist opposition to Monsieur X, the government will fall.

This verbal economic model purports to explain the 1957–58 recession:

> The recession could have been stopped had the defense spending cutback been delayed, had the money rates been eased sooner and business confidence restored before unemployment had passed three million.

The inadequacy of words becomes apparent when a model is presented quantitatively. It is in the attempt to present relationships with precision, as well as quantitatively, that the use of mathematics is growing in model development. The vagueness, the ambiguity, the lack of clear and specific definitions of the character of a situation described verbally are faults which can be avoided by formalized mathematical presentation of problems. This objective is not always achieved. In the minds of many, formalized models take on an aura of authenticity and accuracy which can lead to misapplication. However, the attempt to develop a formalized, mathematical model of a given situation demands a more thorough analysis of the situation than would otherwise be demanded and, consequently, problems are often more properly analyzed.

Translating problems stated in verbal terms to precise mathematical problems is not an easy task because most languages do not lend themselves to precise, unambiguous statements. The following exchange illustrates this point as well as the previous comment on the ambiguity of verbal models:

From the Minutes of a Borough Council Meeting: Councillor Trafford took exception to the proposed notice at the entrance of South Park: "No dogs must be brought to this Park except on a lead." He pointed out that this order would not prevent an owner from releasing his pets, or pet, from a lead when once safely inside the Park.

THE CHAIRMAN (COLONEL VINE): What alternative wording would you propose, Councillor?

COUNCILLOR TRAFFORD: "Dogs are not allowed in this Park without leads."

COUNCILLOR HOGG: Mr. Chairman, I object. The order should be addressed to the owners, not to the dogs.

COUNCILLOR TRAFFORD: That is a nice point. Very well then: "Owners of dogs are not allowed in this Park unless they keep them on leads."

COUNCILLOR HOGG: Mr. Chairman, I object. Strictly speaking, this would prevent me as a dog-owner from leaving my dog in the back-garden at home and walking with Mrs. Hogg across the Park.

COUNCILLOR TRAFFORD: Mr. Chairman, I suggest that our legalistic friend be asked to redraft the notice himself.

COUNCILLOR HOGG: Mr. Chairman, since Councillor Trafford finds it so difficult to improve on my original wording, I accept. "Nobody without his dog on a lead is allowed in this Park."

COUNCILLOR TRAFFORD: Mr. Chairman, I object. Strictly speaking, this notice would prevent me, as a citizen, who owns no dog, from walking in the Park without first acquiring one.

COUNCILLOR HOGG (with some warmth): Very simply, then: "Dogs must be led in this Park."

COUNCILLOR TRAFFORD: Mr. Chairman, I object: this reads as if it were a general injunction to the Borough to lead their dogs into the Park.

Councillor Hogg interposed a remark for which he was called to order; upon his withdrawing it, it was directed to be expunged from the Minutes.

THE CHAIRMAN: Councillor Trafford, Councillor Hogg has had three tries; you have had only two . . . .

COUNCILLOR TRAFFORD: "All dogs must be kept on leads in this Park."

THE CHAIRMAN: I see Councillor Hogg rising quite rightly to raise another objection. May I anticipate him with another amendment: "All dogs in this Park must be kept on the lead."

This draft was put to the vote and carried unanimously, with two abstentions.[1]

It is desirable to distinguish between two types of applications of formal analytical techniques to business problems. The first is known as *descriptive* and involves the determination, by some method or another, of the relationships among variables. The first step in a descriptive analysis would be exactly the one described earlier: construction of a model representing the situation confronting the investigator. The second step would be the determination of the forms of the several functional relationships linking the variables and the estimation of the parameters. This task, which can be formidable, usually involves statistical analysis.

The second type of business application, as contrasted with the descriptive, is called *normative* and involves the use of the relationships among the variables to derive a decision rule that will assist a decision maker in making an optimum decision. The normative model must include a criterion by which a decision is to be judged. This criterion, usually called the objective function, must be made explicit and must be unique. In many of the cases and examples of this book, an earnings function was the objective function.

The normative application thus goes beyond the descriptive, although the first steps may be the same or similar. Although both types of analysis are applicable to business, the normative is of greater interest here. In the discussion of the management science process which follows, it will be assumed that the words "problem" and "model" always refer to normative or decision situations.

After the problem has been abstracted from the real-world environment in which it occurs and has been made explicit in the mathematical world of the model, that is, after the model has been formulated, the stage is set for the next step—solving the model. This step, of course, is not necessary in a purely descriptive analysis, since an optimum solution can be sought only if the model includes an objective function, i.e., only if a normative result is sought.

It is in deriving a solution to the model that mathematical techniques, usually optimizing ones, are of the greatest value. Again, there is a premise that the original problem is too complex for

---

[1] Robert Graves and Alan Hodge, "The Reader Over Your Shoulder"; quoted in Ernest Nagel, "Symbolic Notation, Haddocks' Eyes and Dog-Walking Ordinance," quoted in James R. Newmann, *The World of Mathematics* (New York: Simon and Schuster, Inc., 1956), Vol. 3, pp. 1890–91.

solution by inspection; that is, a formal solution technique is necessary.

The management science approach to a decision-making problem may be summarized as follows:

1. Identify the decision variables and denote the range of feasible alternatives.
2. Specify the objective.
3. Identify parameters, i.e., other factors to be included.
4. Develop the model which expresses the objective as a function of the decision variables and the parameters.
5. Solve the model for the value of the decision variables which optimizes the objective.

These steps are illustrated in Table 1 for two optimization problems which were discussed earlier in a less formal manner. The economic order quantity was presented in Case 1 in Chapter 5, and the linear programming model was formulated in Chapter 13.

Table 1

Step	Economic Order Quantity	Linear Programming
Decision variables and alternatives	x = number of units per order; $0 \leq x \leq Q$	x = number of units of X to produce; $0 \leq x$ y = number of units of Y to produce; $0 \leq y$
Objective function	Minimize total cost (T) = ordering cost + inventory carrying cost	Maximize profit
Parameters	Ordering cost = k Carrying cost = $a + bx$ Total demand = Q	Total time on milling machine = 100 hours Total time on turret lathe = 100 hours Milling machine time to produce one X = 1 Milling machine time to produce one Y = 2 Lathe time to produce one X = 3 Lathe time to produce one Y = 1 Profit on one X = 4 Profit on one Y = 3
Model	$T = \dfrac{kx}{2} + \dfrac{aQ}{x} + bQ$	Max $P = 4x + 3y$ Subject to $x + 2y \leq 100$ $3x + y \leq 100$
Solution	$\dfrac{dT}{dx} = 0; \dfrac{d^2T}{dx^2} < 0$ $x = \sqrt{\dfrac{2aQ}{k}}$	By graphical or enumeration methods $x = 20; y = 40$

After a solution to the model is obtained, the analyst moves to the last stage of the process: relating the normative result, the decision rule, back to the actual situation confronting the decision maker. That is, the solution must be translated from mathematical terms into policy language. This step, also dependent in large part on the skills of the analyst and decision maker, can be a difficult one.

The several stages of the process are summarized in the following diagram:

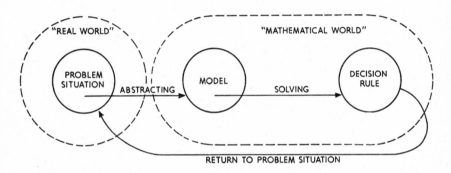

Reading from left to right, the first step is to move from the real world to the mathematical world by formulating the problem in quantitative terms. The next step is to manipulate the model according to the rules of mathematics so that a solution or decision rule is obtained. Finally, the decision rule must be related back to the environment in which the problem actually exists and in which the policy maker must act.

2. LIMITATIONS AND EXTENSIONS OF THE MANAGEMENT SCIENCE APPROACH

The reactions of a manager to the management science approach may be that the procedure is fine for hypothetical problems, but that it cannot be applied because the assumptions are never satisfied in real life. For example, a known uniform demand in inventory problems is rare: the demand is nearly always unknown; the predicting problem invariably involves forecasting into the future, and this cannot be done with complete accuracy; variables and the relationships between them cannot be quantified, etc.

Consider the practical objection that the variables or factors which affect decision-making problems cannot be quantified. It is true that many of the factors which enter into business decision problems are presently thought of as being qualitative variables and, therefore, incapable of being expressed quantitatively. However, the history of science can be stated in terms of the sequence of situations whereby variables which were thought of as being qualitative came to be treated quantitatively. Furthermore, businessmen do make judgments about the relationships of qualitative factors. They will speak, for example, of the productivity of plant A being higher than that of plant B. All that is required to go from ordinal relationships to quantitative measurements is the ability to measure. The development of models should be quite useful in determining what should be measured and how it can be measured.

A second objection, while granting that perhaps some of the variables can be identified and quantified, is that there will be so many variables and the relationships among them will be so complex that it will be impossible to include them all in a quantitative model. This complexity, of course, is the very reason why a human being needs some help as a decision maker, and this help can come only from an objective and abstract treatment of the problem.

Most business problems become extremely complicated if one attempts to consider all the possible factors that might affect the problem. A basic premise made throughout this text is that problems can be simplified by neglecting some factors and simplifying some relationships without necessarily invalidating the subsequent results. It is, of course, possible to oversimplify a problem; the real art is to determine how much a problem should be simplified. The mathematical techniques may even make it possible to determine which of the many factors are influential enough to be retained in the model.

Relationships can be approximated to any desired degree of accuracy by increasing the effort spent in determining the relationships and by making use of the power and complexity of mathematics. The mathematical techniques tend to become complicated as the relationships become more complex. A number of the techniques covered in this text illustrate how the relationships and the mathematics become more difficult as the models become more realistic. In the problems dealing with one decision variable, the linear and polynomial relations were easier to deal with than those involving complex functions such as the logarithm and the exponential. Some problems are trivial when only one decision variable is considered, and it will be remembered that the calculus of two or more variables is considerably more complicated than that of one variable. When a restriction was added to the model, the solution (by Lagrange multipliers) became even more complicated. Another factor which makes models more realistic is the assumption that a parameter is a random variable instead of a fixed quantity. This, it will be recalled, required the optimization of an expected value. Many other ways exist for making models more realistic; however, the necessary mathematics is beyond the scope of this text.

A third objection often raised is that while it may be possible to formulate a complex model, it will not be possible to obtain a solution which is economically practical. It is generally true that the more complicated a model is, the more difficult it is to obtain a solution.

There are different kinds of solution situations. First, when a solution can be expressed as a closed computable function of the parameter, it is said that there is an analytical solution. This is equivalent to saying that it is possible to determine a function s such that $x = s(z)$ gives an optimal value of E for any value of z. The function s is called a decision rule or, sometimes, a strategy.

If the analytical solution can be obtained, the decision problem is reduced to a matter of computation. The decision rule is obtained by solving the equation $f'(x, z) = 0$ for x in terms of the external variables and parameters. If this cannot be done, an analytical decision cannot, in general, be obtained. Note that derivation of an analytical solution depends on the form of f, in particular, on whether f' exists, and on the restrictions on x.

If an analytical solution cannot be obtained, it may be possible to find a solution by an *enumerative method*. If the decision variable x can take a finite number of discrete values, it is theoretically possible to enumerate all possible alternatives, compute E for each one, and identify the optimum alternative by inspection.

In any large problem, the method of enumeration would require the evaluation of far too many alternatives to be practical. It is frequently possible, however, to reduce the number of alternatives which must be examined. For example, suppose a value of x is selected and the function f evaluated at that point. Certain other functions are computed; for example, the derivative of f if f is differentiable. Using this additional information and advanced technique, a new value of x is selected. If the procedure works correctly, the value of f for this new point x will be greater than that for the previous point of x. By repeating this procedure, it is theoretically possible to come to the optimal point. *Linear programming* is an example of a major mathematical technique in which a solution is obtained by an enumerative or an iterative procedure. Such procedures involve the numerical computation of values of f for successively better values of x. An optimal value of x is guaranteed.

Some business problems are so complicated that they cannot be reduced at the present time to the structure described above. Consider, for example, the problem of balancing an assembly line. The number of alternatives is so large that complete enumeration is out of the question. The measure of effectiveness cannot be expressed as a function of the decision variables in any closed or easily computable form. The approach that can be taken is to abandon any attempt at locating the optimum balance and to look instead for a way to improve the present line-balancing method. The term *heuristic problem solving* is used to describe such a procedure. Each step is computable and results in an improved solution to the problem, and as such will represent a further step toward the optimal solution. But it will not, in general, be possible to guarantee that any one solution is optimal.

Some problems in business are so complex that representing them by a mathematical model is impractical. In such cases it may be worthwhile to *simulate* the situation which represents the problem in order to gain useful information. Simulation is a general approach to the synthesis and analysis of systems; it usually concentrates on generating highly specific results from highly specific assumptions. The goal is usually the description of a particular situation rather than the identification of a general solution. It thus is a technique which is useful for studying problems which are otherwise mathematically intractable. Simulation generally involves a large number of calculations; however, it can be used on any problem which can be stated quantitatively. The availability of electronic computers has made simulation a feasible approach to many problems which could not have been attempted before.

A fourth objection is that people do not behave rationally and, therefore, models cannot be constructed for situations involving human decisions. Individuals do not always behave rationally, but sometimes the behavior of a number of people can be modeled with sufficient accuracy by using a probability distribution. When a relatively small number of individuals are involved, it may be possible to apply a branch of mathematics known as the *theory of games.* Experience has shown that it is sometimes possible to develop workable models involving human beings.

3. THE PRESENT STATUS OF MANAGEMENT SCIENCE[1a]

The most aggressive probing into decision-making techniques has come from those seeking to develop a management science.[2] While traditionalists may accept some compromise of the principle of rationality, many management scientists seek devices and procedures which will reduce both nonrationality and irrationality to negligible factors in decision making. Thus their discussions frequently center on more precise ways of describing the choices confronting management. A good deal of attention is given to the precise definition of alternatives within these choices. And more recently a great deal of attention has been directed toward the identification of the probable "outcomes" of a particular alternative. The expected consequences of each anticipated course of action having been estimated, the critical step is that of maximizing utility or disutility by weighting these outcomes within the values of the organization.

One has the impression that there are those who look toward the time when numerical values, representing estimated outcomes, may be substituted for verbal symbols in a formula representing organizational goals, which would then be solved for a decision. Lest this seem incredible, it should be noted that it was done on a lathe operator's decisions long ago by Fredrich Taylor, and his expectations are becoming a reality through the application of today's more powerful tools to a manager's problems.

If it is accidental that the term management science is almost a simple reversal of scientific management, it is not without significance, for there is a sense in which the current scientific, rationalist movement is essentially scientific management with new, vastly more powerful tools. Where Taylor used algebra, arithmetic, engineering knowledge, and common sense, we find calculus, probability statistics, and the scientific method.

But though the labels are similar and there is a continuity of purpose, it would be misleading to suggest that the current man-

---

[1a] Reprinted, with permission, from "A Bibliographical Essay on Decision Making" by William J. Gore and Fred S. Silander, *Administrative Science Quarterly,* Vol. 4, No. 1 (June, 1959), pp. 97–121. Footnotes have been renumbered and, in some cases, expanded.

[2] Two new journals carrying the names *Management Science* and *The Journal of the Operations Research Society of America* manifest some of this vigor.

agement science movement stems from scientific management. Although it has benefited immeasurably by the ready-made acceptance scientific management inadvertently prepared for it, the management science movement seems more accurately characterized as the confluence of several attempts to apply probability theory. Each attempt has had sufficient identity to acquire a different name, e.g., game theory, statistical decision theory, cybernetics, and operations research. The literature of management science can be conveniently reviewed within a description of three of these fields.

In point of time game theory might claim seniority since Von Neumann conceived the essentials of the theory in 1928. His work went largely unnoticed until the first edition of the *Theory and Practice of Games and Economic Behavior* in 1944 and the standard 1947 edition.[3] This theory suggests that major economic policy decisions can be understood by representing them as games of strategy and chance analogous to poker, bridge, or the like. "In general, a game will have a certain number of players, say n. The game is composed of moves, which are of two types: personal, made by the players, and chance, in which one of several possible outcomes is selected by a chance device." As in poker the distribution of cards between the hands is made by a random device, and the players have certain choices as to how to play their hands. The rules of the game prescribe "the conditions under which players are allowed to make their moves, and thus tend to define the character and the context of the alternative moves open to them."[4]

As a number of writers have pointed out, this amounts to translating a decision into a problem in the strategies of choice. The strategy is applied by a player against nature or competing players. This makes possible the second, and crucial, translation where the principles of probability are used to state a problem as a matter of selecting among alternatives each of whose probable expected consequences has been numerically weighted. Laplace is reputed to have explained statistics as the calculus of common sense. Most exponents of game theory echo his sentiments and add that what Von Neumann did was to provide in this analogy of the game a device for bringing reason directly to bear upon choices previously made intuitively, capriciously, or ignorantly.

---

[3] John Von Neumann and Oskar Morganstern (2d ed.; Princeton: Princeton University Press, 1947).

[4] Kenneth J. Arrow, "Mathematical Problems in the Social Sciences," in Daniel Lerner and Harold Lasswell (eds.), *The Policy Sciences* (Stanford: Stanford University Press, 1951), pp. 140, 141.

The layman who would use this tool runs into an initial difficulty: the theory is most frequently presented in another language
—the language of mathematical symbols. Fortunately the literature is now sufficiently extensive to include nonmathematical
sources. One who is interested in only a speaking acquaintance
with the theory may invest an evening in Arrow's chapter in *The
Policy Sciences,* or in McDonald's piece in *Fortune,* "The Theory of
Strategy," or in Snyder's discussion in *Research Frontiers in Politics.*[5] For those willing to invest several evenings three nonmathematical books are available. Although Williams' *The Compleat
Strategyst, Being a Primer on the Theory of Games of Strategy*[6]
has received a good deal of attention, perhaps because of its posture
and relatively detailed explanation of specific techniques, Bross's
shorter and more general work[7] and McDonald's *Strategy in Poker,
Business and War*[8] are both excellent sources. Bross, for example,
presents readily understood materials on probability, values, rules
for action, sequential decisions, models, and statistical techniques.
This would equip most casual readers for a further probing of the
subject, and though it does not purport to serve as a systematic
survey, Shubik's collection of readings is certainly one of the most
useful starting points for many readers.[9]

For those with scientific, mathematical, or statistical training
some of the fundamental works on the subject might represent a
jumping-off point. The 1947 edition of Von Neumann and Morganstern is already a classic and is almost universally referred to by
other students.[10] The two issues of the "Annals of Mathematical
Studies" entitled *Contributions to the Theory of Games* must also
be counted among the most important basic sources.[11] But as of this
moment the most comprehensive and integrated work available is

---

[5] John McDonald, "The Theory of Strategy," *Fortune,* Vol. 34 (June, 1949),
pp. 100–110; and Richard Snyder, "Game Theory and the Analysis of Political Behavior," in Brookings Lectures, *Research Frontiers in Politics and Government*
(Washington, D.C.: Brookings Institution, 1955), pp. 70–103.

[6] New York: McGraw-Hill Book Co., Inc., 1954.

[7] I. D. J. Bross, *Design for Decision* (New York: Macmillan Co., 1953).

[8] New York: W. W. Norton & Co., Inc., 1950.

[9] Martin Shubik, *Readings in Game Theory and Political Behavior* (Garden
City, N.Y.: Doubleday & Co., Inc., 1954). See his more general discussion of decision
making in *Administrative Science Quarterly,* Vol. 3 (December, 1958), pp. 289–306,
as well.

[10] Von Neumann and Morganstern, *op. cit.*

[11] "Annals of Mathematical Studies," Nos. 24 and 28, in H. W. Kuhn and
A. W. Tucker, *Contributions to the Theory of Games* (Princeton: Princeton University Press, 1950, 1953).

the recently published *Games and Decisions* by Luce and Raiffa. As the authors note,

The over-all outline of this book parallels the original structuring given to the theory by Von Neumann and Morganstern . . . [though] in the decade since the second edition of their book there have been many additions . . . and we have tried to include these . . . . Our emphasis is almost totally on the concepts and so relatively little attention is given to the detailed "solutions" of specific games. [Finally], our work is strongly colored . . . by a social science point of view.[12]

The book includes chapters entitled "Utility Theory," "Two-Person Zero-Sum Games," "Two-Person Co-operative Games," "Theories of *n*-Person Games in Normal Form," "Individual Decision Making under Uncertainty," "Group Decision-Making," and an appendix, "A Probabilistic Theory of Utility." It also contains a highly selective bibliography of four hundred entries. McKinsey's *Introduction to the Theory of Games*,[13] is another useful source.

The line between works on game theory and decision theory is tenuous. Several important sources nominally associated with decision theory suggest the richness and complexity of its underlying mathematical assumptions. The classic work is Abraham Wald's *Statistical Decision Functions*.[14] The work of Von Neumann and Wald is often said to form the theoretical foundations for this whole field. Also helpful are both the collected papers from a RAND seminar in Santa Monica in 1952, *Decision Processes*,[15] and a more restricted work, *Decision Making—An Experimental Approach*.[16] A more concise summary of statistical decision theory has been prepared by Savage,[17] whose work on the foundations of statistics is perhaps the most readable source on decision theory.[18] Again for the mathematically inclined, there are three more comprehensive recent discussions. Vajda has a book which is most worth-while as a

---

[12] R. Duncan Luce and Howard Raiffa, *Games and Decisions* (New York: John Wiley & Sons, Inc., 1957).

[13] New York: McGraw-Hill Book Co., Inc., 1952.

[14] New York: John Wiley & Sons, Inc., 1950; see also an article by Wald, "Review of the Theory of Games," *Review of Economics and Statistics*, Vol. 34 (February, 1947), pp. 47–52.

[15] R. M. Thrall, C. H. Coombs, and R. L. Davis (eds.), *Decision Processes*, (New York: John Wiley & Sons, Inc., 1954).

[16] Donald Davidson and Patrick Suppes, *Decision Making* (Stanford: Stanford University Press, 1957).

[17] L. J. Savage, "The Theory of Statistical Decision," *Journal of the American Statistical Association*, Vol. 46 (March, 1951), pp. 55–67.

[18] L. J. Savage, *The Foundation of Statistics* (New York: John Wiley & Sons, Inc., 1954).

source on linear programming and its uses.[19] And Blackwell and Girshick[20] have prepared a book which treats statistical decision theory with great mathematical sophistication.[21]

For both the layman and the administrative practitioner the literature on operations research may prove rewarding. In approaching operations research one must recognize that (a) it is a new and fluid field, (b) it is heavily reliant conceptually upon game theory and statistical decision theory, and (c) it is often as much influenced by the kind of problems undertaken in the name of operations research as by its theoretical foundations. One may also assume that (a) the field is still seeking general acceptance within industry and government; (b) that there is not a well-defined, professionally enforced pattern and approach (many problems are handled more like research projects than management studies); and (c) though hundreds of concrete applications of operations research techniques have been made, we have probably not yet discovered its full potential nor its real limitations. It is not yet clear, for example, whether a new profession of operations researchers will develop to claim a place among existing top staff functionaries or whether the tools of operations research will be applied by industrial engineers or organization and method analysts. For these reasons there is some tendency for operations research to be what people do in the name of operations research.

Yet several general works reveal considerable agreement upon its major techniques. *Introduction to Operations Research,* by Churchman, Ackoff, and Arnoff, is meant to be a basic textbook (which will yield to the efforts of most laymen). In the first two hundred pages the authors explain the strategy of operations research as "Formulating the Problem," which is to be attacked in

---

[19] S. Vajda, *The Theory of Games and Linear Programming* (New York: John Wiley & Sons, Inc., 1956).

[20] David Blackwell and M. A. Girshick, *Theory of Games and Statistical Decisions* (New York: John Wiley & Sons, Inc., 1954). Also see H. Chernoff and L. Moses, *Elementary Decision Theory* (New York: John Wiley & Sons, Inc., 1959).

[21] Included among those sources would be a discussion by the eighteenth century mathematician, David Bernoulli, whose "Exposition of a New Theory of the Measurement of Risk," is translated in *Econometrica,* Vol. 22 (January, 1954), pp. 23–36. This work is seen by some as the birth of the game theory. More modern and comprehensive sources would include Rudolf Carnap, *Logical Foundations of Probability* (2d ed.; Chicago: University of Chicago Press, 1950); Hans Reichenbach, *The Theory of Probability* (Berkeley: University of California Press, 1949); R. E. von Mises, *Probability, Statistics and Truth* (3d ed.; New York: Macmillan Co., 1939); W. Feller, *An Introduction to Probability Theory and Its Applications* (New York: John Wiley & Sons, Inc., 1957); and Savage, *The Foundations of Statistics.*

terms susceptible to systematic analysis; "Construction of a Model," which represents the central dynamics and alternatives within the problem as defined; "Selection of Decision Criteria"; and "Solution" (in the mathematical sense) of the model. In the remaining four hundred pages four classes of models are described, including inventory, allocation or optimization, waiting time (queuing), and replacement models.[22] In a journal article Ackoff adds routine and sequencing models to this list[23] and notes that information-collecting processes may well lend themselves to mathematical models.

The importance of the model is indicated by the fact that its identification and elaboration seems to be one of two crucial steps, the other being the manipulation of values to produce a precise and internally consistent set of objectives. The model is used as a vehicle for simulating the anticipated choice situation by providing a vicarious testing of alternative subgoals and alternative means of realizing them. Since a model is an abstraction of a complex situation, one soon confronts the inevitable difficulty of determining what elements of the larger process to emphasize in the model. Such problems are presently thwarting much more widespread application of the technique. Kenneth Arrow has done much of the theoretical exploration seeking to penetrate this threshold. His chapter on mathematical models in *The Policy Sciences* is most useful.[24] An introductory discussion of this approach to values appears in *Readings in Game Theory*,[25] but most readers will find it worthwhile to look at his *Social Choice and Individual Values*.[26]

It is no slight to operations research to note that there seems to be a place for more complex and subtle models. The inventory control problem which yields so well to existing models is important because hundreds of thousands of hospitals, department stores, army depots, auto parts houses, and other establishments must cope with it every day. But there are types of decisions, such as the selection of a successor to the chief executive, which are much more vital

---

[22] New York: John Wiley & Sons, Inc., 1957.

[23] Russell Ackoff, "The Development of Operations Research as a Science," *Operations Research,* Vol. 4 (June, 1956), pp. 265–95. An alternative source is Franklin Lindsay, *New Techniques for Management Decision-Making* (New York: McGraw-Hill Book Co., Inc., 1958). This discussion is especially useful in the area of concrete application of these techniques.

[24] "Mathematical Models in the Social Science," in Daniel Lerner and Harold Lasswell, *op. cit.*

[25] Shubik, *op. cit.,* pp. 69–72.

[26] New York: John Wiley & Sons, Inc., 1951.

to organizational survival though they arise much less frequently. If management science is to become the science of decision making, models which comprehend the variables in this sort of decision may be needed.

Perhaps the most popular nonmilitary application of operations research has involved inventory models. Individuals in isolated firms have been working toward systematic techniques of inventory control for a generation. These are nicely summarized by Whitin,[27] but the creation of more refined models has revolutionized this work, and the basic techniques are concisely described in an important article by Laderman, Littaur, and Weiss.[28] Central to this problem is optimizing the ratio of inventory carrying costs to the losses following an inventory shortage. Relatively simple in itself, this becomes a highly complicated matter when one seeks to take account of quantity discounts, limited funds, or production facilities. But these models of "static inventory" problems are elementary in comparison with attempts to devise models that reflect the dynamics of inventory flow problems.[29] An extensive, selective bibliography may be found in *Operations Research*.[30]

A second and more universal class of common managerial problems can be attacked with allocation or optimization models, for which the technical device is linear programming.[31] A typical optimization problem is that of minimizing the costs and maximizing the rate at which empty boxcars are moved to the points where they are to be loaded, taking account, for example, of existing traffic densities on alternative routes. This technique has been applied to hundreds of management problems; among them, optimal staffing patterns given present and anticipated personnel,[32] optimal crop rotation,[33] and optimal bombing patterns.

---

[27] T. M. Whitin, *The Theory of Inventory Management* (Princeton: Princeton University Press, 1953).

[28] J. L. Laderman, S. Littaur, and Lionel Weiss, "The Inventory Problem," *Journal of the American Statistical Association*, Vol. 88 (December, 1953), pp. 717–32.

[29] R. Bellman, I. Glickman, and A. Gross, "On the Optimal Inventory Equation," *Management Science*, Vol. 2 (October, 1955), pp. 83–104.

[30] Churchman, *op. cit.*, pp. 232–34.

[31] A linear function is one where, if three gallons of fuel oil are produced for one dollar, six gallons can be produced for two dollars.

[32] D. F. Votaw and A. Orden, "The Personnel Assignment Problem," in *Symposium on Linear Inequalities and Programming*, Project SCOOP, Hdqts. Air Force (Washington, D.C., 1952).

[33] C. Hindreth and S. Reiter, in T. C. Koopmans (ed.), *Activity Analysis of Production and Allocation* (Cowles Commission Monograph 13; New York: John Wiley & Sons, Inc., 1951).

The relative abundance of literature on linear programming gives testimony to its potential theoretical complexity and its vast potential field of application. Several reliable sources are available for those with a specific problem in mind.[34]

Queuing or waiting-line models are much more restricted devices dealing typically with service situations where the objective is to maximize service and minimize costs by optimizing waiting time and facilities. These models have been applied to the scheduling and flow problems of an airport,[35] the design and provision of capacity in automatic telephone exchanges,[36] and the flow of auto traffic at toll booths and intersections.[37] More comprehensive and detailed discussions may be found in a highly regarded discussion by Kendall.[38]

So-called replacement models are much less widely recognized than these first three, though they may soon receive a great deal of attention because they can provide such determinative and conclusive "solutions." Replacement refers to equipment or facilities, such as machinery, light globes, floors, and trucks. In the case where a light globe is simply replaced when it burns out, the problem is much simpler than when mass replacement is used and maximum average life must be determined. Where equipment is involved, there is the question of the possibility of replacement because of obsolescence in addition to the problem of wearing out. The American Management Association has prepared a summary of problems

---

[34] *Ibid.* Among a number of other helpful sources geared to the layman, see W. W. Cooper, *An Introduction to Linear Programming* (New York: John Wiley & Sons, Inc., 1953); W. C. Hood and T. C. Koopmans (eds.), *Studies in Econometric Method* (Cowles Commission Monograph 14; New York, 1953); Robert Dorfman, Paul Samuelson, and Robert Solow, *Linear Programming and Economic Analysis* (New York: McGraw-Hill Book Co., Inc., 1958); and a series of two articles by G. B. Danzig, "Linear Programming under Uncertainty," *Management Science*, Vol. 1 (April–July 1955), pp. 197–207, and G. B. Danzig, "Recent Advances in Linear Programming," *Management Science*, Vol. 2 (January, 1956), pp. 131–45.

[35] R. B. Adler and S. J. Fricker, "The Flow of Scheduled Air Traffic," in *RLE Technical Report,* No. 198 (Cambridge, 1951).

[36] G. S. Berkeley, *Traffic and Trunking Principles in Automatic Telephony* (2d rev. ed.; London: Benn, 1949).

[37] L. C. Edie, "Traffic Delays at Toll Booths," *Journal of Operations Research Society of America*, Vol. 2 (May, 1954), pp. 107–38; and B. D. Green-Shields, D. Shapiro, and E. Erickson, *Traffic Performance at Urban Street Intersections* (New Haven, 1947).

[38] D. G. Kendall, "Some Problems in the Theory of Queuing," *Journal of the Royal Statistical Society,* Vol. 8 (June, 1951), pp. 151–73. See also B. D. Marshall, "Queuing Theory," in J. F. McCloskey and F. N. Trefethen (eds.), *Operations Research for Management* (Baltimore: Johns Hopkins Press, 1954).

and principles.[39] Terborgh's treatment of equipment replacement policy will also be useful.[40] Perhaps the most immediately useful source is the chapter "Operations Research" and the accompanying bibliography.[41]

Those unfamiliar with mathematics may have reservations about the mass of symbolism accompanying these various models. Their question is, Why put relatively simple ideas in this complex form? The management scientist seeks to explain on two different levels. In general terms he feels that techniques of mathematical thought embody a higher order of rationality than words or concepts expressed in words. Granting that the nonmathematician is a reasonable individual, his habits of thought may still be short-circuited by unperceived slips in logic—the *non sequitur,* for instance. In one sense science as a whole and mathematics in particular are elaborate rituals designed to forestall faulty reasoning.

Until recently these rituals have had only limited applicability to management decision making because of their cumbersome and oversimplified assumptions. Through the work of Von Neumann and Wald probabilistic devices have been made available so that the power of science can be brought to management. But the immediate justification for these symbols is that they make possible a previously unknown level of rigor in definition. Elements such as product, mission, organizational objective, or authority and relationships like power-over, accountability-to, or communication-with can be given precision which will support a higher level of problem solving because of the increased strength built into their base. It might be noted incidentally that while more precise terms could produce firmer agreement, less ambiguous conceptions of purpose, and much more detailed plans, they may upon occasion induce conflicts which are more intense just because the elbow room possible within more loose definitions has been reduced.

Precision has an even larger implication, however. One of the unique contributions of the manager has always been the contribution of the broad look, the view from the top. Multivariant models now under development could aid immeasurably in the manager's conception of the whole. With the development of N-person game

[39] American Management Association, *Tested Approaches to Capital Equipment Replacement* (Special Report No. 1; New York, 1954).

[40] B. Terborgh, *Dynamic Equipment Policy* (New York: McGraw-Hill Book Co., Inc., 1949).

[41] Churchman, *op. cit.,* pp. 477–516.

theory and with the unraveling of the problem of representing non-material values in mathematical terms, management science will probably revolutionize day-to-day management.

Conclusions. First, what was once an emergent, often consistent body of administrative theory has been fractured by new approaches such as human relations, operations research, and democratic management. Concurrently the role of the executive in facilitating organizational unity has been diluted, with the result that organizations have become increasingly effective instruments of production and increasingly impossible places to live and work. It would seem that the former cannot continue indefinitely in defiance of the latter. There is a need for a cogent theory of organization. It is conceivable but improbable that a comprehensive decision theory can emerge in the present chaos of organizational theory.

Secondly, there is a large body of literature dealing more or less directly with some facet of decision making. (A generous list might run to five thousand entries.) The sample of one hundred items included here is a true sample to the extent that it reflects no common core, no universal dimensions. It is probably accurate also in reflecting more concern with technical problems than with fundamental organizational problems, such as role conflict and the pluralism of objectives.

While one might attempt to extract universals from this rather considerable body of literature, it is unlikely that they would receive any general acceptance. In short, the literature dealing with decision making, impressive in relation to one man's ability to deal with it, appears to be uneven and chaotic, and in no respect comprehensive. The themes which occur most frequently (centralization-decentralization, authoritarian vs. democratic leadership, control, "two-way communication," and the like) do not seem to confront many of the central problems. Conversely, critical factors such as a topology of decisions, models of various decisional processes, the function of ideology, and the basis of power and its generation receive only infrequent and inadequate attention.

Finally, though we do not now have anything approaching a theory of decision making, administrative practice remains far behind even those conceptions we do have. Most organizational systems imply an ideology half a century out of date, denying the very existence of modern social science. Thus, inadequate as the literature may be from a conceptual point of view, it contains a vast number of ideas through which organizational effectiveness could be increased simply by throwing off outworn administrative ideologies.

EXERCISES, SECTION 1

1. For each of the cases 1–21 identify where possible the—
   Objective function
   Decision variable
   Parameters
   Model
   Solution

EXERCISES, SECTION 2

2. For each of the cases 1–21, indicate factors which might be incorporated to make the models more realistic.

APPENDIX 1

DIFFERENTIATION FORMULAS

From Chapter 3:

1. $D_x(c) = 0$, where c is a constant.
2. $D_x(x) = 1$
3. $D_x(kx) = k$
4. $D_x(x^n) = nx^{n-1}$
5. $D_x(kx^n) = knx^{n-1}$
6. $D_x[f(x) \pm g(x)] = D_x f(x) \pm D_x g(x)$
7. $D_x[f(x) \cdot g(x)] = f(x)D_x g(x) + g(x) \cdot D_x f(x)$
8. $D_x \dfrac{f(x)}{g(x)} = \dfrac{g(x)f'(x) - f(x)g'(x)}{[g(x)]^2}$
9. If $y = f(u)$ and $u = g(x)$,

   then $\dfrac{dy}{dx} = \dfrac{dy}{du} \cdot \dfrac{du}{dx}$
10. If $y = [f(x)]^n$,

    then $\dfrac{dy}{dx} = n[f(x)]^{n-1} \cdot f'(x)$
11. If f and g are inverse functions, and if g' exists and is $\neq 0$, then

$$f'(x) = \frac{1}{g'[f(x)]}, \text{ or equivalently } \frac{dy}{dx} = \frac{1}{\dfrac{dx}{dy}}$$

From Chapter 4:

12. If $f'(c) = 0$, where c is some value of x, and if $f''(x)$ exists for every x in an open interval containing c, then

    i) $f(c)$ is a *maximum* value of f if $f''(c) < 0$; and

    ii) $f(c)$ is a minimum value of f if $f''(c) > 0$.

From Chapter 6:

13. If $f(x) = e^x, f'(x) = e^x$
14. If $f(x) = a^x, f'(x) = a^x \log_e a$

15. If $f(x) = e^{g(x)}, f'(x) = e^{g(x)} \cdot g'(x)$

16. If $f(x) = a^{g(x)}, f'(x) = g'(x) \, a^{g(x)} \log_e a$

17. If $f(x) = \log_e x, f'(x) = \dfrac{1}{x}$

18. If $f(x) = \log_a x, f'(x) = \dfrac{1}{x} \log_a e$

19. If $f(x) = \log g(x), f'(x) = \dfrac{g'(x)}{g(x)}$, provided $g(x) > 0$

From Chapter 7:

20. If the cross-partial derivatives of a function of two variables are continuous in some region, they are equal in that region; i.e.,

$$\frac{\partial^2 f(x, y)}{\partial x \partial y} = \frac{\partial^2 f(x, y)}{\partial y \partial x}$$

21. If $z = f(x, y)$ and $x = g(u, v)$, $y = h(u, v)$,

then $\dfrac{\partial z}{\partial u} = \dfrac{\partial z}{\partial x} \cdot \dfrac{\partial x}{\partial u} + \dfrac{\partial z}{\partial y} \cdot \dfrac{\partial y}{\partial u}$

and $\dfrac{\partial z}{\partial v} = \dfrac{\partial z}{\partial x} \cdot \dfrac{\partial x}{\partial v} + \dfrac{\partial z}{\partial y} \cdot \dfrac{\partial y}{\partial v}$

22. If f is a function of two variables (x, y) and has continuous second-order partial derivatives in some region containing the point $(x = a, y = b)$, then the function is at an extreme point at (a, b) if

$$f_x(a, b) = 0 = f_y(a, b)$$

and

$$f_{xx}(a, b) \cdot f_{yy}(a, b) > [f_{xy}(a, b)]^2$$

The extremum is a maximum if $f_{xx}(a, b) < 0$
and a minimum if $f_{xx}(a, b) > 0$

APPENDIX 2

1. Fundamental theorem of the calculus:

$$\int_a^b f(x)dx = F(a) - F(b) \qquad \text{where } F'(x) = f(x)$$

2. $\displaystyle\int_a^b x^n\, dx = \frac{x^{n+1}}{n+1}\bigg|_a^b, \, n \neq -1$

3. $\displaystyle\int_a^b kg(x)dx = k\int_a^b g(x)dx$, k a constant

4. $\displaystyle\int_a^b [f(x) + g(x)]dx = \int_a^b f(x)dx + \int_a^b g(x)dx$

5. $\displaystyle\int_a^b \frac{1}{x}\, dx = \log x \bigg|_a^b$

6. $\displaystyle\int_a^b \log x\, dx = [x \log x - x]\bigg|_a^b$

7. $\displaystyle\int_a^b e^{kx}\, dx = \frac{e^{kx}}{k}\bigg|_a^b$

8. $\displaystyle\int_a^b a^x\, dx = \frac{a^x}{\log a}\bigg|_a^b$

9. $\displaystyle\int_a^b xe^x\, dx = (x - 1)e^x\bigg|_a^b$

10. $\displaystyle\int_a^b x^n\, e^{\delta x}\, dx = \frac{x^n}{\delta} e^{\delta x}\bigg|_a^b - \frac{n}{\delta}\int_a^b x^{n-1}\, e^{\delta x}\, dx$

APPENDIX 3

NOTES ON PROBABILITY

1. Requirements for a p.d.f.

   i) $\int_a^b f(x)dx = 1; a \leq x \leq b;$

   $\sum_{i=a}^{b} p_i = 1$, summation over all values of i

   ii) $f(x) \geq 0$ for all x. $p_i \geq 0$ for all i.

2. Expectation:

   $$E(x) = \int_a^b xf(x)dx \qquad a \leq x \leq b$$

   $$E(x) = \sum_{i=a}^{b} ip_i$$

3. Probability of an event which is *certain* is 1.
4. Probability of an *impossible* event is 0.
5. If A and B are two events,

   i) $P(A \text{ or } B) = P(A) + P(B) - P(AB)$

   ii) $P(AB) = P(A) \cdot P(B, \text{ given that } A \text{ has occured})$
   $= P(B) \cdot P(A, \text{ given that } B \text{ has occurred})$

   iii) If A and B are independent; i.e., occurrence of A has no effect on the occurrence of B, and vice versa, then
   $P(AB) = P(A) P(B)$

6. Probability density functions referred to in the text:

   i) Uniform distribution

   $$f(x) = \frac{1}{b-a} \text{ for } a \leq x \leq b$$
   $$= 0 \qquad \text{otherwise}$$

305

ii) Exponential distribution:

$f(x) = e^{-x}, x \geq 0$

$\quad = 0 \quad$ otherwise

iii) Normal distribution:

$$f(x) = \frac{1}{\sqrt{2\pi}\,\sigma}\,e^{-\frac{(x-\mu)^2}{2\sigma^2}}$$

iv) Linear distribution:

$$f(x) = \frac{x}{a},\ 0 \leq x \leq \sqrt{2a}$$

$$= 0 \quad \text{otherwise}$$

v) Poisson distribution

$$f(x) = \frac{\lambda^x e^{-\lambda}}{x!},\quad \lambda > 0,\quad x = 0, 1, 2 \cdots$$

APPENDIX 4

PROPERTIES OF EXPONENTS AND LOGARITHMS

Exponents

Note: a and b are numbers greater than zero and different from one; m and n are integers.

1. $\sqrt[n]{a} \cdot \sqrt[n]{b} = \sqrt[n]{ab}$ and $\dfrac{\sqrt[n]{a}}{\sqrt[n]{b}} = \sqrt[n]{\dfrac{a}{b}}$

2. $(\sqrt[n]{a})^m = \sqrt[n]{a^m}$ and $\sqrt[m]{\sqrt[n]{a}} = \sqrt[nm]{a}$

3. $\sqrt[n]{a} = a^{1/n}$

4. $\dfrac{1}{a^n} = a^{-n}$

5. $a^m \cdot a^n = a^{m+n}$; $\dfrac{a^m}{a^n} = a^{m-n}$; $(a^m)^n = a^{mn}$

6. $(ab)^n = a^n b^n$ and $\left(\dfrac{a}{b}\right)^n = \dfrac{a^n}{b^n}$

7. $a^{m/n} = \sqrt[n]{a^m}$ if $a > 0, n > 0$

8. $a^1 = a$; $a^0 = 1$ if $a \neq 0$

Logarithms

Note: a is greater than zero and different from one; the arguments are positive.

1. $\log_a(a) = 1$
2. $\log_a(1) = 0$
3. $\log_a(uv) = \log_a u + \log_a v$
4. $\log_a\left(\dfrac{u}{v}\right) = \log_a u - \log_a v$
5. $\log_a(u^k) = k \log_a u$
6. $\log_a u = (\log_a e)(\log_e u)$

307

APPENDIX 5

TABLES

Table I

Value of $1.00 n Periods Hence with Interest Rate i per Period

$$S(i, n) = (1 + i)^n$$

n	1%	2%	3%	4%	5%	6%	8%	10%	15%	20%
1	1.0100	1.0200	1.0300	1.0400	1.0500	1.0600	1.0800	1.100	1.150	1.200
2	1.0201	1.0404	1.0609	1.0816	1.1025	1.1236	1.166	1.210	1.322	1.440
3	1.0303	1.0612	1.0927	1.1249	1.1576	1.1910	1.260	1.331	1.521	1.728
4	1.0406	1.0824	1.1255	1.1699	1.2155	1.2625	1.360	1.464	1.749	2.074
5	1.0510	1.1041	1.1593	1.2167	1.2763	1.3382	1.469	1.611	2.011	2.488
6	1.0615	1.1262	1.1941	1.2653	1.3401	1.4185	1.587	1.772	2.313	2.986
7	1.0721	1.1487	1.2299	1.3159	1.4071	1.5036	1.714	1.949	2.660	3.583
8	1.0829	1.1717	1.2668	1.3686	1.4775	1.5938	1.851	2.144	3.059	4.300
9	1.0937	1.1951	1.3048	1.4233	1.5513	1.6895	1.999	2.358	3.518	5.160
10	1.1046	1.2190	1.3439	1.4802	1.6289	1.7908	2.159	2.594	4.046	6.192
11	1.1157	1.2434	1.3842	1.5395	1.7103	1.8983	2.332	2.853	4.652	7.430
12	1.1268	1.2682	1.4258	1.6010	1.7959	2.0122	2.518	3.138	5.350	8.916
13	1.1381	1.2936	1.4685	1.6651	1.8856	2.1329	2.720	3.452	6.153	10.699
14	1.1495	1.3195	1.5126	1.7317	1.9799	2.2609	2.937	3.797	7.076	12.839
15	1.1610	1.3459	1.5580	1.8009	2.0789	2.3966	3.172	4.177	8.137	15.407
16	1.1726	1.3728	1.6047	1.8730	2.1829	2.5404	3.426	4.595	9.358	18.488
17	1.1843	1.4002	1.6528	1.9479	2.2920	2.6928	3.700	5.054	10.761	22.186
18	1.1961	1.4282	1.7024	2.0258	2.4066	2.8543	3.996	5.560	12.375	26.623
19	1.2081	1.4568	1.7535	2.1068	2.5270	3.0256	4.316	6.116	14.232	31.948
20	1.2202	1.4859	1.8061	2.1911	2.6533	3.2071	4.661	6.727	16.367	38.338
21	1.2324	1.5157	1.8603	2.2788	2.7860	3.3996	5.034	7.400	18.821	46.005
22	1.2447	1.5460	1.9161	2.3699	2.9253	3.6035	5.437	8.140	21.645	55.206
23	1.2572	1.5769	1.9736	2.4647	3.0715	3.8197	5.871	8.954	24.891	66.247
24	1.2697	1.6084	2.0328	2.5633	3.2251	4.0489	6.341	9.850	28.625	79.497
25	1.2824	1.6406	2.0938	2.6658	3.3864	4.2919	6.848	10.835	32.919	95.396
26	1.2953	1.6734	2.1566	2.7725	3.5557	4.5494	7.396	11.918	37.857	114.475
27	1.3082	1.7069	2.2213	2.8834	3.7335	4.8223	7.988	13.110	43.535	137.370
28	1.3213	1.7410	2.2879	2.9987	3.9201	5.1117	8.627	14.421	50.065	164.845
29	1.3345	1.7758	2.3566	3.1187	4.1161	5.4184	9.317	15.863	57.575	197.813
30	1.3478	1.8114	2.4273	3.2434	4.3219	5.7435	10.063	17.449	66.212	237.376
35	1.4166	1.9999	2.8139	3.9461	5.5160	7.6861	14.785	28.102	133.175	590.668
40	1.4889	2.2080	3.2620	4.8010	7.0400	10.2857	21.725	45.259	267.862	1469.771
45	1.5648	2.4379	3.7816	5.8412	8.9850	13.7646	31.920	72.890	538.767	3657.258
50	1.6446	2.6916	4.3839	7.1067	11.4674	18.4202	46.902	117.391	1083.652	9100.427

Table II

Present Value, P, of $1.00 to Be Received n Periods Hence with Interest Rate i per Period

$$P(i, n) = (1 + i)^{-n}$$

n	1%	2%	3%	4%	5%	6%	8%	10%	15%	20%	25%	30%	35%	40%	45%
1	0.9901	0.9804	0.9709	0.9615	0.9524	0.9434	0.9259	0.9091	0.8696	0.8333	0.8000	0.7692	0.7407	0.7143	0.6897
2	0.9803	0.9612	0.9426	0.9246	0.9070	0.8900	0.8573	0.8264	0.7561	0.6944	0.6400	0.5917	0.5487	0.5102	0.4756
3	0.9706	0.9423	0.9151	0.8890	0.8638	0.8396	0.7938	0.7513	0.6575	0.5787	0.5120	0.4552	0.4064	0.3644	0.3280
4	0.9610	0.9238	0.8885	0.8548	0.8227	0.7921	0.7350	0.6830	0.5718	0.4823	0.4096	0.3501	0.3011	0.2603	0.2262
5	0.9515	0.9057	0.8626	0.8219	0.7835	0.7473	0.6806	0.6209	0.4972	0.4019	0.3277	0.2693	0.2230	0.1859	0.1560
6	0.9420	0.8880	0.8375	0.7903	0.7462	0.7050	0.6302	0.5645	0.4323	0.3349	0.2621	0.2072	0.1652	0.1328	0.1076
7	0.9327	0.8706	0.8131	0.7599	0.7107	0.6651	0.5835	0.5132	0.3759	0.2791	0.2097	0.1594	0.1224	0.0949	0.0742
8	0.9235	0.8535	0.7894	0.7307	0.6768	0.6274	0.5403	0.4665	0.3269	0.2326	0.1678	0.1226	0.0906	0.0678	0.0512
9	0.9143	0.8368	0.7664	0.7026	0.6446	0.5919	0.5002	0.4241	0.2843	0.1938	0.1342	0.0943	0.0671	0.0484	0.0353
10	0.9053	0.8203	0.7441	0.6756	0.6139	0.5584	0.4632	0.3855	0.2472	0.1615	0.1074	0.0725	0.0497	0.0346	0.0243
11	0.8963	0.8043	0.7224	0.6496	0.5847	0.5268	0.4289	0.3505	0.2149	0.1346	0.0859	0.0558	0.0368	0.0247	0.0168
12	0.8874	0.7885	0.7014	0.6246	0.5568	0.4970	0.3971	0.3186	0.1869	0.1122	0.0687	0.0429	0.0273	0.0176	0.0116
13	0.8787	0.7730	0.6810	0.6006	0.5303	0.4688	0.3677	0.2897	0.1625	0.0935	0.0550	0.0330	0.0202	0.0126	0.0080
14	0.8700	0.7579	0.6611	0.5775	0.5051	0.4423	0.3405	0.2633	0.1413	0.0779	0.0440	0.0254	0.0150	0.0090	0.0055
15	0.8613	0.7430	0.6419	0.5553	0.4810	0.4173	0.3152	0.2394	0.1229	0.0649	0.0352	0.0195	0.0111	0.0064	0.0038
16	0.8528	0.7284	0.6232	0.5339	0.4581	0.3936	0.2919	0.2176	0.1069	0.0541	0.0281	0.0150	0.0082	0.0046	0.0026
17	0.8444	0.7142	0.6050	0.5134	0.4363	0.3714	0.2703	0.1978	0.0929	0.0451	0.0225	0.0116	0.0061	0.0033	0.0018
18	0.8360	0.7002	0.5874	0.4936	0.4155	0.3503	0.2502	0.1799	0.0808	0.0376	0.0180	0.0089	0.0045	0.0023	0.0012
19	0.8277	0.6864	0.5703	0.4746	0.3957	0.3305	0.2317	0.1635	0.0703	0.0313	0.0144	0.0068	0.0033	0.0017	0.0009
20	0.8195	0.6730	0.5537	0.4564	0.3769	0.3118	0.2145	0.1486	0.0611	0.0261	0.0115	0.0053	0.0025	0.0012	0.0006
21	0.8114	0.6598	0.5375	0.4388	0.3589	0.2942	0.1987	0.1351	0.0531	0.0217	0.0092	0.0040	0.0018	0.0009	0.0004
22	0.8034	0.6468	0.5219	0.4220	0.3418	0.2775	0.1839	0.1228	0.0462	0.0181	0.0074	0.0031	0.0014	0.0006	0.0003
23	0.7954	0.6342	0.5067	0.4057	0.3256	0.2618	0.1703	0.1117	0.0402	0.0151	0.0059	0.0024	0.0010	0.0004	0.0002
24	0.7876	0.6217	0.4919	0.3901	0.3101	0.2470	0.1577	0.1015	0.0349	0.0126	0.0047	0.0018	0.0007	0.0003	0.0001
25	0.7798	0.6095	0.4776	0.3751	0.2953	0.2330	0.1460	0.0923	0.0304	0.0105	0.0038	0.0014	0.0006	0.0002	0.0001
26	0.7720	0.5976	0.4637	0.3607	0.2812	0.2198	0.1352	0.0839	0.0264	0.0087	0.0030	0.0011	0.0004	0.0002	0.0001
27	0.7644	0.5859	0.4502	0.3468	0.2678	0.2074	0.1252	0.0763	0.0230	0.0073	0.0024	0.0008	0.0003	0.0001	0.0000
28	0.7568	0.5744	0.4371	0.3335	0.2551	0.1956	0.1159	0.0693	0.0200	0.0061	0.0019	0.0006	0.0002	0.0001	
29	0.7493	0.5631	0.4243	0.3207	0.2429	0.1846	0.1073	0.0630	0.0174	0.0051	0.0015	0.0005	0.0002	0.0001	
30	0.7419	0.5521	0.4120	0.3083	0.2314	0.1741	0.0994	0.0573	0.0151	0.0042	0.0012	0.0004	0.0001	0.0000	
35	0.7059	0.5000	0.3554	0.2534	0.1813	0.1301	0.0676	0.0356	0.0075	0.0017	0.0004	0.0001	0.0000		
40	0.6717	0.4529	0.3066	0.2083	0.1420	0.0972	0.0460	0.0221	0.0037	0.0007	0.0001	0.0000			
45	0.6391	0.4102	0.2644	0.1712	0.1113	0.0727	0.0313	0.0137	0.0019	0.0003	0.0000				
50	0.6080	0.3715	0.2281	0.1407	0.0872	0.0543	0.0213	0.0085	0.0009	0.0001					

Table III

Value of $1.00 per Period, n Periods Hence, at Interest Rate i per Period

$$S(i, n) = \frac{(1 + i)^n - 1}{i}$$

n	1%	2%	3%	4%	5%	6%	8%	10%	15%	20%
1	1.0000	1.0000	1.0000	1.0000	1.0000	1.0000	1.000	1.000	1.000	1.000
2	2.0100	2.0200	2.0300	2.0400	2.0500	2.0600	2.080	2.100	2.150	2.200
3	3.0301	3.0604	3.0909	3.1216	3.1525	3.1836	3.246	3.310	3.472	3.640
4	4.0604	4.1216	4.1836	4.2465	4.3101	4.3746	4.506	4.641	4.993	5.368
5	5.1010	5.2040	5.3091	5.4163	5.5256	5.6371	5.867	6.105	6.742	7.442
6	6.1520	6.3081	6.4684	6.6330	6.8019	6.9753	7.336	7.716	8.754	9.930
7	7.2135	7.4343	7.6625	7.8983	8.1420	8.3938	8.923	9.487	11.067	12.916
8	8.2857	8.5830	8.8923	9.2142	9.5491	9.8975	10.637	11.436	13.727	16.499
9	9.3685	9.7546	10.1591	10.5828	11.0266	11.4913	12.488	13.579	16.786	20.799
10	10.4622	10.9497	11.4639	12.0061	12.5779	13.1808	14.487	15.937	20.304	25.959
11	11.5668	12.1687	12.8078	13.4864	14.2068	14.9716	16.645	18.531	24.349	32.150
12	12.6825	13.4121	14.1920	15.0258	15.9171	16.8699	18.977	21.384	29.002	39.580
13	13.8093	14.6803	15.6178	16.6268	17.7130	18.8821	21.495	24.523	34.352	48.497
14	14.9474	15.9739	17.0863	18.2919	19.5986	21.0151	24.215	27.975	40.505	59.196
15	16.0969	17.2934	18.5989	20.0236	21.5786	23.2760	27.152	31.772	47.580	72.035
16	17.2579	18.6393	20.1569	21.8245	23.6575	25.6725	30.324	35.950	55.717	87.442
17	18.4304	20.0121	21.7616	23.6975	25.8404	28.2129	33.750	40.545	65.075	105.931
18	19.6147	21.4123	23.4144	25.6454	28.1324	30.9057	37.450	45.599	75.836	128.117
19	20.8109	22.8406	25.1169	27.6712	30.5390	33.7600	41.446	51.159	88.212	154.740
20	22.0190	24.2974	26.8704	29.7781	33.0660	36.7856	45.762	57.275	102.443	186.688
21	23.2392	25.7833	28.6765	31.9692	35.7193	39.9927	50.423	64.002	118.810	225.025
22	24.4716	27.2990	30.5368	34.2480	38.5052	43.3923	55.457	71.403	137.631	271.031
23	25.7163	28.8450	32.4529	36.6179	41.4305	46.9958	60.893	79.543	159.276	326.237
24	26.9735	30.4219	34.4265	39.0826	44.5020	50.8156	66.765	88.497	184.167	392.484
25	28.2432	32.0303	36.4593	41.6459	47.7271	54.8645	73.106	98.347	212.793	471.981
26	29.5256	33.6709	38.5530	44.3117	51.1135	59.1564	79.954	109.182	245.711	567.377
27	30.8209	35.3443	40.7096	47.0842	54.6691	63.7058	87.351	121.100	283.568	681.852
28	32.1291	37.0512	42.9309	49.9676	58.4026	68.5281	95.339	134.210	327.103	819.223
29	33.4504	38.7922	45.2189	52.9663	62.3227	73.6398	103.966	148.631	377.169	984.067
30	34.7849	40.5681	47.5754	56.0849	66.4388	79.0582	113.283	164.494	434.744	1181.881
35	41.6603	49.9945	60.4621	73.6522	90.3203	111.4348	172.317	271.024	881.168	2948.339
40	48.8864	60.4020	75.4013	95.0255	120.7998	154.7620	259.057	442.593	1779.089	7343.853
45	56.4811	71.8927	92.7199	121.0294	159.7002	212.7435	386.506	718.905	3585.126	18281.297
50	64.4632	84.5794	112.7969	152.6671	209.3480	290.3359	573.770	1163.909	7217.711	45497.156

Table IV
Present Value of $1.00 per Period at Interest Rate i per Period

$$P(i, n) = \frac{1 - (1 + i)^{-n}}{i}$$

n	1%	2%	3%	4%	5%	6%	8%	10%	15%	20%	25%	30%	35%	40%	45%
1	0.9901	0.9804	0.9709	0.9615	0.9524	0.9434	0.9259	0.9091	0.8696	0.8333	0.8000	0.7692	0.7407	0.7143	0.690
2	1.9704	1.9416	1.9135	1.8861	1.8594	1.8334	1.7833	1.7355	1.6257	1.5278	1.4400	1.3609	1.2894	1.2245	1.165
3	2.9410	2.8839	2.8286	2.7751	2.7232	2.6730	2.5771	2.4869	2.2832	2.1065	1.9520	1.8161	1.6959	1.5889	1.493
4	3.9020	3.8077	3.7171	3.6299	3.5460	3.4651	3.3121	3.1699	2.8550	2.5887	2.3616	2.1662	1.9969	1.8492	1.720
5	4.8534	4.7135	4.5797	4.4518	4.3295	4.2124	3.9927	3.7908	3.3522	2.9906	2.6893	2.4356	2.2200	2.0352	1.876
6	5.7955	5.6014	5.4172	5.2421	5.0757	4.9173	4.6229	4.3553	3.7845	3.3255	2.9514	2.6427	2.3852	2.1680	1.983
7	6.7282	6.4720	6.2303	6.0021	5.7864	5.5824	5.2064	4.8684	4.1604	3.6046	3.1611	2.8021	2.5075	2.2628	2.057
8	7.6517	7.3255	7.0197	6.7327	6.4632	6.2098	5.7466	5.3319	4.4873	3.8372	3.3289	2.9247	2.5982	2.3306	2.109
9	8.5660	8.1622	7.7861	7.4353	7.1078	6.8017	6.2469	5.7590	4.7716	4.0310	3.4631	3.0190	2.6653	2.3790	2.144
10	9.4713	8.9826	8.5302	8.1109	7.7217	7.3601	6.7101	6.1446	5.0188	4.1925	3.5705	3.0915	2.7150	2.4136	2.168
11	10.3676	9.7868	9.2526	8.7605	8.3064	7.8869	7.1390	6.4951	5.2337	4.3271	3.6564	3.1473	2.7519	2.4383	2.185
12	11.2551	10.5753	9.9540	9.3851	8.8633	8.3838	7.5361	6.8137	5.4206	4.4392	3.7251	3.1903	2.7792	2.4559	2.196
13	12.1337	11.3484	10.6350	9.9856	9.3936	8.8527	7.9038	7.1034	5.5831	4.5327	3.7801	3.2233	2.7994	2.4685	2.204
14	13.0037	12.1062	11.2961	10.5631	9.8986	9.2950	8.2442	7.3667	5.7245	4.6106	3.8241	3.2487	2.8144	2.4775	2.210
15	13.8651	12.8493	11.9379	11.1184	10.3797	9.7122	8.5595	7.6061	5.8474	4.6755	3.8593	3.2682	2.8255	2.4839	2.214
16	14.7179	13.5777	12.5611	11.6523	10.8378	10.1059	8.8514	7.8237	5.9542	4.7296	3.8874	3.2832	2.8337	2.4885	2.216
17	15.5623	14.2919	13.1661	12.1657	11.2741	10.4773	9.1216	8.0216	6.0472	4.7746	3.9099	3.2948	2.8398	2.4918	2.218
18	16.3983	14.9920	13.7535	12.6593	11.6896	10.8276	9.3719	8.2014	6.1280	4.8122	3.9279	3.3037	2.8443	2.4941	2.219
19	17.2260	15.6785	14.3238	13.1339	12.0853	11.1581	9.6036	8.3649	6.1982	4.8435	3.9424	3.3105	2.8476	2.4958	2.220
20	18.0456	16.3514	14.8775	13.5903	12.4622	11.4699	9.8181	8.5136	6.2593	4.8696	3.9539	3.3158	2.8501	2.4970	2.221
21	18.8570	17.0112	15.4150	14.0292	12.8212	11.7641	10.0168	8.6487	6.3125	4.8913	3.9631	3.3198	2.8520	2.4979	2.221
22	19.6604	17.6580	15.9369	14.4511	13.1630	12.0416	10.2007	8.7715	6.3587	4.9094	3.9705	3.3230	2.8533	2.4985	2.222
23	20.4558	18.2922	16.4436	14.8568	13.4886	12.3034	10.3711	8.8832	6.3988	4.9245	3.9764	3.3253	2.8543	2.4989	2.222
24	21.2434	18.9139	16.9355	15.2470	13.7986	12.5504	10.5288	8.9847	6.4338	4.9371	3.9811	3.3272	2.8550	2.4992	2.222
25	22.0232	19.5235	17.4131	15.6221	14.0939	12.7834	10.6748	9.0770	6.4641	4.9476	3.9849	3.3286	2.8556	2.4994	2.222
26	22.7952	20.1210	17.8768	15.9828	14.3752	13.0032	10.8100	9.1609	6.4906	4.9563	3.9879	3.3297	2.8560	2.4996	2.222
27	23.5596	20.7069	18.3270	16.3296	14.6430	13.2105	10.9352	9.2372	6.5135	4.9636	3.9903	3.3305	2.8563	2.4997	2.222
28	24.3164	21.2813	18.7641	16.6631	14.8981	13.4062	11.0511	9.3066	6.5335	4.9697	3.9923	3.3312	2.8565	2.4998	2.222
29	25.0658	21.8444	19.1885	16.9837	15.1411	13.5907	11.1584	9.3696	6.5509	4.9747	3.9938	3.3316	2.8567	2.4999	2.222
30	25.8077	22.3965	19.6004	17.2920	15.3725	13.7648	11.2578	9.4269	6.5660	4.9789	3.9950	3.3321	2.8568	2.4999	2.222
35	29.4086	24.9986	21.4872	18.6646	16.3742	14.4982	11.6546	9.6442	6.6166	4.9915	3.9984	3.3330	2.8571	2.5000	2.222
40	32.8347	27.3555	23.1148	19.7928	17.1591	15.0463	11.9246	9.7791	6.6418	4.9966	3.9995	3.3332	2.8571	2.5000	2.222
45	36.0945	29.4902	24.5187	20.7200	17.7741	15.4558	12.1084	9.8628	6.6543	4.9986	3.9998	3.3333	2.8571	2.5000	2.222
50	39.1961	31.4236	25.7298	21.4822	18.2559	15.7619	12.2335	9.9148	6.6605	4.9995	3.9999	3.3333	2.8571	2.5000	2.222

Table V

Values of ln (x) for Selected Values of x

x	ln (x)	x	ln (x)	x	ln (x)	x	ln (x)	x	ln (x)
		1.00	0.00000	2.00	0.69315	3.00	1.09861	4.00	1.38629
0.02	-3.91202	1.02	0.01980	2.02	0.70310	3.02	1.10526	4.02	1.39128
0.04	-3.21888	1.04	0.03922	2.04	0.71295	3.04	1.11186	4.04	1.39624
0.06	-2.81341	1.06	0.05827	2.06	0.72271	3.06	1.11841	4.06	1.40118
0.08	-2.52573	1.08	0.07696	2.08	0.73237	3.08	1.12493	4.08	1.40610
0.10	-2.30259	1.10	0.09531	2.10	0.74194	3.10	1.13140	4.10	1.41099
0.12	-2.12026	1.12	0.11333	2.12	0.75142	3.12	1.13783	4.12	1.41585
0.14	-1.96611	1.14	0.13103	2.14	0.76081	3.14	1.14422	4.14	1.42070
0.16	-1.83258	1.16	0.14842	2.16	0.77011	3.16	1.15057	4.16	1.42552
0.18	-1.71480	1.18	0.16551	2.18	0.77932	3.18	1.15688	4.18	1.43031
0.20	-1.60944	1.20	0.18232	2.20	0.78846	3.20	1.16315	4.20	1.43508
0.22	-1.51413	1.22	0.19885	2.22	0.79751	3.22	1.16938	4.22	1.43984
0.24	-1.42712	1.24	0.21511	2.24	0.80648	3.24	1.17557	4.24	1.44456
0.26	-1.34707	1.26	0.23111	2.26	0.81536	3.26	1.18173	4.26	1.44927
0.28	-1.27297	1.28	0.24686	2.28	0.82418	3.28	1.18784	4.28	1.45395
0.30	-1.20397	1.30	0.26236	2.30	0.83291	3.30	1.19392	4.30	1.45862
0.32	-1.13943	1.32	0.27763	2.32	0.84157	3.32	1.19996	4.32	1.46326
0.34	-1.07881	1.34	0.29267	2.34	0.85015	3.34	1.20597	4.34	1.46787
0.36	-1.02165	1.36	0.30748	2.36	0.85866	3.36	1.21194	4.36	1.47247
0.38	-0.96758	1.38	0.32208	2.38	0.86710	3.38	1.21788	4.38	1.47705
0.40	-0.91629	1.40	0.33647	2.40	0.87547	3.40	1.22378	4.40	1.48160
0.42	-0.86750	1.42	0.35066	2.42	0.88377	3.42	1.22964	4.42	1.48614
0.44	-0.82098	1.44	0.36464	2.44	0.89200	3.44	1.23547	4.44	1.49065
0.46	-0.77653	1.46	0.37844	2.46	0.90016	3.46	1.24127	4.46	1.49515
0.48	-0.73397	1.48	0.39204	2.48	0.90826	3.48	1.24703	4.48	1.49962
0.50	-0.69315	1.50	0.40547	2.50	0.91629	3.50	1.25276	4.50	1.50408
0.52	-0.65393	1.52	0.41871	2.52	0.92426	3.52	1.25846	4.52	1.50851
0.54	-0.61619	1.54	0.43178	2.54	0.93216	3.54	1.26413	4.54	1.51293
0.56	-0.57982	1.56	0.44469	2.56	0.94001	3.56	1.26976	4.56	1.51732
0.58	-0.54473	1.58	0.45742	2.58	0.94779	3.58	1.27536	4.58	1.52170
0.60	-0.51083	1.60	0.47000	2.60	0.95551	3.60	1.28093	4.60	1.52606
0.62	-0.47804	1.62	0.48243	2.62	0.96317	3.62	1.28647	4.62	1.53039
0.64	-0.44629	1.64	0.49470	2.64	0.97078	3.64	1.29198	4.64	1.53471
0.66	-0.41552	1.66	0.50682	2.66	0.97833	3.66	1.29746	4.66	1.53902
0.68	-0.38566	1.68	0.51879	2.68	0.98582	3.68	1.30291	4.68	1.54330
0.70	-0.35667	1.70	0.53063	2.70	0.99325	3.70	1.30833	4.70	1.54756
0.72	-0.32850	1.72	0.54232	2.72	1.00063	3.72	1.31372	4.72	1.55181
0.74	-0.30111	1.74	0.55389	2.74	1.00796	3.74	1.31909	4.74	1.55604
0.76	-0.27444	1.76	0.56531	2.76	1.01523	3.76	1.32442	4.76	1.56025
0.78	-0.24846	1.78	0.57661	2.78	1.02245	3.78	1.32972	4.78	1.56444
0.80	-0.22314	1.80	0.58779	2.80	1.02962	3.80	1.33500	4.80	1.56862
0.82	-0.19845	1.82	0.59884	2.82	1.03674	3.82	1.34025	4.82	1.57277
0.84	-0.17435	1.84	0.60977	2.84	1.04380	3.84	1.34547	4.84	1.57691
0.86	-0.15082	1.86	0.62058	2.86	1.05082	3.86	1.35067	4.86	1.58104
0.88	-0.12783	1.88	0.63127	2.88	1.05779	3.88	1.35584	4.88	1.58515
0.90	-0.10536	1.90	0.64185	2.90	1.06471	3.90	1.36098	4.90	1.58924
0.92	-0.08338	1.92	0.65233	2.92	1.07158	3.92	1.36609	4.92	1.59331
0.94	-0.06188	1.94	0.66269	2.94	1.07841	3.94	1.37118	4.94	1.59737
0.96	-0.04082	1.96	0.67294	2.96	1.08519	3.96	1.37624	4.96	1.60141
0.98	-0.02020	1.98	0.68310	2.98	1.09192	3.98	1.38128	4.98	1.60543

Table V—*Continued*

x	ln (x)	x	ln (x)	x	ln (x)	x	ln (x)	x	ln (x)
5.00	1.60944	6.00	1.79176	7.00	1.94591	8.00	2.07944	9.00	2.19722
5.02	1.61343	6.02	1.79509	7.02	1.94876	8.02	2.08194	9.02	2.19944
5.04	1.61741	6.04	1.79840	7.04	1.95161	8.04	2.08443	9.04	2.20166
5.06	1.62137	6.06	1.80171	7.06	1.95445	8.06	2.08691	9.06	2.20387
5.08	1.62531	6.08	1.80500	7.08	1.95727	8.08	2.08939	9.08	2.20607
5.10	1.62924	6.10	1.80829	7.10	1.96009	8.10	2.09186	9.10	2.20827
5.12	1.63315	6.12	1.81156	7.12	1.96291	8.12	2.09433	9.12	2.21047
5.14	1.63705	6.14	1.81482	7.14	1.96571	8.14	2.09679	9.14	2.21266
5.16	1.64094	6.16	1.81808	7.16	1.96851	8.16	2.09924	9.16	2.21485
5.18	1.64481	6.18	1.82132	7.18	1.97130	8.18	2.10169	9.18	2.21703
5.20	1.64866	6.20	1.82455	7.20	1.97408	8.20	2.10413	9.20	2.21920
5.22	1.65250	6.22	1.82777	7.22	1.97685	8.22	2.10657	9.22	2.22138
5.24	1.65632	6.24	1.83098	7.24	1.97962	8.24	2.10900	9.24	2.22354
5.26	1.66013	6.26	1.83418	7.26	1.98238	8.26	2.11142	9.26	2.22570
5.28	1.66393	6.28	1.83737	7.28	1.98513	8.28	2.11384	9.28	2.22786
5.30	1.66771	6.30	1.84055	7.30	1.98787	8.30	2.11626	9.30	2.23001
5.32	1.67147	6.32	1.84372	7.32	1.99061	8.32	2.11866	9.32	2.23216
5.34	1.67523	6.34	1.84688	7.34	1.99334	8.34	2.12106	9.34	2.23431
5.36	1.67896	6.36	1.85003	7.36	1.99606	8.36	2.12346	9.36	2.23645
5.38	1.68269	6.38	1.85317	7.38	1.99877	8.38	2.12585	9.38	2.23858
5.40	1.68640	6.40	1.85630	7.40	2.00148	8.40	2.12823	9.40	2.24071
5.42	1.69010	6.42	1.85942	7.42	2.00418	8.42	2.13061	9.42	2.24284
5.44	1.69378	6.44	1.86253	7.44	2.00687	8.44	2.13298	9.44	2.24496
5.46	1.69745	6.46	1.86563	7.46	2.00956	8.46	2.13535	9.46	2.24707
5.48	1.70111	6.48	1.86872	7.48	2.01223	8.48	2.13771	9.48	2.24918
5.50	1.70475	6.50	1.87180	7.50	2.01490	8.50	2.14007	9.50	2.25129
5.52	1.70838	6.52	1.87487	7.52	2.01757	8.52	2.14242	9.52	2.25339
5.54	1.71199	6.54	1.87794	7.54	2.02022	8.54	2.14476	9.54	2.25549
5.56	1.71560	6.56	1.88099	7.56	2.02287	8.56	2.14710	9.56	2.25759
5.58	1.71919	6.58	1.88403	7.58	2.02551	8.58	2.14943	9.58	2.25968
5.60	1.72277	6.60	1.88707	7.60	2.02815	8.60	2.15176	9.60	2.26176
5.62	1.72633	6.62	1.89010	7.62	2.03078	8.62	2.15409	9.62	2.26384
5.64	1.72988	6.64	1.89311	7.64	2.03340	8.64	2.15640	9.64	2.26592
5.66	1.73342	6.66	1.89612	7.66	2.03601	8.66	2.15871	9.66	2.26799
5.68	1.73695	6.68	1.89912	7.68	2.03862	8.68	2.16102	9.68	2.27006
5.70	1.74047	6.70	1.90211	7.70	2.04122	8.70	2.16332	9.70	2.27213
5.72	1.74397	6.72	1.90509	7.72	2.04381	8.72	2.16562	9.72	2.27419
5.74	1.74746	6.74	1.90806	7.74	2.04640	8.74	2.16791	9.74	2.27624
5.76	1.75094	6.76	1.91102	7.76	2.04898	8.76	2.17020	9.76	2.27829
5.78	1.75440	6.78	1.91398	7.78	2.05156	8.78	2.17248	9.78	2.28034
5.80	1.75786	6.80	1.91692	7.80	2.05412	8.80	2.17475	9.80	2.28238
5.82	1.76130	6.82	1.91986	7.82	2.05668	8.82	2.17702	9.82	2.28442
5.84	1.76473	6.84	1.92279	7.84	2.05924	8.84	2.17929	9.84	2.28646
5.86	1.76815	6.86	1.92571	7.86	2.06179	8.86	2.18155	9.86	2.28849
5.88	1.77156	6.88	1.92862	7.88	2.06433	8.88	2.18380	9.88	2.29051
5.90	1.77495	6.90	1.93152	7.90	2.06686	8.90	2.18605	9.90	2.29253
5.92	1.77834	6.92	1.93442	7.92	2.06939	8.92	2.18830	9.92	2.29455
5.94	1.78171	6.94	1.93730	7.94	2.07191	8.94	2.19054	9.94	2.29657
5.96	1.78507	6.96	1.94018	7.96	2.07443	8.96	2.19277	9.96	2.29858
5.98	1.78842	6.98	1.94305	7.98	2.07694	8.98	2.19500	9.98	2.30058

Values outside the range of the table may be obtained by using the formula
$$\ln xy = \ln x + \ln y$$

Table VI

Values of e^x for Selected Values of x

x	e^x	e^{-x}	x	e^x	e^{-x}	x	e^x	e^{-x}	x	e^x	e^{-x}
0.02	1.02020	0.98020	1.02	2.77319	0.36059	2.02	7.53832	0.13266	3.02	20.49129	0.04880
0.04	1.04081	0.96079	1.04	2.82922	0.35345	2.04	7.69061	0.13003	3.04	20.90524	0.04783
0.06	1.06184	0.94176	1.06	2.88637	0.34646	2.06	7.84597	0.12745	3.06	21.32756	0.04689
0.08	1.08329	0.92312	1.08	2.94468	0.33960	2.08	8.00447	0.12493	3.08	21.75840	0.04596
0.10	1.10517	0.90484	1.10	3.00417	0.33287	2.10	8.16617	0.12246	3.10	22.19795	0.04505
0.12	1.12750	0.88692	1.12	3.06485	0.32628	2.12	8.33114	0.12003	3.12	22.64638	0.04416
0.14	1.15027	0.86936	1.14	3.12677	0.31982	2.14	8.49944	0.11765	3.14	23.10387	0.04328
0.16	1.17351	0.85214	1.16	3.18993	0.31349	2.16	8.67114	0.11533	3.16	23.57060	0.04243
0.18	1.19722	0.83527	1.18	3.25437	0.30728	2.18	8.84631	0.11304	3.18	24.04675	0.04159
0.20	1.22140	0.81873	1.20	3.32012	0.30119	2.20	9.02501	0.11080	3.20	24.53253	0.04076
0.22	1.24608	0.80252	1.22	3.38719	0.29523	2.22	9.20733	0.10861	3.22	25.02812	0.03996
0.24	1.27125	0.78663	1.24	3.45561	0.28938	2.24	9.39333	0.10646	3.24	25.53372	0.03916
0.26	1.29693	0.77105	1.26	3.52542	0.28365	2.26	9.58309	0.10435	3.26	26.04954	0.03839
0.28	1.32313	0.75578	1.28	3.59664	0.27804	2.28	9.77668	0.10228	3.28	26.57577	0.03763
0.30	1.34986	0.74082	1.30	3.66930	0.27253	2.30	9.97418	0.10026	3.30	27.11264	0.03688
0.32	1.37713	0.72615	1.32	3.74342	0.26714	2.32	10.17567	0.09827	3.32	27.66035	0.03615
0.34	1.40495	0.71177	1.34	3.81904	0.26185	2.34	10.38124	0.09633	3.34	28.21913	0.03544
0.36	1.43333	0.69768	1.36	3.89619	0.25666	2.36	10.59095	0.09442	3.36	28.78919	0.03474
0.38	1.46228	0.68386	1.38	3.97490	0.25158	2.38	10.80490	0.09255	3.38	29.37077	0.03405
0.40	1.49182	0.67032	1.40	4.05520	0.24660	2.40	11.02318	0.09072	3.40	29.96410	0.03337
0.42	1.52196	0.65705	1.42	4.13712	0.24171	2.42	11.24586	0.08892	3.42	30.56942	0.03271
0.44	1.55271	0.64404	1.44	4.22070	0.23693	2.44	11.47304	0.08716	3.44	31.18696	0.03206
0.46	1.58407	0.63128	1.46	4.30596	0.23224	2.46	11.70481	0.08543	3.46	31.81698	0.03143
0.48	1.61607	0.61878	1.48	4.39295	0.22764	2.48	11.94126	0.08374	3.48	32.45972	0.03081
0.50	1.64872	0.60653	1.50	4.48169	0.22313	2.50	12.18249	0.08208	3.50	33.11545	0.03020
0.52	1.68203	0.59452	1.52	4.57223	0.21871	2.52	12.42860	0.08046	3.52	33.78443	0.02960
0.54	1.71601	0.58275	1.54	4.66459	0.21438	2.54	12.67967	0.07887	3.54	34.46692	0.02901
0.56	1.75067	0.57121	1.56	4.75882	0.21014	2.56	12.93582	0.07730	3.56	35.16320	0.02844
0.58	1.78604	0.55990	1.58	4.85496	0.20598	2.58	13.19714	0.07577	3.58	35.87354	0.02788
0.60	1.82212	0.54881	1.60	4.95303	0.20190	2.60	13.46374	0.07427	3.60	36.59823	0.02732
0.62	1.85893	0.53794	1.62	5.05309	0.19790	2.62	13.73572	0.07280	3.62	37.33757	0.02678
0.64	1.89648	0.52729	1.64	5.15517	0.19398	2.64	14.01320	0.07136	3.64	38.09184	0.02625
0.66	1.93479	0.51685	1.66	5.25931	0.19014	2.66	14.29629	0.06995	3.66	38.86134	0.02573
0.68	1.97388	0.50662	1.68	5.36556	0.18637	2.68	14.58509	0.06856	3.68	39.64639	0.02522
0.70	2.01375	0.49659	1.70	5.47395	0.18268	2.70	14.87973	0.06721	3.70	40.44730	0.02472
0.72	2.05443	0.48675	1.72	5.58453	0.17907	2.72	15.18032	0.06587	3.72	41.26439	0.02423
0.74	2.09594	0.47711	1.74	5.69734	0.17552	2.74	15.48699	0.06457	3.74	42.09799	0.02375
0.76	2.13828	0.46767	1.76	5.81244	0.17204	2.76	15.79984	0.06329	3.76	42.94843	0.02328
0.78	2.18147	0.45841	1.78	5.92986	0.16864	2.78	16.11902	0.06204	3.78	43.81604	0.02282
0.80	2.22554	0.44933	1.80	6.04965	0.16530	2.80	16.44465	0.06081	3.80	44.70118	0.02237
0.82	2.27050	0.44043	1.82	6.17186	0.16203	2.82	16.77685	0.05961	3.82	45.60421	0.02193
0.84	2.31637	0.43171	1.84	6.29654	0.15882	2.84	17.11577	0.05843	3.84	46.52547	0.02149
0.86	2.36316	0.42316	1.86	6.42374	0.15567	2.86	17.46153	0.05727	3.86	47.46535	0.02107
0.88	2.41090	0.41478	1.88	6.55350	0.15259	2.88	17.81427	0.05613	3.88	48.42422	0.02065
0.90	2.45960	0.40657	1.90	6.68589	0.14957	2.90	18.17415	0.05502	3.90	49.40245	0.02024
0.92	2.50929	0.39852	1.92	6.82096	0.14661	2.92	18.54129	0.05393	3.92	50.40044	0.01984
0.94	2.55998	0.39063	1.94	6.95875	0.14370	2.94	18.91585	0.05287	3.94	51.41860	0.01945
0.96	2.61170	0.38289	1.96	7.09933	0.14086	2.96	19.29797	0.05182	3.96	52.45733	0.01906
0.98	2.66446	0.37531	1.98	7.24274	0.13807	2.98	19.68782	0.05079	3.98	53.51703	0.01869
1.00	2.71828	0.36788	2.00	7.38906	0.13534	3.00	20.08554	0.04979	4.00	54.59815	0.01832

Table VI—*Continued*

x	e^x	e^{-x}	x	e^x	e^{-x}	x	e^x	e^{-x}	x	e^x	e^{-x}
4.02	55.70111	0.01795	5.02	151.41130	0.00660	6.02	411.57860	0.00243	7.02	1118.78662	0.00089
4.04	56.82634	0.01760	5.04	154.47002	0.00647	6.04	419.89303	0.00238	7.04	1141.38761	0.00088
4.06	57.97431	0.01725	5.06	157.59052	0.00635	6.06	428.37544	0.00233	7.06	1164.44517	0.00086
4.08	59.14547	0.01691	5.08	160.77406	0.00622	6.08	437.02919	0.00229	7.08	1187.96852	0.00084
4.10	60.34029	0.01657	5.10	164.02191	0.00610	6.10	445.85777	0.00224	7.10	1211.96708	0.00083
4.12	61.55924	0.01624	5.12	167.33537	0.00598	6.12	454.86469	0.00220	7.12	1236.45043	0.00081
4.14	62.80282	0.01592	5.14	170.71577	0.00586	6.14	464.05357	0.00215	7.14	1261.42839	0.00079
4.16	64.07152	0.01561	5.16	174.16446	0.00574	6.16	473.42807	0.00211	7.16	1286.91093	0.00078
4.18	65.36585	0.01530	5.18	177.68281	0.00563	6.18	482.99196	0.00207	7.18	1312.90826	0.00076
4.20	66.68633	0.01500	5.20	181.27224	0.00552	6.20	492.74904	0.00203	7.20	1339.43076	0.00075
4.22	68.03348	0.01470	5.22	184.93418	0.00541	6.22	502.70323	0.00199	7.22	1366.48906	0.00073
4.24	69.40785	0.01441	5.24	188.67010	0.00530	6.24	512.85851	0.00195	7.24	1394.09397	0.00072
4.26	70.80998	0.01412	5.26	192.48149	0.00520	6.26	523.21894	0.00191	7.26	1422.25654	0.00070
4.28	72.24044	0.01384	5.28	196.36988	0.00509	6.28	533.78866	0.00187	7.28	1450.98803	0.00069
4.30	73.69979	0.01357	5.30	200.33681	0.00499	6.30	544.57191	0.00184	7.30	1480.29993	0.00068
4.32	75.18863	0.01330	5.32	204.38388	0.00489	6.32	555.57299	0.00180	7.32	1510.20397	0.00066
4.34	76.70754	0.01304	5.34	208.51271	0.00480	6.34	566.79631	0.00176	7.34	1540.71211	0.00065
4.36	78.25713	0.01278	5.36	212.72495	0.00470	6.36	578.24636	0.00173	7.36	1571.83656	0.00064
4.38	79.83803	0.01253	5.38	217.02228	0.00461	6.38	589.92771	0.00170	7.38	1603.58977	0.00062
4.40	81.45087	0.01228	5.40	221.40642	0.00452	6.40	601.84504	0.00166	7.40	1635.98443	0.00061
4.42	83.09629	0.01203	5.42	225.87912	0.00443	6.42	614.00311	0.00163	7.42	1669.03351	0.00060
4.44	84.77494	0.01180	5.44	230.44218	0.00434	6.44	626.40680	0.00160	7.44	1702.75022	0.00059
4.46	86.48751	0.01156	5.46	235.09742	0.00425	6.46	639.06106	0.00156	7.46	1737.14806	0.00058
4.48	88.23467	0.01133	5.48	239.84671	0.00417	6.48	651.97095	0.00153	7.48	1772.24078	0.00056
4.50	90.01713	0.01111	5.50	244.69193	0.00409	6.50	665.14163	0.00150	7.50	1808.04241	0.00055
4.52	91.83560	0.01089	5.52	249.63504	0.00401	6.52	678.57839	0.00147	7.52	1844.56729	0.00054
4.54	93.69080	0.01067	5.54	254.67800	0.00393	6.54	692.28658	0.00144	7.54	1881.83003	0.00053
4.56	95.58348	0.01046	5.56	259.82284	0.00385	6.56	706.27169	0.00142	7.56	1919.84551	0.00052
4.58	97.51439	0.01025	5.58	265.07161	0.00377	6.58	720.53933	0.00139	7.58	1958.62897	0.00051
4.60	99.48432	0.01005	5.60	270.42641	0.00370	6.60	735.09519	0.00136	7.60	1998.19590	0.00050
4.62	101.49403	0.00985	5.62	275.88938	0.00362	6.62	749.94510	0.00133	7.62	2038.56213	0.00049
4.64	103.54435	0.00966	5.64	281.46272	0.00355	6.64	765.09499	0.00131	7.64	2079.74382	0.00048
4.66	105.63608	0.00947	5.66	287.14864	0.00348	6.66	780.55094	0.00128	7.66	2121.75743	0.00047
4.68	107.77007	0.00928	5.68	292.94943	0.00341	6.68	796.31911	0.00126	7.68	2164.61977	0.00046
4.70	109.94717	0.00910	5.70	298.86740	0.00335	6.70	812.40583	0.00123	7.70	2208.34799	0.00045
4.72	112.16825	0.00892	5.72	304.90492	0.00328	6.72	828.81751	0.00121	7.72	2252.95958	0.00044
4.74	114.43420	0.00874	5.74	311.06441	0.00321	6.74	845.56074	0.00118	7.74	2298.47238	0.00044
4.76	116.74593	0.00857	5.76	317.34833	0.00315	6.76	862.64220	0.00116	7.76	2344.90461	0.00043
4.78	119.10435	0.00840	5.78	323.75919	0.00309	6.78	880.06872	0.00114	7.78	2392.27482	0.00042
4.80	121.51042	0.00823	5.80	330.29956	0.00303	6.80	897.84729	0.00111	7.80	2440.60198	0.00041
4.82	123.96509	0.00807	5.82	336.97205	0.00297	6.82	915.98501	0.00109	7.82	2489.90541	0.00040
4.84	126.46935	0.00791	5.84	343.77934	0.00291	6.84	934.48913	0.00107	7.84	2540.20483	0.00039
4.86	129.02420	0.00775	5.86	350.72414	0.00285	6.86	953.36707	9.00105	7.86	2591.52038	0.00039
4.88	131.63066	0.00760	5.88	357.80924	0.00279	6.88	972.62636	0.00103	7.88	2643.87256	0.00038
4.90	134.28978	0.00745	5.90	365.03747	0.00274	6.90	992.27472	0.00101	7.90	2697.28233	0.00037
4.92	137.00261	0.00730	5.92	372.41171	0.00269	6.92	1012.32000	0.00099	7.92	2751.77105	0.00036
4.94	139.77025	0.00715	5.94	379.93493	0.00263	6.94	1032.77022	0.00097	7.94	2807.36051	0.00036
4.96	142.59380	0.00701	5.96	387.61012	0.00258	6.96	1053.63356	0.00095	7.96	2864.07295	0.00035
4.98	145.47438	0.00687	5.98	395.44037	0.00253	6.98	1074.91837	0.00093	7.98	2921.93106	0.00034
5.00	148.41316	0.00674	6.00	403.42879	0.00248	7.00	1096.63316	0.00091	8.00	2980.95799	0.00034

Values outside the range of the tables may be obtained by using the formula

$$e^{x+y} = e^x e^y$$

INDEX

*This book has been set on the Linotype in 11
point Modern #21, leaded 2 points, and 9 point
Modern #21, leaded 1 point. Chapter numbers
are in 12 point Spartan Medium; chapter titles
are in 18 point Spartan Medium. The size of the
type page is 27 by 46½ picas.*